James Shoramp

Papers
On
Human
Genetics

PRENTICE-HALL BIOLOGICAL SCIENCE SERIES
William D. McElroy and Carl P. Swanson, *Editors*

BIOCHEMICAL SYSTEMATICS,* by Ralph E. Alston and B. L. Turner
CLASSIC PAPERS IN GENETICS, by James A. Peters
EXPERIMENTAL BIOLOGY, by Richard W. Van Norman
MECHANISMS OF BODY FUNCTIONS, by Dexter M. Easton
MILESTONES IN MICROBIOLOGY, by Thomas D. Brock
PAPERS ON HUMAN GENETICS, by Samuel H. Boyer, IV
PRINCIPLES OF BIOLOGY, by Neal D. Buffaloe
SELECTED BOTANICAL PAPERS, by Irving W. Knobloch
A SYNTHESIS OF EVOLUTIONARY THEORY, by Herbert H. Ross

CONCEPTS OF MODERN BIOLOGY SERIES

BEHAVIORAL ASPECTS OF ECOLOGY,* by Peter H. Klopfer

FOUNDATIONS OF MODERN BIOLOGY SERIES

ADAPTATION, by Bruce Wallace and A. M. Srb
ANIMAL BEHAVIOR, by Vincent Dethier and Eliot Stellar
ANIMAL DIVERSITY, by Earl D. Hanson
ANIMAL GROWTH AND DEVELOPMENT, by Maurice Sussman
ANIMAL PHYSIOLOGY, by Knut Schmidt-Nielsen
THE CELL, by Carl P. Swanson
CELLULAR PHYSIOLOGY AND BIOCHEMISTRY, by William D. McElroy
HEREDITY, by David M. Bonner
THE LIFE OF THE GREEN PLANT, by Arthur W. Galston
MAN IN NATURE, by Marston Bates
THE PLANT KINGDOM, by Harold C. Bold

* These titles are also in the Prentice-Hall International Series in Biological Science. Prentice-Hall, Inc.; Prentice-Hall International, United Kingdom and Eire; Prentice-Hall of Canada, Ltd., Canada; Berliner Union, West Germany and Austria.

Papers
On
Human
Genetics

edited by

Samuel H. Boyer, IV

Assistant Professor of Medicine
The Johns Hopkins University

Prentice-Hall, Inc.
Englewood Cliffs, N.J.

PRENTICE-HALL INTERNATIONAL, INC., *London*
PRENTICE-HALL OF AUSTRALIA, PTY., LTD., *Sydney*
PRENTICE-HALL OF CANADA, LTD., *Toronto*
PRENTICE-HALL FRANCE, S.A.R.L., *Paris*
PRENTICE-HALL OF INDIA PRIVATE LIMITED, *New Delhi*
PRENTICE-HALL OF JAPAN, INC., *Tokyo*
PRENTICE-HALL DE MEXICO, S.A., *Mexico City*

©—1963 by Prentice-Hall, Inc., Englewood Cliffs, N.J.

Library of Congress Catalog Card Number: 63-18122

Printed in the United States of America
C

Table of Contents

Early Mathematical Approaches

Part One   **3**

Über den Nachweis der Vererbung beim Menschen
(*On the Demonstration of Heredity in Man*) by W. Weinberg, *4*

Die Bedeutung der Statistisch Ermittelten mit Blutverwandtschaft der Eltern
(*The Meaning of the Statistically Determined Trait with Consanguinity of the Parents*) by F. Lenz, *16*

Origins and Syntheses of Blood Group Genetics

Part Two   **27**

Über Allutinationserscheinungen Normalen Menschlichen Blutes
(*On Agglutination Phenomena of Normal Human Blood*) by Karl Landsteiner, *27*

Serological Differences Between the Blood of Different Races.
The Result of Researches on the Macedonian Front by Dr. Ludwik Hirschfeld and Dr. Hanka Hirschfeld, *32*

An Unusual Case of Intra-group Agglutination by Philip Levine and Rufus E. Stetson, *43*

Studies on an Agglutinogen (Rh) in Human Blood Reacting with Anti-Rhesus Sera and with Human Isoantibodies by Karl Landsteiner and Alexander S. Wiener, *46*

Possible Genetical Pathways for the Biosynthesis of Blood Group Mucopolysaccharides by Winifred M. Watkins and W. T. J. Morgan, *59*

Biochemical Genetics: The Enzymatic Defects

Part Three—Section One   **81**

The Incidence of Alkaptonuria: A Study in Chemical Individuality by Archibald E. Garrod, *82*

Über Ausscheidung von Phenylbrenztraubensäure (ppa) in den Harn als Stoffwechselanomalie in Verbindung mit Imbezillität
(*The Excretion of Phenylpyruvic Acid (ppa) in the Urine, an Anomaly of Metabolism in Connection with Imbecility*) by Asbjörn Fölling, *95*

Galactosemia, a Congenital Defect in a Nucleotide Transferase: A Preliminary Report by Herman W. Kalckar, Elizabeth P. Anderson, and Kurt J. Isselbacher, *103*

Biochemical Genetics: The Hemoglobinopathies

Part Three—Section Two   **109**

The Inheritance of Sickle Cell Anemia by James V. Neel, *110*

Sickle Cell Anemia, a Molecular Disease by Linus Pauling, Harvey A. Itano, S. J. Singer, and Ibert C. Wells, *115*

C^{14}-Hybrids of Human Hemoglobins. II. The Identification of the Aberrant Chain in Human Hemoglobin S by J. R. Vinograd, W. D. Hutchinson, and W. A. Schroeder, *126*

Formation of Normal and Doubly Abnormal Haemoglobins by Recombination of Haemoglobin I with S and C by Harvey A. Itano and Elizabeth Robinson, *129*

Study of Two Abnormal Hemoglobins with Evidence for a New Genetic Locus for Hemoglobin Formation by Ernest W. Smith and John V. Torbert, *133*

Gene Mutations in Human Haemoglobin: the Chemical Difference Between Normal and Sickle Cell Haemoglobin by V. M. Ingram, *141*

Allelomorphism and the Chemical Differences of the Human Haemoglobins A, S and C by J. A. Hunt and V. M. Ingram, *146*

A Terminal Peptide Sequence of Human Haemoglobin? by J. A. Hunt and V. M. Ingram, *149*

Protection Afforded by Sickle-Cell Trait Against Subtertian Malarial Infection by A. C. Allison, *153*

Gene Evolution and the Haemoglobins by Vernon M. Ingram, *164*

Biochemical Genetics: The Serum Proteins

Part Three—Section Three **177**

Biochemical Aspects of the Inherited Variations in Human Serum Haptoglobins and Transferrins by O. Smithies and G. E. Connell, *178*

Chromosomal Rearrangements and the Evolution of Haptoglobin Genes by O. Smithies, G. E. Connell, and G. H. Dixon, *191*

Hereditary Serological Human Serum Groups by R. Grubb and A. -B. Laurell, *202*

Localization of Two Genetic Factors to Different Areas of γ-Globulin Molecules by M. Harboe, C. K. Osterland, and H. G. Kunkel, *213*

The Structural Basis for Genetic Variations of Normal Human γ-Globulins by Edward C. Franklin, Hugh Fudenberg, Martin Meltzer, and Denis R. Stanworth, *217*

Cytogenetics

Part Four **231**

The Chromosome Number of Man by Joe Hin Tjio and Albert Levan, *232*

Étude des chromosomes somatiques de neuf enfants mongoliens (*Study of the Somatic Chromosomes of Nine Mongoloid Idiot Children*) by Jerome Lejeune, Marthe Gautier, and Raymond Turpin, *238*

A Case of Human Intersexuality Having a Possible XXY Sex-determining Mechanism by Patricia A. Jacobs and Dr. J. A. Strong, *240*

A Sex-Chromosome Anomaly in a Case of Gonadal Dysgenesis (Turner's Syndrome) by C. E. Ford, K. W. Jones, P. E. Polani, J. C. de Almeida, and J. H. Briggs, *243*

Sex Chromatin and Gene Action in the Mammalian X-Chromosome by Mary F. Lyon, *250*

Mutation

Part Five   **269**

Parental Age and Mutation by L. S. Penrose, *270*

Radiation and the Sex Ratio in Man.
Sex Ratio Among Children of Survivors of Atomic Bombings Suggests Induced Sex-linked Lethal Mutations by William J. Schull and James V. Neel, *276*

A Reappraisal

Part Six   **291**

Cross Currents in the History of Human Genetics by L. C. Dunn, *292*

Introduction

The study of human genetics is a synthesis of what began 60 years ago as isolated observations by serologists, chemists, mathematicians, biologists and physicians. To this day human genetics and, in fact, genetics in general, remains eclectic and in its essentials provides new ways of looking at old problems and generates new problems often, by their nature, relevant not only to man but to the study of all living things. One consequence of this philosophy is the increasing unity of interest which exists among those who study man and those concerned with other organisms. Indeed the present popularity of human genetics may in part stem from the promise of broad exchange between the various life sciences in an age of exact specialization. Thus the medical reader of this collection should realize at the outset that the proper study of human genetics is necessarily grounded in general genetics. Just so the biologist should recognize that man is a fit subject for some forms of genetical enquiry.

It is the particular purpose of this collection to reprint in one place some of the scientific papers which illustrate the various ways in which the study of human genetics has proceeded. All the examples have been chosen primarily to benefit the newcomers: the students of various rank and training who have become intrigued with human genetics and its problems and wish to know something, firsthand, of its origins. In many instances the papers reprinted here are masterpieces of scientific intuition, investigation, and inference. In other instances papers have been included as examples or summaries of particular areas of interest. Brief introductory annotations have been provided for the purpose of offering perspective rather than summary.

Any such collection, selected from thousands of papers, is necessarily the editor's choice and will naturally reflect less than universal interests. In particular it is immediately obvious that this collection does not contain many of the mathematical treatments which have been so valuable to the development of human genetics. Such papers have been omitted since, in the editor's experience, their content is not easily grasped except by that minority of persons familiar with mathematics beyond algebra. Moreover, the lasting worth of many such papers rests with the methodology which they develop rather than with an examination of genes, their products and their interrelationships. The reader should, however, be quite clear that the omission of such papers does not in the least mean that they are to be denigrated. On the contrary, the mathematical approaches to human genetics have often provided the first sure evidence of simple inheritance and thereby permitted the later description of what a particular gene is doing. The methods of family analysis developed by R. A. Fisher, J. B. S. Haldane and others are cases in point.

I wish to thank the many persons at Johns Hopkins who have given their opinions and criticism. Mrs. Hermine Bird and Dr. and Mrs. Paul Lichtlen assisted in translations from the German and French.

Papers

On

Human

Genetics

Early
Mathematical
Approaches

Part One

A great part of the advance of human genetics has been due to the development of essentially simple concepts whether algebraic, serologic or physicochemical in nature. This is so in the first paper where Weinberg describes a mathematically trivial expression but recognizes and develops the consequences of what is now called the Hardy-Weinberg equilibrium. Hardy (1), an English mathematician, and Weinberg, a German physician, independently found a means of describing the outcome of Mendelian inheritance in a randomly mating population. Both men recognized that simple expansion of the binomial provides a description of genotype frequencies in a randomly mating (panmictic) population and in its descendants. Specifically, if there be two allelic genes, say A and B, which have frequencies of m and n respectively, then in a randomly mating population the genotypes AA, AB and BB will occur in the parental and also all subsequent generations in the ratio of $m^2: 2 mn: n^2$. Not stated by Weinberg but essential for the maintenance of such equilibrium is the equal viability and fertility of all genotypes. The magnificent efforts of Sewall Wright (2), R. A. Fisher (3), and J. B. S. Haldane (4) have indicated the ways in which natural selection may disrupt this generation-to-generation equilibrium of gene frequencies.

In itself the Hardy-Weinberg equilibrium is a touchstone and a point of beginning for much in human genetics. Weinberg's own particular application, indeed the spur toward his derivation, was the problem of inheritance of dizygotic twinning. His conclusion that dizygotic twinning is recessively inherited is highly inferential and not proof in itself. More persuasive inferential uses of the equilibrium have been employed in judging the presence and form of simple inheritance in human populations. For example, elsewhere in this volume application of the Hardy-Weinberg formulation is made by Neel to the inheritance of sickle cell anemia.

3

However, even if Weinberg's formulation had proved of little use his paper would be worth the reading for in it he shows a marvelous understanding of the problems still present in the analyses of human families and populations.

(1) G. H. Hardy. 1908. Mendelian proportions in a mixed population. Science. **28**: 49-50, reprinted in James H Peters (editor). 1959. Classic papers in genetics, Prentice-Hall, Inc., Englewood Cliffs, N. J.

(2) S. Wright. 1931. Evolution in mendelian populations. Genetics. **16**: 97-159.

(3) Ronald A. Fisher. 1958. The genetical theory of natural selection. 1929. Reprinted by Dover Publications, Inc., New York.

(4) J. B. S. Haldane. 1932. The causes of evolution. Harper & Row, Publishers, New York and London: 235.

Über den Nachweis der Vererbung beim Menschen* (On the Demonstration of Heredity in Man)

W. WEINBERG

Under the term heredity we understand the fact that on fertilization of the egg by the semen, species and individual qualities of the parents are received by the forming individual. In this procedure the most substantial part is attributed to the nucleus and, specifically, to the chromosomes of the germ cells, a view which, to be sure, is again hotly disputed. The mature sex cell undergoes a double division just before fertilization. According to a broad view, a part of the genetic composition originating in the two parents is liberated by this process. This process is of the utmost importance in regulating the relationship of the individual to his ancestors and in establishing genetic hypotheses. If we construct the genealogical table of an individual,

* Reprinted by publisher's permission from Jahreshefte des Vereins für Vaterländische *Naturkunde in Württemberg*, *Stuttgart*. 1908. **64**: 368-382. Lecture at the scientific evening at Stüttgart, January 13, 1908.

that is a schematic synopsis of his ancestors, we have a synopsis of those individuals who may have influenced, through the germ plasm, certain qualities of the individual under consideration. However, among all theoretical possibilities only a few are actually to be taken into consideration. There is no continuity of the germ plasm for all ancestors with reference to all qualities, and in the concurrence most of the ancestors are eliminated for the determination of the individual with regard to each particular quality. We do not know how many ancestors actually determine the individual with regard to a certain quality; we can only say that it must be at least two, one on the paternal and one on the maternal side. The more ancestors that are actually involved, the larger is the number of gradations or variations produced. From the significance of reduction division it further follows that the connection with a certain ancestor becomes more improbable the further removed the degree of kinship. Since the number of ancestors is doubled through each step of relationship, the probability that any one ancestor will influence a certain quality is halved in each degree of kinship. According to the Mendelian rule it appears that each quality in the final analysis is determined by only two ancestors and thereby the most rigorous selection of ancestors is expressed.

These are the most essential viewpoints we must take if we wish to explore and evaluate the facts of human genetics. It may be said at once that the limits of genetic research on man are considerably narrower than can be set in general biology. Essentially we can only be concerned with establishing in what cases heredity is present, what influence heredity has as compared to other factors which influence a certain manifestation, and what specific genetic rules enter into consideration of a particular quality. Only general biology can offer us an understanding of the nature of heredity from the point of view of cellular history; man, in particular, is not a profitable subject for its study since it is not possible to expose him to numerous well thought out breeding experiments as can be done with lower plants and animals and which have led to such beautiful results as the discovery of Mendel's rule of inheritance. The study of human heredity can only be a matter of subsequent evaluation of experiments which life has provided without deliberation. In the case of man, the statistical evaluation of mass phenomena must substitute, in a poor way, for experiments. The question of whether a selection has occurred in a positive or a negative direction, whether there has been partial inbreeding or random mixing—panmixis— and to what degree, brings an element of uncertainty into the analysis of the findings. The consequences of strictest inbreeding, that is, sib matings, with which the classical experiment of Mendel dealt, cannot be determined for man and the relatively rare matings of more distant relatives can offer no complete substitute.

But this is only a part of the difference between research on plants and animals and that on man.

The essential difference is due more to the manner of obtaining the material to be investigated and the method of analyzing it. In the case of plants and animals one can personally observe the results of breeding experiments through several generations. In the case of man, one observer can know only fractional portions of the history of two generations of one family, except possibly for those qualities such as color which are established at birth. Even pathological manifestations, as well as some normal ones, can first come to observation at an age when the individual lives far distant from his parents. Many familial traits can therefore be known only by way of tradition, which is frequently incomplete and even with the best intentions (which may not always be assumed), deceptive. How many people are unable to give correctly and completely even the number of children their mother gave birth to, or the causes of death or even the names of their grandparents?

Many questions can therefore be solved conclusively only with the aid of documentary material, the exploration of which will essentially be a thing of the future. Up to the present two directions have become important in this regard. One, as representatives of which I would like to mention Goehlert and Ottokar Lorenz, seeks to analyze the history of prominent families, namely, princely houses and families of the nobility. But these kinds of investigations offer neither a sufficiently large material nor assure a uniform reliability and completeness of data. Moreover, such families represent the product of selection, the analysis of which can never give a picture of average situations.

The other direction, in which Ammon and Riffel have been active, seeks to discover the anthropological and pathological relationships of the total population of entire regions and communities over a rather long period of time. This is also the method I have adopted in my investigations. I was fortunate in being spared the great effort of compiling the composition of the families from church and local registers, since the Württemberg family registers permitted me to learn the demographic history of a family household and its connection with ancestors and descendants. I had only to enter the causes of death on the abstracts placed at my disposal.

Although it is true that the unreliability of the material obtained from studies in man can be considerably corrected or sometimes even removed by the choice of a suitable method, there remain considerable difficulties. For the most part it is impossible to follow the descendants of the personally observed persons for a rather long time or over several generations. In contrast to investigations which follow the descendants of crosses in plants and animals, one is very substantially and often predominantly dependent on establishing the ratios in the ascendant and collateral kinships. Insofar as numerical determinations are concerned, the results must suffer not unimportant numerical displacements, as I will show you later.

The numerous errors which explain the decade-long standstill of genetics are situated in the domain of method.

One of these errors was due to the fact that the relatives of an individual were followed only insofar as pathological conditions could be ascertained. The pedigrees thus obtained were mostly very incomplete and offered only one aspect. Ottokar Lorenz was correct in drawing attention to the fact that such pedigrees are worthless and in pointing out the difference between pedigrees and genealogical tables. However, instead of recommending the correct analysis, i.e., complete pedigrees, he believed that the genealogical table should, on the whole, be given preference and expected from it especially a reduction of exaggerated views on the importance of pathological inheritance. A comparison with the biological research on plants and animals should have been able to teach him that successful investigation examines the results of certain crossings in the descendants. His view that very extensive genealogical tables give a more correct picture of the influence of heredity is based on two mistakes. First of all, he misinterprets the influence of reduction division and the importance of the different degrees of relationship. Secondly, he disregards the favorable selection due to marriage which, especially in the mentally ill, leads to the exclusion in rather high degree of the opportunity for, and possibility of, reproduction. Therefore one seldom finds idiots among the parents of idiots. For this reason a correctly constructed pedigree is preferable to a genealogical table since it offers greater security against a biased selection.

The failure of research in pathological genetics was, in fact, founded on biased casuistics and on the initially erroneous statistical method of inspection which gradually took its place, without completely suppressing it. It was not enough to recognize that the negative case had the same value as the positive one. For example, instead of counting up the typical cases there was a tendency, by extensive investigation of the kinship, to seek the trait among other family members and thereafter to calculate an absolute high percentage of the trait. This was the reason why the studies of Riffel on the inheritance of tuberculosis were harshly criticized by bacteriologists. The same error, i.e., the misinterpretation of the different importance of the different degrees of kinship to the genetic composition of an individual, also led Lorenz and Riffel to entirely opposite and equally false views on the meaning of transmission. Only by the comparative method was it possible to obtain a measure of the influence of heredity. The first attempts in this direction, by Koller on mental diseases and by Kuthry on tuberculosis, however, still gave too little consideration of the influence of age and external living conditions.

The demonstration of a familially increased trait is not directly identical with inheritance in the genetic sense. Familial occurrence of a trait can also be based on common factors of environmental conditions and habits. Thus the family history of persons with gout or diabetes do not readily prove that these illnesses have a genetic foundation. In mental diseases the influence of environmental conditions has been studied too little, whereas in tuberculosis there probably has been overemphasis. In all these diseases the influence of heredity can be recognized only insofar as a trait, whose nature we do not yet know in tuberculosis, remains as a familial trait even after elimination of the influence of age and external environment. In order to study this in tuberculosis, I compared the incidence of familial tuberculosis in affected people and in their spouses. I found familial evidence of tuberculosis among affected subjects to be 50% higher than in their spouses. In well off persons familial evidence was 100% higher among the patients.

A certain inbreeding among tuberculous persons is the necessary result of a definite, if not strong, effort on the part of healthy persons to avoid marriages with susceptible individuals. Therefore my figures representing the relative familial burden of tuberculous persons may be too low, and for the same reason, the mortality from phthisis among spouses of tuberculous persons, which I likewise established, perhaps appears somewhat too high. With this I believe I have given you a picture of the difficulties encountered in determining and evaluating the influence of pathological inheritance in man.

Of particular interest for the theory of heredity are those qualities whose inheritance is, or appears to be, linked more or less to a certain sex. Color blindness and hemophilia belong here. According to the literature to date, both diseases occur many times more frequently in men than in women. Women play a role as intermediaries in transmission from grandfather to grandson. However, recently some doubts have arisen, at least with regard to color blindness, whether color blindness does not occur considerably more often in women than has hitherto been believed, and it has been especially recommended that school physicians should look for it in their examinations. It is not excluded that color blindness has been found more often in men only because it is troublesome in their occupations. Such demonstration would throw some light on the inheritance of color blindness and in this event the question of the carrier would become more complicated. Hemophilia is also not entirely limited to the male sex and here too the question arises whether the male, as a consequence of his occupation and different mode of life from childhood on, more often gives the disease an opportunity to become manifest.

In contrast to these diseases, the ability to bear twins from two ova is a quality in which the male plays only the role of agent of transmission. According to my investigations, begun over 7 years ago, it is quite certain that this quality is doubtless inheritable, as Darwin assumed only on the basis of the casuistic literature. This quality is due to a difference in the ovaries at least in a portion of mothers of non-identical twins in such a way that the abundance of eggs, existing in childhood in all females, persists in some adult women and thereby allows a more frequent loss of eggs from the adult ovaries. In contrast, the majority of adult women have ovaries which are relatively poor in eggs. The ovaries of mothers of twins therefore resemble those of multiparous animals and in this respect a twin birth represents an atavism not only physiologically but also from the viewpoint of comparative anatomy. From this we see, as I stated at that time, that there is no fundamental difference between heredity and atavism. The fact that children of unlike sex occur only among binovular twins and the justified assumption that the frequency of unlike sex twins is almost exactly 50% of the total binovular twins have made it possible for me to determine a series of qualities of binovular twins and their mothers in a large material of population statistics and in specially collected family registers. From this the fact emerges that unlike sex pairs, and consequently binovular twins, occur in very different frequencies among the different peoples of Europe, when compared with the total births. In particular, nations of German origin are distinguished by a high frequency of binovular twins, whereas these are relatively rare among the Latin peoples. For this reason it is probably not justified to consider the occurrence of twins in a family as a sign of degeneration, as Rosenfeld in Vienna tried to do. The fact that the frequency of non-identical twins presents racial variation supports a Mendelian form of inheritance for twinning. At the suggestion of Professor Hacker I studied my previously collected material to find out whether evidence could be found which would support a Mendelian mode of inheritance in twins. However, it would have been very difficult to collect a sufficient number of cases in which children of mothers of twins had married each other and then determine the frequency of twin births among their children. I have therefore tried to construct a formula for the frequency of dominant and recessive traits among the mothers, daughters, and sibs of persons affected with such traits of the same character, under the assumption that absolute panmixis is present.

Before I pursue the problem of Mendelian behavior, I must explain how I demonstrated the fact of inheritance among twins. The proof was a double one.

First, I established that not every woman has the ability to bear twins in the same measure. I could demonstrate this by studying how frequently twins occur again among the later or earlier births of mothers of twins. Among the binovular I found a frequency of 1/30, that is, one would have to examine on the average 30 further births to mothers of twins before finding another monovular or binovular twin birth. This apparently low ratio appears significant, however, if one considers that in Württemberg a twin birth occurs, on the average, once in 75 births and in Stuttgart only once in 90 births. Among the mothers of triplets, quadruplets and quintuplets, of which I collected a total of about 400 cases in Württemberg, the figure for repeated multiple births rose to 1/19, 1/13, and 1/3, respectively.

Second, I was able to establish that there is a direct correlation between the frequency with which multiple births are repeated by a mother, and the frequency of multiple births among mother, sisters and daughters. In these relatives the frequency of multiple births rises to about double, and among triplets the value of 1/9 is reached.

From this relatively low figure for repeatability, to the cause of which I may perhaps still have the opportunity to return, I concluded that since the average number of births to a mother of twins is only about 4-5, numerous women with a tendency to twin births do not manifest this trait because they have not performed the experiment often enough.

Moreover, I have proved that among mothers, sisters and daughters of mothers of twins, triplets, etc., multiple births occur considerably more frequently than among the total number of births. Here it was not that a daughter of a woman who had had twins once in 5 births would have had, on the average, twins among 10 children (because the intensity of the trait among the children represented the mean of that found in the parents); rather the ratio was such that it could be assumed that the mothers of twins had transmitted their ability with that frequency with which, on the average, she repeated having twins, that is, the frequency of 1/30, while the father inherited, on the average, the frequency of 1/90, in the Stuttgart cases. Thus by means of mixing, the actual frequency with which twins were repeated among mothers, sisters and daughters of twins was $1/30 - 1/90 = 1/45$. Seven years ago I, like many others, knew nothing about Mendelian genetics, and I was inclined to consider these figures as proof that we were dealing with a simple mixture of characters. In so doing I had overlooked that the ratio among the relatives of mothers of triplets, quadruplets and quintuplets did not agree with this; such discrepancy I attributed to the smallness of the numbers. For these one does not obtain among mothers and sisters (I have not been able to investigate the daughters) the simple average of the repetition figure and the general figure, but rather considerably smaller values, which, moreover, are somewhat higher among the sisters than among the mothers.

I have now asked myself whether these striking phenomena among the triplets could not perhaps be related to the action of Mendel's rule and arrived at the conclusion that this is actually the case. However, in the presentation of the train of thought which led me to this I must refer to what was said at the beginning of my lecture.

As far as my investigations up to the present could show—I hope soon to be able to extend them considerably—neither a conscious nor unconscious selection takes place with reference to the inherited factors for twinning. The existence of a rather extensive panmixis with regard to this character is also supported on theoretical grounds.

I was therefore confronted with the question: How does the numerical influence of Mendelian inheritance behave under the influence of panmixis? The typical Mendelian rule represents only the effect of the splitting of the inherited factors in the germ cells under the influence of the most absolute inbreeding. Such inbreeding does not occur in man.

If one continues the exclusive crossing of pure types and hybrids for several generations and further counts the hybrids AB among the dominant type AA (whereas the recessive is designated BB), then the relative frequency in the nth generation after the first cross is[1]

$$\mathbf{A} = 2^{n-1} + 1$$
$$\mathbf{B} = 2^{n-1} - 1.$$

The difference then shows the excess of hybrids, which is 2 each time, and becomes relatively less frequent with each generation, since for each generation increasing numbers of $\mathbf{A}$ and $\mathbf{B}$ are obtained.

The situation is entirely different when Mendelian inheritance is examined under the influence of panmixis. I start with the general hypothesis that there are initially m males and females who are pure representatives of type $\mathbf{A}$, and likewise n individuals who are pure representatives of type $\mathbf{B}$ present. If these are crossed at random the composition of the daughter generation is obtained by using the symbolism of the binomial theorem:

$$(m\,AA + n\,BB)^2 = \frac{m^2}{(m+n)^2}\,AA + \frac{2mn}{(m+n)^2}\,AB + \frac{n^2}{(m+n)^2}\,BB$$

or if $m + n = 1$

$$m^2\,AA + 2mn\,AB + n^2\,BB.$$

If the male and female members of the first generation are crossed at random the following frequency of the different combinations of crosses are obtained:[2]

$$m^2 \cdot m^2\,(AA \times AA) = m^4\,AA$$
$$2 \cdot m^2 \cdot 2mn\,(AA \times AB) = 2m^3n\,AA + 2m^3n\,AB$$
$$2 \cdot m^2 \cdot n^2\,(AA \times BB) = 2m^2n^2\,AB$$
$$2mn \cdot 2mn\,(AB \times AB) = m^2n^2\,AA + 2m^2n^2\,AB + m^2n^2\,BB$$
$$2 \cdot 2mn \cdot n^2\,(AB \times BB) = 2mn^3\,AB + 2mn^3\,BB$$
$$n^2 \cdot n^2\,(BB \times BB) = n^4\,BB$$

or the relative frequencies are for

$$AA : m^2\,(m+n)^2$$
$$AB : 2mn\,(m+n)^2$$
$$BB : n^2\,(m+n)^2$$

[1] Editor's note: $\mathbf{A}$ and $\mathbf{B}$ represent phenotype frequencies. The first cross represents the hybrid generation where $n = 1$.

[2] Editor's note: The expression to the left of the equality sign represents the frequency of the cross (mating type) while the figure to the right represents the relative proportions of types among children of these matings determined for Mendelian expectation. The operation thus combines the facts of binomial expectation with those of Mendelism.

and the composition of the second or daughter generation is again

$$m^2\ AA + 2mn\ AB + n^2\ BB.$$

We thus obtain the same distribution of pure types and hybrids for each generation under the influence of panmixis and therewith the possibility of calculating for each generation how the representation of these types is arranged in panmixis and Mendelian inheritance among the parents, sibs and children of the various types and hybrids.

If the original distribution of the two types and hybrids is

$$m^2\ AA + 2mn\ AB + n^2\ BB$$

and among the relatives the representatives of the dominant type (AA) and hybrids (AB) are considered together in that they are designated by the same single letter $(\mathbf{A})$, then when $\mathbf{A}$ is dominant the frequency of $\mathbf{A}$ and $\mathbf{B}$ is

among the parents of $\mathbf{A}$: $(1 + mn)\mathbf{A}:n^2\mathbf{B}$,
among the children of $\mathbf{A}$: $(1 + mn)\mathbf{A}:n^2\mathbf{B}$,
among the sibs of $\mathbf{A}$: $[4(1 + mn) + mn^2]\mathbf{A}:n^2(3 + n)\mathbf{B}$.

[Editor's note: The derivation of these ratios may not be immediately obvious and the following elaboration is provided.

An individual with the dominant phenotype $\mathbf{A}$ may have genotypes AA or AB. The relative frequencies of phenotypes $\mathbf{A}$ and $\mathbf{B}$, i.e., the $\mathbf{A}:\mathbf{B}$ ratio, among the parents of $\mathbf{A}$ individuals may be determined by a series of steps which combine the Hardy-Weinberg expectations with those of Mendelism.

The first step is to set out the mating types which are potentially productive of an $\mathbf{A}$ child. This is done in the first column of the table below. Only the $BB \times BB$ mating type is incapable of producing an $\mathbf{A}$ phenotype child. This mating is therefore omitted. The second step, shown in the second column below, is to indicate the frequency with which these mating types occur in the population. The next step is firstly to indicate, in each mating type, the probability that one parent will have phenotype $\mathbf{A}$ and secondly the probability that the other parent will have phenotype $\mathbf{B}$. These probabilities are shown in columns three and four. The fourth step is to provide, as done in the fifth column, the Mendelian expectation that a specific mating will produce an $\mathbf{A}$ child.

Genotype mating	Frequency genotype mating	Probability one parent is phenotype **A**	Probability one parent is phenotype **B**	Probability child is phenotype **A**
$AA \times AA$	m^4	1	0	1
$AA \times AB$	$4m^3n$	1	0	1
$AA \times BB$	$2m^2n^2$	1/2	1/2	1
$AB \times AB$	$4m^2n^2$	1	0	3/4
$AB \times BB$	$4mn^3$	1/2	1/2	1/2

The probability that a parent will be phenotype $\mathbf{A}$ when given that a child is phenotype $\mathbf{A}$ may be symbolized Pr ($\mathbf{A}$ parent | $\mathbf{A}$ child) and may be calculated by compound probabilities. Thus by cross multiplication

$Pr\,(\mathbf{A}\text{ parent} \mid \mathbf{A}\text{ child}) = m^4(1)(1) + 4m^3n(1)(1) + 2m^2n^2(\tfrac{1}{2})(1) + 4m^2n^2(1)(\tfrac{3}{4}) + 4mn^3(\tfrac{1}{2})(\tfrac{1}{2})$

Summed this expression becomes

$$m^4 + 4m^3n + 4m^2n^2 + mn^3.$$

Simplification depends on the use of identities such as $(m + n) = 1$. Thus $1 + n = m + n + n = m + 2n$. In turn, $m^4 + 4m^3n + 4m^2n^2 = m^2(m^2 + 4mn + 4n^2) = m^2(m + 2n)^2 = m^2(1 + n)^2$.

Thereby Pr (**A** parent | **A** child) $= m^2(1 + n)^2 + mn^3$.

The Pr (**B** parent | **A** child), obtained in a similar fashion, $= 2m^2n^2(1/2)(1) + 4mn^3(1/2)(1/2) = m^2n^2 + mn^3$.

The ratio of the Pr (**A** parent) : Pr (**B** parent) thus becomes

$$\frac{m^2(1 + n)^2 + mn^3}{m^2n^2 + mn^3} = \frac{m(1 + n)^2 + n^3}{mn^2 + n^3}$$

$$= \frac{m(1 + n)^2 + n^3}{n^2(m + n)} = \frac{m(1 + n)^2 + n^3}{n^2}$$

$$= \frac{m + 2mn + mn^2 + n^3}{n^2} = m + 2mn + n^2(m + n)$$

$$= \frac{m + 2mn + n^2}{n^2} = \frac{m + mn + n(m + n)}{n^2}$$

$$= \frac{m + mn + n}{n^2} = \frac{1 + mn}{n^2}.$$

The balance of the expressions for the relative proportions of **A** and **B** phenotypes among other classes of relatives and in the case of other forms of inheritance may be derived in a similar manner. Such derivations are still occasionally employed today for the demonstration of simple inheritance in those instances where data, for example, is limited to parent-child combinations.]

But if **A** is recessive, one obtains:

for the parents of **A**: m**A**:n**B**
for the children of **A**: m**A**:n**B**
for the sibs of **A**: $(1 + m)^2$**A**:$n(3 + m)$**B**.

Thus it appears that in Mendelian inheritance the representation of types obtained for sibs differs from the proportion among parents and children. In qualities that are measurable, as in our case, this must lead to different average values among parents and sibs. In a non-Mendelian character, where the hybrids represent several intermediary stages, the average representation of measurable qualities would be the same in parents and sibs. There is, therefore, a real difference between Mendelian and non-Mendelian characters. I have found with respect to the tendency for triplet birth that the sibs and parents exhibit essentially different numbers, which speaks for a Mendelian trait. There are similar small differences in the tendency for twinning.

It is now apparent that where **A** is dominant, type **A** is always represented in at least half of the parents.

Where **A** is recessive one obtains limiting values for frequencies of **A**, of $1:0$ and $0:1$ for the parents and $1:0$ and $1:3$ for sibs. At the same time we learn that rare recessive characters can be detected easier in sibs than in parents. The possibility of calculating the expected figures for Mendelian inheritance has enabled me to utilize not only the absolutely few cases in which children of mothers of twins married each other but also my entire earlier material.

It is now a question of determining the value of m. For this the following consideration is needed. A binovular twin birth occurs once in 35 births among mothers with a tendency to twinning, but only once in 140 among all mothers, as in Stuttgart, then the former represent only one fourth of all mothers. If their frequency is placed at $m^2 = 1/4$, then that of the other women is $2mn + n^2 = 3/4$, and we obtain $m = n = 1/2$ where **A** is recessive. In the case of dominance of twinning we would obtain the ratio $m:n = 1:6.5$, if $m^2 + 2mn:n^2 = 1:3$.

Likewise, if a triplet birth occurs in ca. 6000 births, and in mothers with a tendency to triplet births, a triplet birth occurs once to every 200 single births, the value

$$m = 1/5 \text{ in the case of recessivity}$$
$$m = 1/60 \text{ in the case of dominance.}$$

In each of these cases, however, a twin birth would occur in 84 births in Württemberg women without a tendency to triplet births.

If the value thus found is inserted into the above formula for the hereditary trait through parents, sibs and children, one obtains, from the comparison of the calculated probable number with the actual ratios, the assumption which comes closest to the mode of inheritance.

According to whether the trait for multiple births as opposed to single birth is (I) recessive, (II) dominant or (III) equivalent, the following expected numbers are obtained as the expected frequency of multiple births in the kinships of mothers of twins and triplets in Stuttgart and Württemberg:

	I	II	III
(a) among the mothers of mothers of twins	1/52	1/46	1/45
(b) among the daughters of mothers of twins	1/52	1/46.8	1/45
(c) among the sisters of mothers of twins	1/49	1/46.6	1/45
(d) among the mothers of mothers of triplets	1/52	1/29	1/29
(e) among the sisters of mothers of triplets	1/37	1/29	1/29

The observed births in the individual groups were

a)	1365
b)	1464
c)	1022
d)	2638
e)	1666

Accordingly the absolute number of expected multiple births is:

In group	According to the assumption			Observed
	I	II	III	
(a)	26	27	30	27
(b)	28	31	33	24
(c)	21	22	23	27
(d)	51	91	91	45
(e)	45	57	57	36
Totals	171	228	234	159

The assumption that the trait for twin births is recessive is therefore obtained from the expected numbers which are closer to the observed than under any other assumption. The difference in 12 cases lies within the mean error, which is close to $\sqrt{171} = 13$.

The situation found in the inheritance of twinning best finds its explanation in the assumption that the trait for twinning is inherited according to the Mendelian rule and is recessive.

This investigation (a more thorough presentation based on a new collection of material that I have in the meantime obtained from another source will follow) may show that one can gain an insight into the nature of human inheritance by suitable changes in the investigative methods.

Die Bedeutung der Statistisch Ermittelten Belastung mit Blutverwandtschaft der Eltern*
(The Meaning of the Statistically Determined Trait with Consanguinity of the Parents)

F. LENZ

In this paper Lenz gives the first exact treatment of the role of consanguinity in the appearance of recessively inherited disturbances. The manner of approach is straightforward and is easily grasped by the reader uncomfortable with mathematics. The simple devices employed provide an estimate of gene frequencies and, as such, are still applied. Perhaps more impressive than the formulae derived is that Lenz recognized the limitations of his method. He observed that it depended heavily upon a precise knowledge of the proportion of marriages between blood relations; upon the assumption of genetic, as opposed to acquired, origin of a given disorder; and finally upon the assurance of genetic homogeneity among all the examples of a given disorder. The latter assumption is, as Lenz recognized, often untenable, and it becomes possible that genetic heterogeneity of loci and mutant genes responsible for many disorders is the rule rather than the exception. In turn the dependence of mathematical genetics upon a precise characterization of genes and their products becomes manifest.

In any case, the principle of an increased proportion of cousin marriages in a rare recessive disorder stands, and as a means in itself suggesting simple inheritance of a given condition was clearly recognized, for example, by Garrod in his remarks included in this collection.

Very much that is erroneous and only little that is correct has been written about the harmful consequences of consanguineous marriages. Mayet (1) devoted an excellent statistical investigation to this problem, and Kraus and

* Reprinted by publisher's permission from Münchener Medizinische Wochenschrift. 2: 1340-1342.

Döhrer (2) discussed the problem very thoroughly with the aid of Mayet's tables. Even so, it cannot be said that very much has resulted from this. Yet the statistical work up to the present has shown that carriers of certain afflictions descend from consanguineous marriages in a higher than average percentage. In a material of 16,146 feeble-minded and idiots Mayet found that 1.44 per cent descended from consanguineous marriages, while consanguineous marriages constitute only 0.647 per cent of all marriages. Englemann (3) found that the percentage of consanguineous marriages among the parents of 3524 deafmutes was 6.8. Earlier, Hartmann had found 7.0 per cent and Bezold 6.6 per cent for deafmutism. Higher figures are given by others, especially by American investigators. The percentage is still higher in so-called retinitis pigmentosa which therefore is customarily mentioned first in discussions of traits due to inbreeding. On the basis of a compilation of 513 cases, Schmidt reported a percentage of 25.5 (1). Likewise, Ayres found 22 per cent, Hirschberg 25 per cent, Mooren 33 per cent, v. Wecker 33 per cent, Jäger 33 per cent.[1]

It is therefore not to be doubted that consanguineous marriage is of significance in the occurrence of some afflictions; it is also established that the percentage of the trait due to consanguineous marriage differs greatly for different afflictions, but is fairly constant for one and the same affliction. However, an understanding of this constancy and this difference has not yet been obtained by workers on this subject. Most of them have concluded that consanguinity disposes in especially high degree to retinitis pigmentosa, also in high degree to deafmutism, in low degree to idiocy, etc. Why this is so remained obscure. And yet the solution is very simple. The percentage of the trait through consanguineous marriage depends upon the frequency or rarity of the affliction for which blood relationship is of importance. This will become clear immediately.

Practically all workers on the problem are in agreement that the harmfulness of consanguineous marriages rests on an "increase of the genetic effect." Of course, in an age of exact research in genetics this is expressed very vaguely, but yet contains a kernel of truth. We know that there are many abnormal genetic factors, one of which by itself alone does not lead to manifest disease but must first meet one of a similar kind for this to occur. Such hereditary factors are commonly called recessive. The harmfulness of consanguineous marriages then rests mainly on the fact that they give recessive abnormal hereditary factors the opportunity to meet, appear homozygously, and thereby become manifest. Consanguineous marriages are practically of no importance with respect to dominant hereditary traits since a dominant character becomes manifest by itself alone, that is, heterozygously. If, therefore, the percentage of consanguinity among parents of carriers of a certain trait is increased with regularity, there is reason to assume that the condition is inherited recessively. The magnitude of this percentage,

[1] Cited by Kraus.

however, is simply a result of the frequency distribution of the recessive factor in the population and increases with the rarity of the factor.

If a character is present in only one family it can, nevertheless, be made homozygous through consanguineous marriage but not through marriage between unrelated persons; in this case 100 per cent of the affected individuals are offspring of consanguineous marriages. If, on the other hand, an abnormal recessive character is very widespread in a population, the probability of coming together with a similar one is not much greater in consanguineous marriages than in other marriages; the appearance of affected individuals among consanguineous matings has increased only a little over the average. But if a certain group of affected individuals is weighted no higher than the average with consanguineous marriages, this speaks against a recessive inheritance of the defect.

I have now traced these situations numerically and have compiled into a table how high a percentage of consanguineous marriages among the parents of the affected individuals is to be expected for different frequencies of an affliction if a simple recessive mode of inheritance is present. For the sake of clarity, the percentages were calculated exclusively for marriages between children of cousins; therefore only the most frequent kind of consanguineous marriage is considered; that between uncle and niece and aunt and

Table 1. FREQUENCY OF THE TRAIT THROUGH COUSIN MARRIAGES OF THE PARENTS IN ITS DEPENDENCE ON THE GENERAL FREQUENCY OF RECESSIVE AFFLICTIONS (ASSUMPTION: 1 PER CENT OF ALL MARRIAGES ARE CONTRACTED BETWEEN FIRST-DEGREE COUSINS)

Frequency of afflicted persons, whose parents were not blood relations	Frequency if those from consanguineous marriages are included	Percentage of cousin marriages among the parents
1: 1		1
1: 2		1
1: 10		1.2
1: 100		1.6
1: 400		2.2
1: 900		2.9
1: 1600		3.5
1: 2500		4.0
1: 4900		5.1
1: 10000		6.8
1: 40000		12
1: 90000		16
1:160000	1:125000	21
1:490000	1:300000	31
$1:10^6$	1:540000	38
$1:4 \times 10^6$	$1:1.5 \times 10^6$	55
$1:25 \times 10^6$	$1:4.6 \times 10^6$	76
$1:100 \times 10^6$	$1:10.5 \times 10^6$	86

nephew is, on the contrary, not considered. This is important to know if the table is to be used for comparative purposes. Marriages between first-degree cousins must first be sorted out from a statistical material that contains marriages in addition to those between children of cousins, e.g., those between uncle and niece or marriages between second-degree cousins, before the material can be compared with this table.

For this computation it was necessary to use the general percentage frequency of cousin marriages as a base. Unfortunately, the true percentage is not known. It was found statistically that of 5,922,439 marriages between 1875 and 1899 in Prussia 0.587 per cent were cousin marriages; in Bavaria, 0.582. This percentage is, however, certainly too low because for many marriage contracts the relationship is not ascertained at the registry. Therefore the figures are minimum figures. In France a percentage of 0.970 was determined. In England the percentage is still higher. Since in France some cases could have eluded discovery, I believed it permissible to assume 1 per cent as the percentage of cousin marriages and to use it as a base in the table.

To explain the computation it will first be shown how the frequency of a recessive affliction, p, can be obtained from the proportion of affected individuals whose parents were first-degree cousins, b. If the general proportion of cousin marriages is a, then a heterozygous carrier of a latent recessive disorder has the probability a of entering into a cousin marriage; and since the probability that two cousins have a certain gene in common is $1/8$,[2] he has the probability of $a/8$ of contracting a cousin marriage and in this marriage come together with such a carrier of the gene. One-fourth of the children, on the average, from such a marriage have the recessive affliction. The probability that two carriers of the latent recessive character come together in non-cousin marriage is about $1/b$ times as large, since b is the proportion of cousin marriages of parents. In the mating of two carriers of the latent character the probability of producing affected children is just as great if the parents are related by blood as if they are not. The probability that a carrier of the recessive factor acquires a carrier spouse who is not related to him by blood is therefore $\frac{a}{8} \cdot \frac{1}{b}$, or more exactly $\frac{a}{8}\left(\frac{1-b}{b}\right)$, at least for a relatively rare character, that is, a large b. Therefore, $\frac{a}{8}\left(\frac{1-b}{b}\right)$ must at the same time be the frequency distribution of carriers of the factor in the population (m). Since according to Mendel's law, each individual has two sets of genes, the frequency of the gene for the recessive character is $n = \frac{1}{2} \cdot \frac{a}{8} \cdot \left(\frac{1-b}{b}\right)$. Then the frequency of the recessive affliction without

[2] Every human being has, on the average, one half of his hereditary factors in common with each of his parents and with each of his sibs; consequently, on the average, 1/4 with one of his grandparents, an uncle or an aunt, and therefore 1/8 with a cousin. This is according to Mendel's law.

consanguineous marriage is $p = n^2$, since the affliction arises from the meeting of two factors, each of which has the frequency n.

The computation will perhaps be most easily clarified by an example. Let the load through cousin marriages be 20 per cent for an affliction. Then

$$m = \frac{1}{100} \cdot \frac{1}{8} \cdot \left(\frac{1 - 1/5}{1/5} \right) = \frac{4}{800} = \frac{2}{400}. ^3$$

Therefore $n = m/2 = 1/400$; and $p = n^2 = 1:160,000$. If of the parents of carriers of a certain affliction 20 per cent come from cousin marriages, it is to be assumed that only every 160,000th in the population has the affliction, whereby, however, the affected children of consanguineous marriages have not been included in the computations.

To this must still be added the frequency of the affliction in children from consanguineous marriages and this can be easily calculated since it is known how large a proportion of affected individuals come from consanguineous marriages, namely, b. Therefore

$$p = n^2 + \frac{b}{1 - b} \cdot n^2.$$

Therewith a close connection has been made between p and b; the frequency of the affliction can also be calculated easily from the percentage of cousin marriages among the parents.

For frequent afflictions the probability that a heterozygous carrier of a gene acquires a spouse with the same trait in a consanguineous marriage, is not $a/8$, but larger, because by consanguineous marriage he can acquire a spouse of the same kind first by blood relationship and second because of the general frequency of the gene. The probability is therefore $a/8 + am$. Thus m is calculated from the formula $m = \left(\frac{a}{8} + am \right) \frac{1 - b}{b}$.

The reverse calculation is more convenient, that is, to calculate the carrier from the frequency of the affliction in individuals who do not come from consanguineous marriages. First, $n = \sqrt{p}$; m is then $= 2\sqrt{p}$, at least for rare afflictions. In frequent ones $m = 2\sqrt{p} - p$, because here two genes often meet in the same individual. As p becomes smaller it soon becomes insignificant for the calculation with respect to $2\sqrt{p}$. b is then easily calculated according to the formula

$$m = \left(\frac{a}{8} + am \right) \frac{1 - b}{b}.$$

If one wishes to proceed not only from affected individuals whose parents are not related by blood, but directly from all affected individuals, the computation would become much more intricate. Instead, in the table I have

---

³ Editor's note: The term $1/100$ is taken to be the proportion a of consanguineous unions in the population.

calculated in all conditions where the frequency is less than 1:100,000, how many affected individuals from consanguineous marriages are to be expected. If p is the number of affected persons from consanguineous marriages, $p\dfrac{b}{1-b}$ is the number of affected individuals from cousin marriages. According to this, one can also calculate the number of affected individuals from marriages between uncle and niece, and aunt and nephew, and between second-degree cousins. A regular correlation exists between the frequency of cousin marriages and that with sibs of parents. I have assumed the frequency of these latter marriages as 0.06 per cent, marriages with children of cousins as 0.30 per cent and that with second-degree cousins as 1 per cent. If all consanguineous marriages up to second-degree cousins are counted in, a frequency of about 2.3 per cent of consanguineous marriages is found. Of course, the frequency of children with recessive afflictions differs with the different degrees of consanguineous marriages. The following formulation illustrates the relative ratios:

	Frequency	Proportion of the combined hereditary property, on the average		Numerical ratio of affected children
Marriages with sibs of the parents	0.06 per cent:	$\dfrac{1}{4}$	=	0.01
Marriages with first-degree cousins	1.00 per cent:	$\dfrac{1}{8}$	=	0.12
Marriages with children of cousins	0.30 per cent:	$\dfrac{1}{16}$	=	0.02
Marriages with second-degree cousins	$\dfrac{1.00 \text{ per cent:}}{2.36 \text{ per cent}}$	$\dfrac{1}{64}$	=	$\dfrac{0.02}{0.17}$

Under these assumptions, the total frequency of recessive afflictions, including those from consanguineous marriages up to second-degree cousins, has been computed and presented in the middle column of Table 1.

Not considered in the computation was the circumstance that the number of children from consanguineous marriages is, on the average, not as large as from other marriages, a fact which Weinberg (4) correctly pointed out, in contradiction to Mayet. Since consanguineous marriages are quite often contracted in the interest of holding estates together, they occur predominately among the well-to-do and wealthy, who have a smaller number of children than the less well-to-do. The same rationalized motives which lead to consanguineous marriage, also often act toward keeping the number of children small. Not quite so many children with heritable disease issue from consanguineous marriages as would be the case if the fertility in all marriages were the same. Since the degree of the lower fertility in consanguineous marriages is not known more precisely, it could not be considered in the computations. This omission could be made quite comfortably since, on the one hand, it could not be very significant, and, on the other hand, in the calculation of the totals it would give only approximate values.

We would now like to make some tests of this example.

In the case of idiocy and feeble-mindedness, 1.44 per cent of the parents were found to be blood relations as compared with the average of 0.647 (2). Taken as absolute, these figures are certainly too small due to the paucity of the statistics as mentioned at the beginning. But relatively they show that in idiocy the hereditary taint in consanguineous marriages exceeds the average by more than double. Since this could also hold true for cousin marriages, the general average of which we have placed at 1 per cent, about 2.2 per cent of the trait in idiots would correspond to cousin marriages. In Table 1, we see that it represents a frequency of 1:400. That would lead to the number of 150,000 idiots and feeble-minded in Germany, which actually would be in agreement with the approximate number of inherited feeble-mindedness. Consequently, idiocy and feeble-mindedness could represent a simple recessive hereditary affliction. However, it is quite probable that only a part of this weakened condition of the brain is a simple recessive. The higher figure that would accordingly be expected for the trait in consanguineous marriages is lowered by the unavoidable inclusion of idiocy due to other causes (syphilis, alcohol).

The deafmutes are, as we heard, charged in about 7 per cent to demonstrable consanguineous marriages. If all cases could be detected this figure would no doubt be somewhat higher. For the trait only in marriages between first-degree cousins the figure of about 5.1 per cent of the table enters into consideration. This corresponds to a frequency of 1:5000. This would make about 12,000 deafmutes in Germany; actually there are about 50,000. However, about half of these afflictions are due to other causes (meningitis, etc.). The number remaining is still too high, especially if one considers that the percentage rate of the hereditary taint would increase accordingly. It cannot therefore very well be assumed that deafmutism is a uniformly recessive affliction. The pedigrees also correspond to this. In the simple recessive mode of inheritance, two deafmute parents must have only deafmute children. This agrees with a part of the cases, but not with most. It therefore appears that there are different recessive afflictions which can become manifest as deafmutism. The organ of hearing is indeed so complex that it is immediately understandable that a deficiency in various hereditary factors can each by itself cause deafmutism. Probably there are several kinds of hereditary deafmutism. The pedigrees as well as the numerical situation are in accord with this.

In retinitis pigmentosa the proportion of cases due to consanguineous marriage is about 25 per cent. In the table, the figure of about 16 per cent could represent cousin marriages alone. This gives a frequency of 1:90,000 and for Germany about 700 affected persons. Since this concerns a rather rare affliction, this number is probably correct. Other experiences also confirm that most cases of atrophy of the retinal pigment are determined by simple recessive abnormal hereditary factors. A pedigree with a dominant mode of inheritance and one with a recessive sex-linked one have been described by Nettleship (5). But these pedigrees are isolated ones. To be sure, they show that atrophy of the retinal pigment can also be determined by other than the usual abnormal hereditary factors. The great majority, however, are obviously simple recessives. Such a severe affliction could not maintain itself at all through a dominant mode of inheritance since it would be eliminated in a short time by natural selection. The recessive traits can, on the contrary, disseminate unhindered since they remain preeminently latent; according to the table in the ratio of 1:300.

Of course, there is still a large number of other recessive afflictions in which corresponding considerations would be indicated. But due to the lack of sufficient statistical material this has so far not been possible. I would like to go briefly into the subject of dementia praecox. I am indebted to Professor Rüdin, Director of the Genetic Research Division of the German Research Institute for Psychiatry, Munich, for reliable information on this subject. In a material of 700 cases of dementia praecox, Rüdin found that in 14 cases, i.e., 2 per cent, the parents were cousins. This figure is a minimum figure; however, it could not lag much below the true one since this material could be investigated thoroughly. If we assume that 2.2 per cent in the table is the actual number, then this would correspond to a frequency of dementia praecox of 1:400, if this were a simple recessive affliction. Now, what is the true frequency of dementia praecox? In Bavaria in 1910, 3,400 mental patients were admitted to institutions out of a population of 6,800,000, that is, 1 out of every 2,000 inhabitants. Of course, not all mental patients are admitted to institutions; according to the census of December 1, 1910, only 152 of 196 cases were admitted. On the other hand, not a few cases are admitted several times, either because they change institutions or are discharged temporarily. If one assumes that these two errors approximately equalize each other, the figure of 1:2000 denotes the annual frequency of onset of mental diseases. According to Kraepelin about 10 per cent of the cases admitted in Munich were dementia praecox. The admittance frequency for dementia praecox would therefore be about 1:20,000. This would be the magnitude of the probability that an inhabitant would succumb to dementia praecox in a given year. Since the mean duration of life is 50 years, the probability of acquiring dementia praecox at any time during a lifetime would be 50 times as great, or about 1:400. This would be precisely the figure we found according to the table. The agreement is, nevertheless, only seemingly good; in fact, it is too good. If we assume that the factor for dementia praecox is a simple recessive, we must make the further assumption that the disease becomes manifest in only a fifth of those with a tendency to it. Rüdin (6) found that only 4.5 per cent of the sibs of dementia praecox patients likewise succumbed, whereas this percentage must be 25 if the factor is developed in every case by a simple recessive mode of inheritance. The frequency of 1:400 for affected persons would thus correspond to a frequency of 1:80 for persons with a tendency for it, and this figure does not agree with the 2 per cent taint through cousin marriages. First to be considered as a source of error is that, like deafmutism, dementia praecox is not an idiotypic entity. Second, there is the possibility that the percentage of cousin marriages among healthy individuals is higher than the 1 per cent I assumed in computing the table. If the general frequency of cousin marriages were 1.3 per cent instead of 1 per cent, there would be complete agreement between the hypothesis and reality. Finally, as a third source of error there must be taken into consideration that the probability error in 700 cases could still be too large to establish the percentage as generally valid. In such cases the standard deviation is calculated according to the formula

$$m = \sqrt{\frac{p \cdot 9}{s^3}},$$

or in our case

$$m = \sqrt{\frac{14 \cdot 686}{700^3}} = \text{ca. } 0.5 \text{ per cent.}$$

The percentage rate of cousin marriages would therefore be noted as 2 ± 0.5 per cent. As a result of this possibility for the discrepancy, the number calculated according to this hypothesis is obviously in agreement with the true number, even though less demonstrable. However, in any case here also the order of magnitude agrees, and only this is of importance.

SUMMARY

The percentage rate of consanguineous marriages which is found among the parents of carriers of certain afflictions depends upon the general frequency with which the hereditary factor for the specific affliction occurs in the population. The correlation is numerically ascertainable. A comparison with the actual figures in idiocy, deafmutism, retinitis pigmentosa and dementia praecox shows that there is agreement at least with respect to the order of magnitude.

LITERATURE

(1) Mayet, P.: Verwandtenehe und Statistik. Jahrb. d. internat. Vereinigung f. vergl. Rechtswissenschaft und Volkswirtschaftslehre. Vol. 6 and 7.

(2) Kraus, F. and Döhrer, H.: Blutverwandtschaft in der Ehe und deren Folgen für die Nachkommenschaft. In: Krankheiten und Ehe. Edited by v. Noorden and Kaminer. 2nd edition. Leipzig, 1916.

(3) Englemann: Die Ergebnisse der fortlaufenden Statistik der Taubstummen während der Jahre 1902 bis 1905. Mitteilungen aus dem Kais. Gesundheitsamt. Vol. 12.

(4) Weinberg, W.: Verwandtenehe und Geisteskrankheit. Archiv f. Rassen-u. Gesellschaftsbiologie. 4 Jg., 1907.

(5) Nettleship, E.: On some hereditary diseases of the eye. Transactions of the Ophthalmological Society, 1909.

(6) Rüdin, E.: Zur Vererbung und Neuenstehung der Dementia praecox. Berlin, 1916.

Origins
and
Syntheses
of
Blood
Group
Genetics

Part Two

> *The discovery by Landsteiner of what are now called the ABO blood groups provides the prime illustration of a simple observation which has become of fundamental importance to the study of human variation. Fortuitously this discovery coincided with the reappearance of Mendelism, and the two events have since done much to complement one another.*
>
> *Landsteiner's concern with the possible relationship of his finding to disease foreshadowed a long debate. Later observation established that associations between blood groups and disease do indeed exist.[1]*

Über Agglutinationserscheinungen Normalen Menschlichen Blutes* (On Agglutination Phenomena of Normal Human Blood)

KARL LANDSTEINER,

Assistant at the Pathological-Anatomical Institute, Vienna.

[1] The topic of association between blood groups and disease has been reviewed by C. A. Clarke in Progress in medical genetics. A. G. Steinberg (editor). 1961. Grune and Stratton, New York: 81-119.

* Reprinted by publisher's permission from Wiener klinische Wochenschrift. 1901. 14: 1132-1134.

Some time ago I observed and reported[1] that blood serum of normal human beings is often capable of agglutinating red blood corpuscles of other healthy individuals. At that time I had the impression that this clumping property of the blood serum against foreign blood corpuscles was particularly evident in some cases of illness and I thought that it could be related to the great dissolving power of pathological sera for normal corpuscles, discovered much earlier by Maragliano,[2] since agglutinating ability and dissolving power do indeed often, but not always, change in parallel. The circumstance that it is not heating, but rather the addition of salt up to an amount equivalent of the normal that increases the dissolving power of sera, speaks against equating Maragliano's reactions with the hemolytic reactions of the blood sera so often studied at present. Maragliano himself differentiates his observations from Landois' phenomenon—hemolysis due to serum from a different species—in that in his case the hemoglobin is not only dissolved but also destroyed. A real difference between my observations and Maragliano's is that in Maragliano's case the serum acts also on corpuscles which come from the same individual and that the reaction is obtained only with abnormal blood. My observations, however, show differences of a rather striking kind between blood serum and corpuscles of different apparently entirely healthy human beings.

From Shattock's description and illustrations[3] his observations undoubtedly are pertinent here even though he detected the reaction only in febrile cases and missed it in normal blood. Shattock attributes the reaction to increased coagulability and rouleaux formation of febrile blood.

The agglutination of human blood by human serum to be discussed further here is called isoagglutination according to Ehrlich and Morgenroth's[4] method of notation. Shortly after the publication of my paper these two authors described experiments in which they succeeded in producing isolysins and isoagglutinins, that is, sera acting on corpuscles of the same species, by injection of blood of similar kind. Due to the variety of situations among the individual experimental animals these very thorough experiments confirm the not presupposed presence of clearly demonstrable blood differences within an animal species.

In Ehrlich and Morgenroth's work the phenomena of isolysis receive an accurate review from the standpoint of Ehrlich's theory.

Since the appearance of the communications by Shattock and by me, several investigators have been occupied with the behavior of isoagglutination in man. The criticism of those works[5] which consider the reaction specific

[1] Centralblatt für Bakteriologie, XXVII. February 1900. **10**: 361.

[2] XI Congress für innere Medizin. Leipzig. 1822.

[3] Jour. Pathol. and Bacteriology. February, 1900.

[4] Berliner klinische Wochenschrift. 1900.

[5] For the literature see Eisenberg. Wiener klinische Wochenschrift. 1901: 42.

for a certain disease results per se from its presence in healthy persons. Other works recorded observations on the intensity and frequency of the reaction in cases of illness.

Donath[6] found the phenomenon more frequently in different forms of anemia than in healthy persons, but not every time. Ascoli[7] observed the phenomenon in healthy individuals, but in greater intensity in sick persons. Like other authors, he got the result that the reaction is frequent in sick persons and only exceptional in healthy ones. My data contradict this finding.[8]

Since I have expressed myself very briefly in the above-mentioned communication, I will mention in the following the results obtained in some recent experiments. The tables are self-explanatory. About equal amounts of serum and approximately 5% blood suspension were mixed in 0.6% saline solution and observed in hanging drops or in test tubes (the plus sign denotes agglutination).

Table I. CONCERNING THE BLOOD OF SIX APPARENTLY HEALTHY MEN

Sera	Blood corpuscles of:					
	Dr. St.	Dr. Plecn.	Dr. Sturl.	Dr. Erdh.	Zar.	Landst.
Dr. St........	−	+	+	+	+	−
Dr. Plecn......	−	−	+	+	−	−
Dr. Sturl......	−	+	−	−	+	−
Dr. Erdh......	−	+	−	−	+	−
Zar..........	−	−	+	+	−	−
Landst........	−	+	+	+	+	−

Table II. REGARDING THE BLOOD OF SIX APPARENTLY HEALTHY PUERPERAE

Sera	Blood corpuscles of:					
	Seil.	Linsm.	Lust.	Mittelb.	Tomsch.	Graupn.
Seil..........	−	−	+	−	−	+
Linsm........	+	−	+	+	+	+
Lust.........	+	−	−	+	+	−
Mittelb.......	−	−	+	−	−	+
Tomsch.......	−	−	+	−	−	+
Graupn.......	+	−	−	+	+	−

[6] Wiener klinische Wochenschrift. 1900: 22.

[7] Münchener medizinische Wochenschrift. 1901: 1229.

[8] Although Eisenberg attacks the data of my work, he mentions the work in bibliography but not with a single word in the text.

Table III. Concerning the Blood of Five Puerperae and Six Placentae
(Umbilical Cord Blood)

Sera	Blood corpuscles of:					
	Trautm.	Linsm.	Seil.	Freib.	Graupn.	Mittelb.
Lust..........	+	+	−	−	−	+
Tomsch.......	−	−	+	−	−	−
Mittelb.......	−	−	+	−	−	−
Seil..........	−	−	+	−	−	−
Linsm.........	+	+	+	−	−	+

A fourth, similar, table dealing with the sera of Table II, combined with the corpuscles of Table I and several other sera, e.g., from two persons with hemophilia and purpura, showed completely comparable regularities and could therefore be omitted. In the investigation of ten other normal persons (in 42 combinations of the same) the situations were similar.

The experiments demonstrate that my data require no correction. All 22 examined sera from healthy persons gave the reaction. The result obviously would have been different had I not used a number of different corpuscles for the test.

Halban,[9] Ascoli and, finally, Eisenberg, called attention to a different resistance of the blood corpuscles against the reaction. This is also evident from the tables presented. In addition, however, a remarkable regularity appeared in the behavior of the 22 blood specimens examined. If one excludes the fetal placental blood, which did not produce agglutination—Halban also found that fetal blood rarely produces hemagglutination—from some of the blood serum examinations, in most cases the sera could be divided into three groups:

In several cases (group A) the serum reacted on the corpuscles of another group (B), but not on those of group A, whereas the A corpuscles are again influenced in the same manner by serum B. In the third group (C) the serum agglutinates the corpuscles of A and B, while the C corpuscles are not affected by sera of A and B.

In ordinary speech, it can be said that in these cases at least two different kinds of agglutinins are present: some in A, others in B and both together in C. The corpuscles are naturally to be considered as insensitive for the agglutinins which are present in the same serum.

It is not to be denied that the affirmation of the presence of few different agglutinins in the examined cases sounds rather remarkable, even though somewhat similar situations were found in Ehrlich and Morgenroth's experiments, and that it would be more satisfactory to find another explanation by continued observations.

[9] Wiener klinische Wochenschrift. 1900: 24.

It is now natural to look for these regularities in pathological cases. Eisenberg traces the formation of agglutinins back to the resorption of constituents of red blood corpuscles. This idea is not entirely new; it was already advanced by Halban and Ascoli as a possible solution. I did not mention this explanation at that time because I had not succeeded in producing in animals the ability for isoagglutination by injection of their own corpuscles in solution.

As I believe, Ehrlich also did not report positive results in this direction; to be sure, Ascoli had positive, but not constant, findings. Halban pointed out the difficulties in the interpretation mentioned. Especially, the formation of the naturally occurring hemagglutinins and that of the normal agglutinins that act on bacteria must perhaps be explained in different ways.

Moreover, my investigations show that the different sera do not act identically with respect to agglutination. If one believes, therefore, that they owe their agglutination ability to a kind of autoimmunization through resorption of cell constituents, then one must again assume individual differences to obtain the different sera. In fact, the blood corpuscles also behave differently in the fetal blood (see Table III). Assuming that differences of sera or corpuscles exist, one can understand with the same ease or difficulty agglutination within the species as that through serum from another species. In spite of this the explanation just mentioned cannot be excluded by any means. Indeed, if the nonrefuted experiments of Ascoli are correct, then the physiological destruction of the body tissues must, in general, be considered a source of formation of the active substances of the serum.

To exclude the assumption that perhaps past disease processes are of importance, I regarded investigations on the blood of children and animals utilizable. Halban's investigations do not support such a connection.

The described agglutination can also be produced with serum which has been dried and then dissolved. I did this successfully with a solution from a drop of blood which had been dried on linen and preserved for 14 days. Thus the reaction may possibly be suitable for forensic purposes of identification in some cases, or, better, for the detection of the nonidentity of blood specimens, if, as is possible, rapid fluctuations of the property do not occur, thus making them useless. To be sure, on the second test the six sera in Table I exhibited the same behavior as the specimens taken 9 days earlier.[10]

Finally, it must be mentioned that the reported observations allow us to explain the variable results in therapeutic transfusions of human blood.

[10] Dr. Richter in collaboration with me intends to test the usefulness of the indicated method.

Serological Differences Between the Blood of Different Races
The Result of Researches on the Macedonian Front*

DR. LUDWIK HIRSCHFELD,
Dozent at the University of Zurich;

DR. HANKA HIRSCHFELD,
Of the Central Bacteriological Laboratory, Royal Serbian Army.

The study of accurately assessed variation between different peoples essentially begins with this investigation by the Hirschfelds. The subsequent use of blood groups by anthropologists probably owes as much to the authors' conclusions as it does to their large body of data and manner of approach. The conclusion that man has a dual origin was, and is today, highly controversial and prompted much similar investigation. In the case of this paper such conclusion rested on the assumption that human blood types A and B are determined by genes at independent genetic loci and that the relative frequencies of the two types provided a "biochemical race index." The manner in which the assumption perished is in fact partially evident in Table III where there is a marked tendency for the calculated probabilities to yield higher proportions of O types than those found. This discrepancy together with further data led Bernstein (1) to propose the view, later corroborated by family studies and accepted today, that the genes determining A, B and, O behave as alleles, i.e., occur at a single genetic locus.

(1) F. Bernstein. 1925. Ergebnisse einer biostatistischen zusammenfassenden Betrachtung über die erblichen Blutstrukturen des Menschen. Klinische Wochenschrift. **3:** 1495-1497.

RACE PROBLEMS AND RESEARCHES
IN IMMUNISATION

It is a well-known fact that it is possible to produce antibodies by injecting an animal of one species with the red blood corpuscles of an animal of a

* Paper read before the Salonika Medical Society, June 5, 1918. Reprinted by publisher's permission from Lancet. 1919. ii: 675-679.

different species. These antibodies, which we call hetero-antibodies are capable of reacting with the erythrocytes of all representatives of the species used for immunising. A rabbit immunised with the blood of a man of any race will produce agglutinins or hæmolysins which can influence to a greater or lesser degree the blood corpuscles of men of any race. The hetero-antibodies are thus specific for a species and cannot bring us nearer to the solution of the race problem.

But, as Ehrlich showed in goats and von Dungern and Hirschfeld[1] in dogs, we do possess a means of finding serological differences within a species. This is effected by immunisation *in the species*. The reason for this can be explained in a few words. These antigen properties which are common to the giver and receiver of blood cannot give rise to any antibodies, since they are not felt as foreign by the immunised animal. The antibodies produced within the species which we call iso-antibodies do not, therefore, act against the whole of the antigen properties of the species, but only against the differences between the blood of the animal which provides the blood for injection and that of the recipient. The iso-antibodies thus do not influence all representatives of the species, but only the blood used for injection and other kinds of blood similar to it. If we inject into dogs the blood of other dogs it is in many cases possible to produce antibodies. By means of these antibodies we have been able to show that there are in dogs two antigen types. These antigen types, which we recognise by means of the iso-antibodies, we may designate biochemical races.

It was, therefore, clear to us from the beginning that we could only attack the human race problem on serological lines if we could succeed in making use of antibodies of this kind. The iso-antibodies alone are capable of selecting from the whole of the biochemical elements, which serologically characterise human blood as such, those elements that are characteristic of the blood of only a part of the human species.[2]

Such a differentiation of the human species is now possible by means of the iso-agglutinins first analyzed by Landsteiner. If the serum and the blood corpuscles of different pairs of human beings are brought together agglutination sometimes occurs. Accurate analysis of the agglutinable properties of the blood and of the agglutinating properties of the serum showed that this phenomenon has nothing to do with disease. It depends on the following physiological facts. There are present in human blood two agglutinable properties, which, however, are not equally marked in all individuals. In the serum there is never present an agglutinin reacting with its own blood, but always an agglutinin which reacts with that property which is absent in that particular blood. As has often been pointed out in the literature of the subject, these properties are of great importance in blood transfusion, for a blood

---

[1] Von Dungern: Münchener medizinische Wochenschrift, 1911. Von Dungern and Hirschfeld: Zeitschrift für Immunitätsforschungen, 1911, Comm. I, II, III.

[2] This only applies to non-absorbed sera.

must never be injected which can be agglutinated by the recipient. Either of the two agglutinable properties may be present or both together, or both may be absent, and we can therefore distinguish four different combinations in man. In the literature of the subject we therefore most often find the statement that there are in the human species four different groups. But since we have, indeed, four groups but only two agglutinable properties, von Dungern and Hirschfeld[1] introduced another definition which is shown in the accompanying table. (Table I.) They called the agglutinable property,

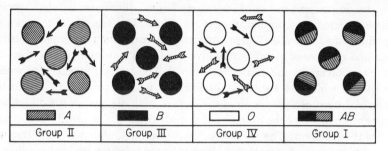

Table I. Landsteiner's Law of Iso-agglutinins

which is common in Central Europe, A, the other, which is rare in Central Europe, B. In the figure the blood corpuscles possessing the A property are shown shaded, those with the B property are black. Landsteiner's rule lays down that there are always present in the serum agglutinins against the agglutinable property which is absent in the blood corpuscles of the same blood. If the individual has in the blood corpuscles the A property, he has in his serum agglutinin anti-B, and vice versa. These agglutinins are represented diagrammatically by arrows corresponding with the agglutinable property, the anti-A being shaded, the anti-B black. We see in the first square of the figure the shaded red blood corpuscles A surrounded by the black arrows anti-B, while in the second square are the black blood corpuscles B with the shaded anti-A agglutinins. In the third square we see the non-agglutinable red blood corpuscles which possess neither A nor B property, called by von Dungern and Hirschfeld the Group O. In accordance with Landsteiner's rule that in the blood there are always agglutinins against the qualities lacking in the corpuscles we have here both the shaded anti-A and the black anti-B arrows. Finally, in the fourth square are represented the red corpuscles, which have both A and B properties, and accordingly no agglutinins. Below our diagram we have given the classification used by English writers on the subject. The English Group I. corresponds to our A B. Group II. is our A, and Group III. our B. As against Mosse, we wish to point out that Group I. does not represent any special individuality, but merely, as can easily be proved by absorption experiments, the combination of the properties A and B. For the differentiation of the groups, therefore, we require not three, but only two sera, A and B.

RESULTS OF EXPERIMENTS

What biological significance, then, has this peculiar differentiation of the blood within the human species, and how are these marks of the biochemical race inherited? Von Dungern and Hirschfeld first undertook experiments on the inheritance of these characteristics in dogs, and found that the biochemical properties of the blood are sometimes inherited and sometimes disappear in the offspring. They established, further, that the anatomical and biochemical characteristics are inherited independently of one another. Young dogs which had the general structure and colour of the mother showed the agglutinable properties of the father and vice versa.

Researches on the inheritance of the biochemical group properties in man as differentiated by means of Landsteiner's iso-antibodies permitted von Dungern and Hirschfeld to come to an important conclusion as to the nature of these properties. We succeeded in showing that the A and B properties are generally inherited, but sometimes may disappear in the offspring. When the parents had A or B we found sometimes the Group O occurring in the children. On the other hand, we never found either A or B property in a child when it was absent in the parents. This observation will permit under certain circumstances medico-legal decisions to be made in order to find the real father of a child. If we find in a child either A or B property when it is absent in the mother it must be present in the real father.

The analysis of our numerical results proved that we can apply Mendel's law to the inheritance of the biochemical properties A and B. Since the A and B properties may disappear but never appear spontaneously, we can regard them according to Mendel's law as those properties which once present in the germ-plasm must also be outwardly visible. Mendel, as we know, named such a property or quality, which always gives the species its outward appearance, the dominant, while the absence of the property (which property may appear in children although absent in the parents) is considered as latent or recessive, and is set in contra-distinction to the dominant. If, for example, the dominant is *red* the Mendelian quality or property antagonistic to it—e.g., *white*—is described as *non-red*. If we introduce the Mendelian terminology we can in our cases speak of non-A and non-B. With certain premises, which are discussed in the second part of von Dungern and Hirschfeld's paper, the figures showing the frequency of occurrence of A and B in central Europe can be brought into harmony with Mendel's law, the properties A and B being recognised as dominant, the properties non-A and non-B (the combination of which gives Group O) as recessive. A and non-A thus may be regarded as Mendelian pairs and similarly B and non-B.

What are the laws, then, governing the relationships of A and B with each other? The calculation showed that they simply fit in with the calculation of probability according to which A and B can come together when they do not influence each other. When A, for instance, occurs in half of all cases and B in one-tenth, A B will be found together in about one-twentieth—i.e., in 5 per cent. Experience has shown that the occurrence of Group I. (our Group A B) approximates to this figure. If, therefore, Landsteiner's rule is regarded from the broad biological point of view it can be stated as follows: There are within the human species four properties of blood, A, non-A, B, and non-B. A and non-A, B and non-B behave to each other according to Mendel's law, while A and B, non-A and non-B do not influence one another. Experience has shown that the inheritance of the biochemical blood properties in man is not influenced by sex and does not correspond with the inheritance of anatomical qualities (family resemblance, etc.), so that we have to do with an independent heredity. The agglutinable properties appear already in embryonic life; we have observed them in a six-months' fœtus. We have succeeded in finding these properties in the placental blood even when they were absent in the mother. The iso-agglutinins, however, do not appear until the second year of life. We can confirm Landsteiner's observation that these group-properties have nothing to do with disease. They appear also not to alter with time. We ourselves possess the same groups and agglutinins which we found in our blood eight years ago in spite of the fact that one of us has had typhoid and now suffers from chronic malaria. The experiments in heredity, also, point to the constancy of the biochemical properties of the blood. There exist, indeed, weakly agglutinable blood corpuscles and weakly agglutinating sera. An accidental coming together of these might simulate Group O where in reality A or B was present.

We have often examined hundreds of specimens of blood with 10 different sera and found mostly only quantitative differences between the different A and B sera for the agglutinin is seldom absent. Rarely there are to be found certain anti-A (Group B) sera which agglutinate the corpuscles of rather more individuals than other sera. The corresponding groups are distinguished by von Dungern and Hirschfeld as Large-A and Small-a. We have therefore always used several sera for the examination of a people or a race, and, on the other hand, always used the same set of sera for the examination of different races. We have never observed that malaria has any influence on the agglutinations. The clumping in the blood of anæmic patients has nothing to do with the agglutinations, as one of us has succeeded in proving.[3] The red blood corpuscles always sink in their own plasma as soon as their number is so small that they cannot support each other. The rate of sinking thus runs parallel with the anæmia. It seemed, therefore, that it would be of interest to make use of the properties of blood, as defined by Landsteiner's rule, to form an anthropological criterion for the discovery of hitherto unknown and anatomically invisible relationships between different races. Through the accident of the war we happened to come to a part of the globe where more than elsewhere various races and peoples are brought together, so that the

[3] L. Hirschfeld. 1917. Korrespondenzblatt für Schweizer Aerzte.

problems we are discussing, which otherwise would have necessitated long years of travel, could be brought in a relatively short time nearer to solution.

TECHNIQUE

The technique is as follows. We add a few drops of blood from the ball of the finger to a mixture of sodium chloride and sodium citrate solution (normal saline 9 parts, 2.5 per cent, Na citrate 1 part). A drop of the blood mixture is brought in contact in a small test tube with a drop each of the A and B sera, of which the activity and specificity have always been established by a control experiment. The result was never read off in less than half an hour—a point of great importance, as particularly Group B is but slowly agglutinated. We used only Serbians as providers of serum. For each race several sera are used, but the same set of sera for all races. Our material consists for the most part of soldiers from various districts. This is to be regarded as a very favourable circumstance, since they are mostly unrelated to each other, so that the possibility that the frequency of a group might depend on family relationship is excluded. The refugees, as our statistics for the Jewish race particularly show, give evidence of great individual differences in the first, second, and other hundreds examined, so that the results must be confirmed by tests on more extensive material. The exact statistics with regard to the different tribes, provinces, anatomical structure, etc., will appear in an anthropological journal. We examined 500-1000 persons of each race. For the Germans we quote from memory the results of von Dungern and Hirschfeld as the statistical table for these is unfortunately not to hand. For the Austrians we used the Vienna statistics of L. Landsteiner. For the Jews we used the refugees from Monastir belonging to a people which came from Spain about 400 years ago. For the Greeks we examined 300 soldiers from Old Greece and the Islands and 200 refugees from Asia Minor and Thrace. For the Turks we used Macedonian Mohammedans. These last must certainly contain a large admixture of Slav blood, and the statistics should be confirmed in Turkey. We wish to emphasise particularly that all these people, except the Indians, who are as a nation for the most part vegetarians, are receiving exactly the same food and are exposed to the same hardships and diseases, so that it would not be correct to refer the great differences we have found in the frequency of A and B Groups to special climatological or pathological conditions.

STATISTICAL ANALYSES

We wish to point out as the first important fact that we found the Groups A and B present in all races examined. Table II shows the percentage of A and B. The figures in the right-hand column of Table II represent the total numbers of each race examined. A glance at the table shows that we find marked differences in the incidence of A and B in the different races. From the English onward we see that A always diminishes, whereas B increases.[4] In order to give an exact analysis we will first look at our data from the point of view developed by von Dungern and Hirschfeld in the second part of their paper.[5] The group A B was regarded by them as the accidental coming together of A and B. If we analyse our statistics from this point of view we reach the following figures: If A is present in 43.4 per cent and B in 7.2 per cent. For the calculation of probability we must multiply 43.4/100 by 7.2/100, which gives 301/10,000 = 3.1 per cent. In reality we found 3.0 per cent.

Table II.

	A in per cent	B in per cent	A B in per cent	O in per cent	Total number examined
English............	43.4	7.2	3.0	46.4	500
French............	42.6	11.2	3.0	43.2	500
Italians...........	38.0	11.0	3.8	47.2	500
Germans..........	43.0	12.0	5.0	40.0	ca. 500
Austrians..........	40.0	10.0	8.0	42.0	?
Serbs.............	41.8	15.6	4.6	38.0	500
Greeks............	41.6	16.2	4.0	38.2	500
Bulgarians.........	40.6	14.2	6.2	39.0	500
Arabs.............	32.4	19.0	5.0	43.6	500
Turks.............	38.0	18.6	6.6	36.8	500
Russians...........	31.2	21.8	6.3	40.7	1000
Jews..............	33.0	23.2	5.0	38.8	500
Malagasies.........	26.2	23.7	4.5	45.5	400
Negroes (Senegal)}......	22.6	29.2	5.0	43.2	500
Annamese.........	22.4	28.4	7.2	42.0	500
Indians...........	19.0	41.2	8.5	31.3	1000

Since A occurs in 43.4 per cent and A B in 3.0 per cent, we have the property A altogether in 46.4 per cent, and correspondingly the non-A in 53.4 per cent. Similar calculations given for non-B 89.8 per cent. The calculation of probabilities thus gives for Group O: $\frac{53.4}{100} \times \frac{89.8}{100} = \frac{4795}{10,000} = 47.9$ per cent. We actually found 46.4 per cent.

[4] In the English literature of the subject we find that the frequency of occurrence of B is higher and corresponds to the figures given by Landsteiner for Vienna. We cannot corroborate this. We examined our English material several times with seven different anti-B sera without finding a greater frequency than that here given.

[5] Loc. cit.

Table III.

	A B		O	
	Really found	Calculation of probability	Really found	Calculation of probability
	%	%	%	%
English............	3.1	3.1	46.4	47.9
French............	3.0	4.7	43.2	46.6
Italians............	3.8	4.1	47.2	49.5
Germans..........	5.0	5.1	40.0	43.1
Austrians.........	8.0	4.0	42.0	42.6
Serbs.............	4.6	6.5	38.0	42.7
Greeks............	4.0	6.7	38.2	43.4
Bulgarians........	6.2	5.7	39.0	42.3
Arabs.............	5.0	6.1	43.6	47.5
Turks.............	6.6	7.0	36.8	39.9
Russians..........	6.3	6.8	40.7	44.9
Jews..............	5.0	7.6	38.8	44.5
Malagasies........	4.5	6.2	45.5	49.5
Negroes (Senegal).......	5.0	6.5	43.2	47.6
Annamese.........	7.2	6.4	42.0	45.3
Indians...........	8.5	7.8	31.3	43.7

We made the same calculations for each people and race, and have shown the results in Table III. The table shows only slight differences between the calculation and the facts, the calculation giving somewhat higher results.

Basing our opinion on the whole of our material embracing about 8000 cases we look on Group O (the English Group IV) as the accidental conjunction of the two groups non-A and non-B, while Group I, our A B, is to be regarded as the accidental conjunction of the groups A and B. If, then, we wish to find exactly the frequency of A and B, we must add the English Group I (our A B) to the Groups II and III. Thus in the English subjects instead of 43.4 per cent A, 7.2 per cent B, and 3 per cent A B, we read 46.4 per cent A and 10.2 per cent B.

In Table IV the figures arrived at are shown diagrammatically, Group A being shaded and Group B black. The result is remarkable.

The prevalence of the Group A is characteristic of the European peoples. Most European peoples have not less than 45 per cent A; in the Italians alone we found 41 per cent. This frequency of A only applies to Europe. In Africa and in Asia we find far fewer cases of A; the Malagasies have 30 per cent, Negroes 27 per cent, Annamese 29 per cent, and Indians 27 per cent of A. The countries lying between Asia and Central Europe, with the exception of the Macedonian Turks who have the European A frequency, show

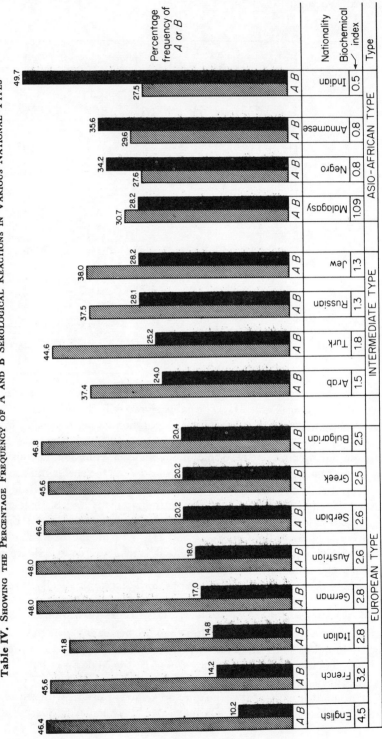

Table IV. Showing the Percentage Frequency of A and B Serological Reactions in Various National Types

the intermediate type; the Arabs 37 per cent, the Russians 37 per cent, the Jews 38 per cent. Thus we see that going southwards and eastwards the frequency of A constantly diminishes. If we now consider Group B we find the exact opposite: the English who are farthest west have only 10 per cent, the French and Italians 14 per cent, the German Austrians 17 to 18 per cent. Of the Balkan peoples the Serbians and Greeks have the same frequency of 20.2 per cent, the Bulgars 20.4. The contrary is found in Africa and Asia. Group B, which is numerically low in Europe, reaches 28 per cent in the Malagasies, in Negroes 34 per cent, in Annamese 35 per cent, and finally in Indians a maximum of 49 per cent. The peoples of the Mediterranean basin and the Russians in this also show the intermediate type: the Arabs have 24 per cent, Turks 25 per cent, Russians and Jews 28 per cent. The Russians arranged according to districts show the following relationships:

Table V.

	A %	B %	Total
Central Russia..........	37.6	25.2	400
Siberia...............	36.5	29.0	321
Ukraine..............	35.1	33.3	111
Perm, Vologda, etc......	36.8	34.5	84

Central Russia and Siberia show the intermediate type. Little Russia and the Volga District have the Asiatic type.

We see thus that A and B are present in different proportions in different races. The serological formula for a particular race is in no way affected by the anthropological characteristics. The Indians, who are looked on as anthropologically nearest to Europeans, show the greatest difference from them in the blood properties. The Russians and the Jews, who differ so much from each other in anatomical characteristics, mode of life, occupation, and temperament, have exactly the same proportion of A and B. On the other hand, it is clear that the distribution of A and B corresponds with surprising accuracy to geographical situation. The nearer to Western and Central Europe the more A and the less B, the nearer to Africa and Asia, especially to India, the less A and the more B. The peoples lying between Central and Western Europe on one side, and Africa and Asia on the other—that is to say, the peoples of the Mediterranean basin—show the intermediate type. In order to designate these relationships by a number we will call the proportion of A to B the biochemical race-index. We see that the race-index in the European peoples varies between 4.5 and 2.5, in the Asio-African peoples it is 1 or less, while the intermediate type is characterised by the race-index 1-2 (Table IV).

This remarkable fact, that A and B are represented in very different proportions in different races may be discussed from two standpoints. One can imagine that when man appeared on the earth A and B were present in the same proportions in different races. In this case the differences which are now present in different races would depend on the assumption that for unknown reasons A is more suitable for increased resistance of the organism to disease in a temperate climate, while B is more suitable in a hot climate. The hypothesis is improbable.

We see that the Russians in Siberia have the same proportion of B as the natives of Madagascar. The Jews who have lived for centuries in Monastir show a type of blood different from that of the other Balkan peoples. It is also a priori improbable that the climatic conditions should influence the frequency of A and B. If B could not be acclimatised in a temperate climate it should have died out in those climates long ago in the extended periods of time which we can take into consideration. It is very difficult to imagine one single place of origin for the human race in view of our statistics, since it would then be inexplicable why A diminishes from west to east and south, while B increases. The figures arrived at by us are most easily explained on the assumption that A and B had different points of origin and that there are two different biochemical races which arose in different places. In this case the mutual infiltration of these races is the cause of the varying proportion of A and B. Since the greatest frequency of B is found in India,[6] we should then look for the moment on India as the cradle of one part of humanity— namely, of the biochemical race B. Both to the east (Indo-China) and to the west, towards Europe and Africa, a broad stream of Indians poured out, ever lessening in its flow, which finally, although continually diminishing, penetrated to Western Europe. A similar single place of origin for A cannot be indicated, since all European peoples show a greater or less preponderance of A, which only seems to diminish somewhat in the Italians. Since, however, the Asiatic and African peoples are poor in A, we must assume hypothetically that A arose in North or Central Europe and spread out thence southwards and eastwards. A detailed examination of the northern races may lead us to unexpected and important conclusions on this point.

CONCLUSION

We see then that the analysis of the figures we obtained has led us to remarkable results and that the highly interesting problem of a possible double origin of the human race has become a question which can be studied by means of serological methods. A problem of such dimensions may be propounded, but can hardly be resolved by the experimental results of a science, the introduction of which into these problems is here attempted for the first time. Still, we believe that we have shown in this paper that experiments in immunisation deserve to be made use of for the solving of anthropological questions. A close cooperation would be necessary between

[6] Of the greatest importance are the researches from the Central Asia plateau.

anthropologists and serologists, and the researches should be conducted on an international basis. The present war has brought so many races and peoples together that the main problems should certainly be capable of solution in a short time and without great labour. A series of important special researches, such as the examination of various stocks, primitive races, and anthropoid apes, should be begun without delay.

In our experiments we received much help from many medical and other officers of the Allied Armies in Macedonia. We owe our gratitude to the Directors of the Medical Services of the several armies for permission to examine soldiers and for other assistance. Major Stefanovitch and Captain W. L. Murphy, the liaison officers of the Serbian and British Army Medical Services, have undertaken the translation of the paper into English, for which we offer them our best thanks.

An Unusual Case of Intra-group Agglutination*

PHILIP LEVINE, M.D., Newark, N. J.

RUFUS E. STETSON, M. D., New York

Few discoveries having a genetic aspect have had as much practical importance to medicine as this almost casual observation by Levine and Stetson. In their note the consequences of immunization of a mother by a heterozygous, antigenically distinct fetus are clearly set out. In the succeeding paper Landsteiner and Wiener independently provide a superb description of the serology and inheritance of the Rh system. In these two papers two quite different means of observation, one purely clinical and the other, in its inception at least, purely experimental converge upon the same problem.

This report deals with a rare property in the blood of a patient whose serum showed an iso-agglutinin of moderate activity, which agglutinated about

* From the Department of Laboratories, Newark Beth Israel Hospital, Newark, N. J., and the Blood Transfusion Betterment Association of New York City. Dr. William E. Studdiford, director, and Dr. John S. Labate, resident, of the Obstetrical and Gynecological Service at Bellevue Hospital, gave the authors permission to study this case. Reprinted by senior author's and publisher's permission from J. Am Med. Assn. 1939. **113**: 126-127.

80 per cent of the bloods of her own group. In view of the fact that this agglutinin tended to disappear after an interval of several months and the fact that this agglutinin gave an equally strong reaction at 37 and 20 C., it would seem to resemble agglutinins resulting from iso-immunization following repeated transfusions. This phenomenon is readily reproduced in some species (cattle, chickens, rabbits), by several repeated transfusions, but in the case of man only two clearcut instances of such iso-immunization to cellular elements are described in the literature.[1] The case to be described differs from these in that the immune iso-agglutinin must have been stimulated by a factor other than repeated transfusion. The nature of this factor becomes evident from a summary of the case history.

REPORT OF CASE

M. S., a woman aged 25, a secundipara, was registered in the antepartum clinic of Bellevue Hospital July 12, 1937, at which time she showed some pretibial edema and a blood pressure of 130 systolic, 90 diastolic. (The expected date of delivery was in the last week of October.) Two weeks later the blood pressure was 154 systolic, 106 diastolic, and there was a faint trace of albumin in the urine. Hospitalization and rest in bed resulted in subsidence of all symptoms. The fetal heart sounds were not heard, but there were no X-ray signs of fetal death.

Labor pains and vaginal bleeding started on September 8 (the thirty-third week of the gestation), and at midnight September 9 the patient was admitted to the hospital, at which time labor pains lasting one minute occurred every five minutes. There was considerable bleeding before the membranes were ruptured, and a macerated stillborn fetus weighing only 1 pound 5 ounces (595 gm.) was delivered. After the placenta was expelled, bleeding was finally controlled and the patient (group O) was given her first transfusion of 500 cc. of whole blood from her husband (group O). Ten minutes after she received the blood a chill developed and she complained of pains in her legs and head. About twelve hours later a piece of membrane was passed and this was followed by more bleeding. At 4 p. m. a second transfusion of 750 cc. of whole blood was given, apparently without any reactions. In view of the renewed bleeding, hysterectomy was performed, followed by a third transfusion of 800 cc. of whole blood with no reaction.

Nineteen hours after the first transfusion and eight hours after the hysterectomy the patient voided 8 ounces (240 cc.) of bloody and dusky urine. At this time tests done with a more delicate technic revealed that, although the patient and her husband—the first donor whose blood caused a reaction—were in group O, the patient's serum nevertheless agglutinated distinctly her husband's cells and, indeed, the cells of most group O donors.

[1] Karl Landsteiner, Philip Levine and M. L. Janes. May 1928. Proc. Soc. Exper. Biol. and Med. **25**: 672; Erwin Neter. March 1936. J. Immunol. **30**: 225.

Subsequently the patient received six more uneventful transfusions from compatible professional donors very carefully selected by the Blood Transfusion Betterment Association.

Subsequent intensive treatment—diathermy over the kidneys, forced fluids by vein, rectum and mouth, the repeated transfusions mentioned and high hot colonic irrigations—resulted in gradual recovery of kidney function.

COMMENT

The blood was referred to us during the patient's convalescence, October 9, a month after the hysterectomy. Tests previously performed at the Donor Bureau of the Blood Transfusion Betterment Association showed that only eight of fifty group O donors did not react with the patient's serum and hence were compatible. In our series of fifty-four bloods of group O, thirteen failed to react with the patient's serum. Thus, of a total of 104 group O bloods twenty-one were compatible.

It could be readily shown that these reactions differ from those due to so-called atypical agglutinins occasionally found in the serums of normal persons. The former reactions were just as active at 37 as at 20 C., while reactions of the latter variety as a rule do not occur at 37 C. or else are considerably diminished. In other words, identical results were obtained when tests with serums of the patient were kept either at 20 or at 37 C. or were read after centrifuging and resuspending the sedimented cells.

The reactions were found to be independent of the M, N or P blood factors. Owing to the lack of suitable quantities of the blood, it was not possible to perform absorption experiments in order to supply data on the incidence of the reactions in bloods of groups A, B and AB.

Another specimen drawn two months later, December 3, still exhibited the agglutinin, which however gave far weaker reactions. Here again the reactions at 37 C. were just as intense as those at room temperature or lower. It was not possible to examine the serum of this patient until a year later, when all traces of reactions had disappeared.

In several respects this iso-agglutinin, as already mentioned, resembles the iso-agglutinins described by Landsteiner, Levine and Janes and that of Neter, namely (1) reactions within the same group equally active at room temperature and at 37 C. and (2) the temporary character of the agglutinin. In both of these cases the agglutinin was not demonstrable until an interval of several weeks had elapsed following repeated transfusions. In the present case, however, it is evident that the unusual iso-agglutinin must have been present at the time the patient was given her first transfusion with the blood of her husband, which subsequently was shown to be sensitive. Furthermore, this first transfusion was not uneventful in view of the resulting chills, pains in the legs and intense headache.

It is well established that in instances of iso-immunization in animals the iso-agglutinin serves as a reagent to detect dominant hereditary blood factors in the red blood cells and presumably also in the tissue cells. In view of the fact that this patient harbored a dead fetus for a period of several months, one may assume that the products of the disintegrating fetus were responsible not only for the toxic symptoms of the patient but also for the iso-immunization. Presumably the immunizing property in the blood and/or tissues of the fetus must have been inherited from the father. Since this dominant property was not present in the mother, specific immunization conceivably could occur.

No data are available as to the relationship to one another of the immune iso-agglutinin in the two previously reported cases and in the present case. Judging from the frequency of positive and negative reactions, it is evident that the iso-agglutinin in this case is distinct from the other two; i.e., 20 per cent nonreacting bloods in contrast with 75 per cent in the case of Neter and 60 per cent in that of Landsteiner, Levine and Janes.

Agglutinins of this sort can rarely be investigated thoroughly because of their tendency to diminish in activity and eventually to disappear. Consequently attempts were made to produce a hetero-immune agglutinin of identical or similar specificity by repeated injections of sensitive blood into a series of rabbits. These experiments met with failure, since suitable absorption tests with such serums failed to reveal the presence of the desired agglutinin.

Studies on an Agglutinogen (Rh) in Human Blood Reacting with Anti-Rhesus Sera and with Human Isoantibodies*

KARL LANDSTEINER, M.D.

ALEXANDER S. WIENER, M.D.

From some observations made with immune sera, and particularly from the evidence provided by tests with occasionally occurring normal and post-

* *From the Laboratories of The Rockefeller Institute for Medical Research, and the Serological Laboratory of the Office of the Chief Medical Examiner of the City of New York, New York.* Reprinted by junior author's and publisher's permission from J. Exp. Med. 1941. 74: 309-320.

transfusion human sera containing irregular agglutinins (*cf.* reviews in 1, 2) one can conclude that there exist individual properties of human blood other than those which are demonstrable by readily available reagents such as A_1, A_2, B, M, N. Doubtless numerous attempts have been made to discover additional agglutinogens by the familiar technique used for the demonstration of the factors M and N (3), that is, with immune sera prepared by the injection of human blood into rabbits, but only few results were obtained (*e.g.* 4, 5), and these were not followed up because it was difficult to produce the immune sera again. Other ways of approaching the problem were therefore desirable and it was thought that new results might be obtained by immunizing with animal instead of human blood, considering that the blood of some animals contains antigens related to agglutinogens present in individual human bloods, for instance the Forssman substance related to A in sheep cells. A result that favored this plan was the observation that certain anti-*rhesus* immune sera contain agglutinins specific for the human agglutinogen M (6).

Pursuing this idea, by immunizing rabbits with *rhesus* blood an immune serum was obtained with which an agglutinable factor different from A, B, M, N, or P was detected (7), and this new factor was designated as Rh to indicate that *rhesus* blood had been used for the production of the serum. The property was then found to be present in the blood of about 85 per cent of white individuals examined (7, 8).

Evidence that the property Rh is of clinical importance was obtained when one of the writers came into possession of blood samples from patients who had shown hemolytic reactions, one with fatal outcome, after receiving repeated transfusions of blood of the proper group (8). The serum of these patients contained anti-Rh isoagglutinins while in the blood cells the factor was lacking. This showed that the agglutinogen in question, unlike M and N, is endowed with the capacity to induce the formation of immune isoantibodies in certain human beings.

Another related fact is the appearance of immune isoantibodies in pregnancy. Levine and Stetson (9) had previously reported a severe accident following a transfusion of apparently compatible blood in a woman after a stillbirth and offered the explanation that the patient had been immunized by an antigen in the dead fetus, inherited from the father. Furthermore, in a review of the literature by Wiener and Peters (8) it was pointed out that apparently every recorded instance in which a hemolytic reaction followed a first transfusion with blood of the proper group had occurred with intra- or postpartum patients. This supported the above mentioned hypothesis that isoimmunization can result from pregnancy. Further cases of transfusion reactions attributable to isoimmunization of pregnancy were reported by Levine and Katzin (10). The serum from one of the cases, in which the isoagglutinin was identified, was found to give reactions corresponding to those of Rh.

In a recent paper, Levine, Katzin, and Burnham (11) described a number of cases of erythroblastosis foetalis, stillbirths, and miscarriages, which appear to be due to isoimmunization in pregnancy. From their results, the authors conclude that most of the mothers developed antibodies against the Rh factor. Significant additional evidence has been obtained since (23). Previously the idea of a serological explanation of erythroblastosis was advanced by Ottenberg (12) and Darrow (13).

The purposes of our own studies were to develop a practical method of testing for the presence of the Rh factor, and to investigate its heredity.

EXPERIMENTAL

The rabbit immune serum described in our preliminary communication gave reactions which were definite, although considerably weaker than those obtained with common reagents for blood grouping or MN tests. Subsequent attempts at producing immune sera in rabbits by injecting *rhesus* blood gave unsatisfactory results even though feeble Rh antibodies were detectable in some of the sera. Such difficulties have also been encountered in work with immune sera against other factors (P, O, etc.). We then turned to the immunization of other laboratory animals and obtained sera from guinea pigs which gave reactions corresponding in specificity to those of the rabbit antibodies.

For the production of the sera large guinea pigs were injected intraperitoneally with a suspension of washed red cells of *rhesus* monkeys, each animal receiving a dose corresponding to 1 cc., in later experiments to 2 cc. of whole blood. The injection was repeated after 5 days and 1 week later the animals were bled. The sera of the majority of animals were found to show a difference between the two sorts of blood, Rh+ and Rh−, and in a group of ten animals usually one or more were found that yielded sera suitable for practical diagnosis. The manner of selecting the sera is given below.

While in the case of the immune rabbit sera the reagent was prepared in the customary way by absorbing the diluted serum with negatively reacting blood, it was found with several guinea pig sera that absorption with human blood resulted merely in a non-specific diminution of the agglutinin content, no matter whether positive or negative blood was used. This led us to test the effect of simple dilution, and indeed it was found that a distinction between positive and negative bloods could be made directly without absorbing the sera. (As an analogy, mention may be made of rabbit immune anti-A sera which cannot be specifically absorbed with A_2 cells to produce a reagent for A_1, absorption with A_2 blood serving merely to diminish the agglutinin titer.)

The method for determining suitable sera consists in making serial dilutions by halves and testing with known negative and positive blood. Those sera which show in three (or more) successive dilutions negative reactions with the former and positive ones with the latter blood are usable.

The actual tests can usually be carried out simply by selecting a dilution of the serum, *e.g.*, 1 to 10, which gives no reactions with negative but definite reactions with positive bloods, those sera that contain appreciable amounts of anti-A or anti-B agglutinins having been previously absorbed with small quantities of A and B blood. Since the sera are used diluted, inactivation is mostly unnecessary. The blood to be tested should be fresh.

Another method, alternative to dilution alone, is to absorb the sera diluted, *e.g.* 1:4, with a quantity of blood (using A or B cells if indicated) sufficient to remove the reaction with Rh-negative blood.

Two drops (0.1 cc.) of the test fluid are then mixed with one drop of 2 per cent (in terms of blood sediment) washed blood suspension, freshly prepared, in a narrow tube of 7 mm. inner diameter and allowed to stand at room temperature. Readings are taken after sedimentation has occurred, usually after 30 minutes to 1 hour, by direct inspection of the bases of the tubes, with a hand lens. Negatively reacting bloods then show a circular deposit with a smooth edge, while positive bloods have a wrinkled sediment with a serrated border or show a granular deposit (*cf.* Figs. 1 to 6). From these readings, as a rule, the diagnosis can readily be made. The readings are facilitated by using racks having small holes beneath the bottom of the tubes. Following the reading the tubes are shaken and the sediment examined after it forms again. A further examination is made after 2 hours, again inspecting the sediment. The tubes are then gently shaken and the suspension is examined microscopically: the negative blood samples are mostly perfectly homogeneous; the positive ones show various degrees of agglutination, not infrequently visible to the naked eye. At times, the clumping is quite weak in spite of a distinctly positive sediment picture. Needless to say, positive and negative control bloods should be included in each test.

As already mentioned, with the great majority of specimens the distinction between positive and negative reactions is quite definite but the positive reactions vary in strength and some bloods offer difficulties because of their weak reactions. However, after sufficient practice, and by repeating the tests if necessary with fresh blood samples and several sera, only in some few instances were the reactions questionable. Marked differences in the intensity of the reactions were also observed in tests made with human anti-Rh sera. Whether the variations in strength of agglutination are due to homo- and heterozygosity or to the existence of other differences in the agglutinogen has not been determined.

In order to ascertain whether sera from various sources give corresponding reactions, comparative tests were made with series of human blood specimens. The immune rabbit serum originally obtained (7) was found to give parallel reactions with two human sera (8) from post-transfusion cases

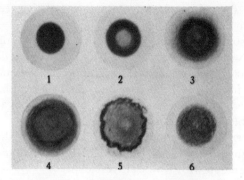

Figs. 1 and 2. Negative reactions; the inner light disc in Fig. 2 is
due to slight convexity in the bottom of the tube. **Fig. 3.** Faintly
positive reaction. **Fig. 4.** Weak reaction. **Figs. 5 and 6.** Typical
positive reactions. Magnification 1:2.

in a series of 42 bloods (29 positive and 13 negative). Additional tests have
now been made to compare the reactions of different guinea pig sera with
each other and with human Rh isoagglutinins. Three of the guinea pig sera
were examined with a random series of 110 bloods (89 positive, 21 negative)
and in no case was a discrepancy encountered. Furthermore, parallel tests
were carried out with a guinea pig serum, which gave good differentiation,
and a human serum[1] (human serum 3) obtained from the mother of a child
with erythroblastosis. 159 bloods gave corresponding reactions with both
sera of which 109 were positive and 50 negative.[2] In three cases, there were
definite discrepancies; one blood reacted distinctly with the human, not
with the guinea pig serum, the other two were agglutinated by the guinea
pig serum, not by human serum 3, though one of these was agglutinated by
two other human sera (Nos. 2, 4). Furthermore, three specimens gave
doubtful reactions with the guinea pig serum, one reacting distinctly, one
weakly, and one faintly with human serum 3. In addition to the blood
mentioned above, which gave divergent reactions with the two human sera,
a second such blood (not retested) was found, and in a larger series of comparisons made with several human anti-Rh sera, Dr. Philip Levine[3] observed
that the reactions ran parallel in the great majority of cases, but bloods were
encountered which were agglutinated differently, *e.g.* one by one serum, the
other by a second serum. These observations raise the question whether there
actually exist variants of the property Rh, more different than those found
for agglutinogens A (14-16), M (17), and N (18), and whether human sera
may contain more than one kind of anti-Rh agglutinin.

Of interest in this connection is a serum, obtained from a post-transfusion

---

[1] For this serum we are indebted to Dr. Philip Levine and Dr. P. Vogel.

[2] The large number of negative bloods is due to selection, in order to increase the
significance of the comparison.

[3] Personal communication.

case (19), which differed strikingly from the other human sera in that it gave many more negative reactions. The results are summarized in Table I and show that in spite of the difference in the reactions there is a marked correlation, establishing a relationship between this serum and the other human sera. If this distribution is compared with that to be expected on the assumption that the reactions of this patient's serum would be unrelated to Rh, we obtain a value of χ^2 equal to approximately 19.9, n being 1 (*cf.* Fisher (20)). The likelihood that this value is due to chance alone is very small.

To date a total of 448 white individuals has been examined with guinea pig sera, human sera, or both.[4] Among these, there were 379 positive and 69 negative reactions, that is, 84.6 per cent Rh+ and 15.4 per cent Rh−. The distribution in the sexes, and among the blood groups and M,N types (*cf.* Tables II to IV) did not reveal a definite correlation. Likewise in a series of 133 specimens tested for Rh and P there was no definite correlation between these two properties. The high incidence of Rh-negative individuals in group B (27.5 ± 4.4 per cent) may still be accidental in view of the small size of the series.

In a series of 113 Negro bloods, only 9 were found to give clearly negative reactions, suggesting the possibility of a racial difference in the distribution.

STUDIES ON HEREDITY

Sixty families with 237 children were tested for the presence or absence of the factor Rh in the red cells. The bloods were examined not later than 1 day following their collection. All the bloods were examined for the properties A,B, and in most cases for M,N, and the subgroups A_1 and A_2. The tests for Rh

Table I.

| | Reactions with human serum Wa | |
Reactions with typical human Rh sera	Positive	Negative
Positive....................................	31	8
Negative....................................	1	11

Table II. DISTRIBUTION OF THE RH FACTOR IN THE TWO SEXES

| | Males | | Females | | Totals | |
	Rh+	Rh−	Rh+	Rh−	Rh+	Rh−
Number......	299	53	80	16	379	69
Per cent......	84.9	15.1	83.3	16.7	84.6	15.4

[4] The children of the family material and the few instances in which the reactions with the two sorts of sera disagreed have not been included in the number.

Table III. DISTRIBUTION OF THE RH FACTOR IN THE FOUR BLOOD GROUPS

	Group O		Group A		Group B		Group AB		Totals	
	Rh+	Rh−	Rh+	Rh−	Rh+	Rh−	Rh+	Rh−	Rh+	Rh−
Number....	191	29	148	27	29	11	11	2	379	69
Per cent....	86.8	13.2	84.6	15.4	72.5	27.5	84.6	15.4	84.6	15.4

Table IV. DISTRIBUTION OF THE RH FACTOR IN THE THREE M,N TYPES

	Type M		Type N		Type MN		Totals	
	Rh+	Rh−	Rh+	Rh−	Rh+	Rh−	Rh+	Rh−
Number.........	93	20	70	9	205	39	368	68
Per cent.........	82.3	17.7	88.6	11.4	84.0	16.0	84.4	15.6

presented in Tables V and VI were made either with guinea pig immune sera, or with a post-transfusion human serum,[5] or both. While it is realized that the use of two reagents introduces an inaccuracy, this is so small in view of the almost complete correspondence shown above between these sera that the results cannot be appreciably affected.

As is apparent from the results with the families in which both parents are Rh-negative, evidently the property Rh is inherited as a dominant. In six such matings encountered in our series, all 31 children proved to be Rh-negative.[6] (This number of Rh− × Rh− families, larger than would be expected by chance, is in part due to selection of families with a known negative parent.)

In analogy to the other individual human blood properties whose heredity has been investigated, one may presume that the factor Rh is transmitted by means of a pair of genes, *Rh* and *rh*, where the dominant gene *Rh* determines its presence. Hence, three genotypes would exist, *RhRh*, *Rhrh*, and *rhrh*, the first two corresponding to the phenotype Rh+, the last to Rh−. By the usual simple calculation, one obtains from the distribution of the phenotypes in the population the frequencies of the two genes. In our random series of 448 individuals there were 69 or 15.4 per cent Rh− individuals. Accordingly, the frequency of gene *rh* is $\sqrt{0.154}$ or 39.2 per cent, and the frequency of gene *Rh* 60.8 per cent. From these figures the frequencies of the three genotypes are as follows: genotype *RhRh*, $(0.608)^2$ or 37.0 per cent; genotype *Rhrh*, $2(0.608)$ (0.392) or 47.6 per cent; and genotype *rhrh*, 15.4 per cent.

[5] With the exception of 4 families, a single human serum (No. 3) was used.

[6] Actually, in one of these families, in which blood specimens were taken from 8 children, the oldest boy was Rh-positive, but on investigation it was learned that he was the child of a previous marriage. All individuals in this family were tested with human as well as with guinea pig serum.

From the genotype frequencies one can calculate the distribution in the offspring of various matings of the Rh factor to be expected on the hypothesis of simple dominance. In the matings Rh+ × Rh+, there are three possibilities; namely, (1) both parents of genotype *RhRh*, (2) one parent of genotype *RhRh*, the other *Rhrh*, and (3) both parents *Rhrh*. Only in case (3) can Rh— children occur. The relative frequency of this mating among Rh+ × Rh+ families is $\dfrac{(0.476)^2}{(0.370 + 0.476)^2}$ or 31.6 per cent. Since one-fourth of all the children of these matings should be Rh—, only 7.9 per cent of all the children of Rh+ × Rh+ matings should be Rh-negative. The observed incidence of 7 Rh— individuals among 158 offspring, or 4.4 ± 1.1 per cent, is less than the expected value; to decide whether this is accidental or significant, examination of a larger series is necessary.

In the matings Rh+ × Rh—, two cases exist: (1) genotype *RhRh* × *rhrh*, or (2) *Rhrh* × *rhrh*. Rh-negative children will result only from the second sort of mating. The frequency of such matings among Rh+ × Rh— families should be the same as that of genotype *Rhrh* among Rh+ individuals, or 56.3 per cent. Hence half of 56.3, or 28.15 per cent of the children from all the Rh+ × Rh— matings should be Rh-negative. The figure observed was 11 among 48 children, or 22.9 ± 4.0 per cent, which does not differ significantly from the predicted value.

The usefulness of the blood property Rh for forensic exclusion of paternity is small, on account of the low incidence of matings Rh— × Rh— (0.15 × 0.15, or only 2.25 per cent), these being the only ones which permit a decision.[7] For individual identification in medico-legal cases, determination of the Rh factor doubles the number of classifications, but only fresh blood, not dried blood stains, can be tested.

Perusal of the data listed in Table V indicates that the property Rh is not a sex-linked dominant factor. This follows firstly from the equal distribution of the factor in the two sexes (*cf.* Table II), and secondly from the analysis of families in which the father is positive and the mother negative (families 4, 24, 53, and 59 of Table V), where on the usual hypothesis only the offspring of one sex, most probably the daughters, would exhibit the character.

Significant data relating to the question of the linkage relation of property Rh and the agglutinogens A and B are provided by family 6, and also by family 54 if one makes use of the subgroups A_1 and A_2. In family 6, the mother is heterozygous for both A and Rh, the father, who belongs to group O, only for Rh. In this family only Rh-negative children yield information as to linkage (*cf.* 21); that one of the two Rh-negative children belongs to group A, the other to group O, is evidence against close linkage. Similarly, the mother

---

[7] By chance such a case was encountered among a few forensic examinations in which tests for Rh were made. The test showed the following: putative father, BMRh—; mother, A_2BMRh—; child, A_1BMNRh+. Consequently, a paternity exclusion could be made from three independent results; namely, the subgroups, the M,N types, and the Rh factor.

Table V. List of Family Material.

Family number	Parents		Children					
	Father	Mother						
1	OMNRh−	OMRh−	OMNRh−♂	OMNRh−♂	OMNRh−♀	OMNRh−♀	OMNRh−♂	
2	A₂NRh+	OMNRh+	ONRh+♂	A₂MNRh+♀	OMNRh+♂	ONRh+♂	OMNRh+♀	
3	A₁MNRh−	ONRh+	OMRh+♀♀	A₁NRh++♀	OMNRh+♂	OMNRh−♂		
4	A₁MNRh+	A₁NRh+	A₁NRh+♀♂	A₁NRh−♂♀	A₁NRh−♂♂	A₁NRh−♂	A₁NRh−♂	
5	A₁MRh+	A₁MRh+	OMRh+♂	OMRh+♂	OMRh+♀	A₁MRh+♀	OMRh+♂	
6	OMNRh+	A₁MRh+	OMNRh−♂	OMNRh−♂	OMRh+♂	A₁MRh+♂		
7	BMRh−	OMRh−	BMRh−♀	BMRh−♀				
8	BMNRh−	A₂MNRh−	BNRh−♀*	A₂MNRh−♂*	A₂MNRh−♂*			
9	A₁MRh+	OMRh+	OMRh+♀♀	OMRh+♂	OMRh+♂			
10	OMNRh+	OMNRh+	A₂MNRh+♀	A₂MNRh+♂	A₁NRh+♀♀	OMRh+♂		
11	A₁NRh+	A₁NRh+	A₂NRh−♀	A₁MNRh+♂	OMNRh+♀	A₁MNRh+♀		
12	OMNRh+	OMNRh+	ONRh+♂	OMNRh+♂	OMNRh+♂			
13	A₁MNRh−	A₁MNRh+	A₁MRh+♂	A₁MRh−♂	OMNRh−♂	OMRh+♀		
14†	OMNRh+	A₁MNRh+	A₁MNRh+♀♀	OMNRh+♂	OMNRh+♀	OMNRh+♂		
15	OMNRh+	A₁MNRh+	A₁MNRh+♀	OMNRh+♂	OMNRh+♀	A₁MNRh+♂		
16	A₁MNRh+	A₁NRh+	OMNRh+♀	OMNRh+♂	A₁NRh+♂	A₁MNRh+♀		
17	A₁MNRh+	A₂MRh+	A₁NRh+♂	A₁MRh+♀	OMNRh+♂	A₁MRh+♂	A₂MRh+♀	
18	A₂NRh−	ONRh+	ONRh−♂	ONRh−♂	ONRh−♀	ONRh−♂		
19	ONRh−	A₂MNRh−	ONRh−♂‡	A₂NRh−♀	A₂MNRh−♂	A₂NRh−♀	A₂NRh−♂	
20	AMNRh+	AMNRh+	OMNRh+♀♀	AMNRh+♀	AMNRh+♂	AMRh+♂		
21	OMNRh+	A₁MNRh+	A₁NRh+♀	A₁NRh+♀				
22	AMNRh+	BMRh+	OMRh+♂	AMNRh+♀				
23	A₂MRh+	BNRh+	A₂BMNRh+♀	BMNRh+♂				
24	OMNRh+	BMNRh−	ONRh+♂	BMNRh+♂	BNRh+♂			
25	A₁MNRh−	A₂BMNRh+	BMNRh+♂	A₁BNRh+♂				
26	OMRh+	BNRh+	OMNRh+♂	OMNRh+♂	OMNRh+♀			
27	OMRh+	A₁MNRh+	A₁MNRh+♂	A₂MNRh+♂	A₂MRh+♂	A₂MRh+♂		
28	A₂MNRh+	A₁MNRh+	A₁MNRh+♀	A₁MNRh+♀	A₁MNRh+♂	A₁MNRh+♂		
29	OMNRh+	OMRh+	OMNRh+♀*	OMRh+♀♀*	OMRh+♀♀*			
30	A₁MNRh+	OMNRh+	OMNRh+♂	OMNRh+♂	OMNRh+♂	ONRh+♂		
31	OMNRh+	A₁NRh+	A₁NRh+♂	A₁MNRh−♀	A₁NRh+♀	A₁NRh+♀	OMNRh+♀	

Table V. (*Continued*)

Family number	Parents		Children
	Father	**Mother**	
32	A₁BMNRh−	A₁MNRh−	A₂BMNRh−♀, A₂BMNRh−♀, A₁MNRh−♂, A₁BMNRh−♂, A₁NRh−♂, A₁MRh−♂, A₁MNRh−♀, A₁MNRh−♂, A₁MRh−♂
33	OMNRh+	A₂MRh+	A₂MRh+♂, A₂NRh+♂
34	A₂BMNRh+	OMNRh+	A₂MRh+♂, A₂MNRh+♀, A₂MNRh+♀, A₂NRh+♀
35	A₁BMNRh+	A₁NRh+	BMNRh+♀, A₁MNRh+♀, A₁NRh+♂, A₂MNRh+♀, A₁MNRh+♀, BMRh+♂
36	BMRh+	OMNRh+	OMRh+♀, OMNRh+♀, A₁NRh+♀, BMNRh+♂, OMNRh+♀
37	A₂MNRh+	BMRh+	BMRh+♂, BMRh+♀, BMNRh+♂, OMNRh+♀
38	A₁MRh+	A₁BNRh+	A₂MRh+♀, A₁BMNRh+♂
39	BMRh+	OMNRh+	A₁BMNRh+♂, BMNRh+♂, BMRh+♀, BMRh+♀, BMNRh+♀
40	A₁MNRh+	A₁NRh+	BMRh+♂, A₁MNRh+♂, A₁NRh+♂, OMNRh+♂
41	ONRh+	OMNRh+	A₁MNRh+♂, OMNRh+♂, OMNRh+♂, A₁NRh+♀
42	BMRh+	A₂BMNRh+	OMNRh+♂, BMNRh+♂, BMNRh+♂
43	ONRh+	OMNRh+	BMRh+♂, ONRh+♂, ONRh+♀, A₁MRh+♀, ONRh+♂
44	A₁MNRh+	A₂MNRh+	ONRh+♂, A₁MNRh+♂, OMRh+♀, A₂MNRh+♀, A₁MNRh−♂
45	OMNRh+	A₁MNRh+	A₁MNRh+♂, OMNRh+♂, A₁MNRh+♂, OMNRh+, A₁NRh+♂, A₁MRh+♂, OMNRh+♂, A₁MRh+♂
46	OMRh+	BMNRh+	OMRh+♂, BMNRh+♀, BMNRh+♀, OMRh+♂
47	A₁BMNRh−	OMNRh+	A₁NRh+♂, A₁MRh+♀, A₁NRh+♀, OMNRh+♂, A₁MRh+♀
48	OMRh+	OMRh+	OMRh−♂, OMRh−♂, OMRh+♂, OMRh+♂
49	OMNRh+	OMRh+	OMNRh+♀, OMNRh+♀, OMRh+♂
50	A₁BMRh+	OMRh+	BMRh+♂, BMRh+♀, BMRh+♂
51	BMRh+	OMRh+	OMRh+♂, OMRh+♂, BMRh+♂
52	OMNRh+	A₁MNRh+	OMNRh+♂, OMRh+♀, OMNRh+♂, ONRh+♀, ONRh+♀, A₁MRh+♀, OMNRh+♂, A₁MNRh+♀, A₁MNRh+♀
53†	OMRh+	OMNRh−	OMRh+♂, OMRh+♀, OMNRh+♂, OMRh+♀, A₁MRh+♂, A₂MNRh+♂, OMNRh+♀
54	OMNRh−	A₁MRh+	A₂MRh+♂, A₁MNRh+♂, A₂MRh+♂, A₁MRh+♂, A₂MNRh+♂, A₂MRh+♂
55	OMNRh−	AMRh−	OMNRh−♂, OMNRh−♂, OMRh−♂, OMNRh−♂
56	BNRh−	OMNRh+	BNRh+♂, BMNRh+♂, BMRh+♂, BMNRh+♂, A₂BMNRh+♀
57	A₂BMNRh+	A₁MNRh+	A₂MNRh+♂, A₂BMRh+♂, A₂MNRh−♂, A₂MNRh+♂, ONRh+♂, A₂MNRh+♂, A₂MNRh−♀
58	AMNRh−	BMRh+	ABMRh+♂, AMNRh+♂, AMNRh+♂, A₂MNRh+♂, OMNRh+♂
59	A₁MNRh+	ONRh−	ONRh+♀, OMNRh+♂, ONRh+♂, ONRh+♂, A₂MNRh+♂
60	A₁MRh+	A₁MNRh+	OMNRh+♀, OMNRh+♀, A₁MNRh+♂, A₁MRh+♀

* Twins. † Colored family. ‡ Oldest child, and is from a previous marriage.

Table VI. Summary of Family Material

Mating	Number of families	Number of children		
		Rh+	Rh−	Totals
Rh+ × Rh+	42	151	7	158
Rh+ × Rh−	12	37	11	48
Rh− × Rh−	6	0	31	31
Totals........	60	188	49	237

in family 54 is evidently of genotype A_1A_2Rhrh, the father of genotype $OOrhrh$. In a mating of this kind children of types A_2Rh+ and A_1Rh− belong to one category (either linked or crossover), those of types A_1Rh+ and A_2Rh− to the other. As there are 5 children of one sort and 1 of the other, this family does not furnish evidence for close linkage.

Information as to the linkage relations of property Rh and agglutinogens M,N is provided only by families 4, 6, and 13. In family 4, three of the children belong to one class, two to the other class; in family 6 two children can be used, and one of these belongs to each class; finally, in family 13 only two of the children can be used, and again one belongs to each class. These results point strongly to independent assortment, though the possibility of a loose linkage cannot be excluded.

COMMENT

From the clinical facts mentioned in the introduction, it is apparent that a test by which Rh+ and Rh− individuals can be distinguished is of practical importance for the selection of blood donors in certain instances. This occasion arises in cases of repeated transfusion to Rh− patients, in whom the injection of Rh+ blood is sometimes harmful. The same indication obtains even at the very first transfusion in pregnancy when the woman is of type Rh−. For these reasons, where blood donor organizations exist, it will be helpful to examine the donors in order to have available a list of Rh− individuals. The fact that occasionally doubtful reactions may be encountered is of no consequence for the selection of Rh− donors, as such individuals can be excluded. To perform compatibility tests will be important, even when the donor's blood has been tested with anti-Rh sera, and should be conducted also at body temperature (22).

The test that has been described is not as perfect as one would desire, since the reactions are not strong, but with proper attention reliable results can as a rule be obtained. A favorable circumstance is the ease with which the reagent was prepared. The tests can also be made with the occasionally occurring human sera containing Rh agglutinins, but such sera are not always at hand, and unless a sufficient number of individuals previously tested for the factor are available, it may not be possible to establish the identity of a given irregular iso-agglutinin with anti-Rh. Therefore, it is of value to possess in the guinea pig antisera a reagent which can be obtained at will. Moreover, indications were found of differences in the reactions of various human sera reacting on Rh+ blood, while the guinea pig sera appeared to be uniform and most likely can be used as a standard. If the agglutinable property proves to be a species character in the monkey, this could account for the uniformity of the antibodies induced by *rhesus* blood, but it has not yet been determined whether there are individual differences in *rhesus* blood with regard to the factor.

As regards the nature of the reactions described, it might be questioned whether they actually indicate a special agglutinable property or merely differing degrees of agglutinability, in view of the failure to separate Rh agglutinins from the guinea pig sera by absorption with negative bloods. The second assumption can be eliminated, however, because a separation was possible with rabbit immune sera, and the Rh agglutinins in human sera do not react at all on negative bloods and can be specifically absorbed.

The investigation of families leads one to conclude that the factor is inherited as a simple Mendelian dominant, which is not sex-linked. If further studies should prove the factor to be linked to neither A,B nor M,N, as one might surmise from our own scanty data, the property Rh may serve to mark a new pair of chromosomes for linkage studies.

The authors are indebted to Mr. Jack Black and Miss E. H. Tetschner for their assistance.

SUMMARY

Studies are reported on an individual agglutinogen (Rh) in human blood which has been found to be of clinical importance because occasionally it gives rise to the formation of immune isoantibodies in man, a peculiarity which leads to untoward transfusion reactions.

A method for the determination of the presence or absence of the new blood factor is described, which can be used for typing patients and prospective blood donors.

Examination of families showed that the agglutinogen is inherited as a simple Mendelian dominant. The distribution of the factor Rh among white individuals and Negroes may indicate racial differences. The property is probably genetically independent of the blood groups and the factors M and N.

BIBLIOGRAPHY

(1) K. Landsteiner and P. Levine. 1929. J. Immunol. **17**: 1.

(2) A. S. Wiener. 1939. Blood groups and blood transfusion, 2nd ed. Charles C. Thomas, Springfield, Illinois: 183.

(3) K. Landsteiner and P. Levine. 1928. J. Exp. Med. **47**: 757.

(4) K. Landsteiner, W. R. Strutton and M. W. Chase. 1934. J. Immunol. **27**: 469.

(5) P. H. Andresen. 1935. Z. Immunitätsforsch. **85**: 227.

(6) K. Landsteiner and A. S. Wiener. 1937. J. Immunol. **33**: 19.

(7) K. Landsteiner and A. S. Wiener. 1940. Proc. Soc. Exper. Biol. and Med. **43**: 223.

(8) A. S. Wiener and H. R. Peters. 1940. Ann. Int. Med. **13**: 2306.

(9) P. Levine and R. E. Stetson. 1939. J. Am. Med. Assn. **113**: 126.

(10) P. Levine and E. M. Katzin. 1940. Proc. Soc. Exper. Biol. and Med. **45**: 343.

(11) P. Levine, E. M. Katzin and L. Burnham. 1941. J. Am. Med. Assn. **116**: 825.

(12) R. Ottenberg. 1923. J. Am. Med. Assn. **81**: 295.

(13) R. R. Darrow. 1938. Arch. Path. **25**: 378.

(14) E. von Dungern and L. Hirschfeld. 1911. Z. Immunitätsforsch. **8**: 526.

(15) V. Friedenreich. 1936. Z. Immunitätsforsch. **89**: 409.

(16) A. S. Wiener and I. J. Silverman. 1941. Am. J. Clin. Path. **11**: 45.

(17) V. Friedenreich and A. Lauridsen. 1938. Acta Path. Microbiol. Scand. **38**: 115.

(18) V. Friedenreich. 1936. Deutsch. Z. ges. gerichtl. Med. **25**: 358.

(19) A. S. Wiener. 1941. Arch. Path. **32**: 229.

(20) R. A. Fisher. 1936. Statistical methods for research workers, 6th ed. Oliver and Boyd, London: 88.

(21) A. S. Wiener. 1932. Genetics. **17**: 335.

(22) P. Levine, E. M. Katzin and L. Burnham. 1940. Proc. Soc. Exp. Biol. and Med **45**: 346.

(23) P. Levine and S. H. Polyes. 1941. Ann. Int. Med. **14**: 1907.

Possible Genetical Pathways for the Biosynthesis of Blood Group Mucopolysaccharides*

WINIFRED M. WATKINS

W. T. J. MORGAN

Human genetics, as illustrated in this section on the blood groups, often proceeds from simple to complex descriptions of a given character. These complexities result from an ever closer inspection of what genes do. Invariably genes are found to operate in a milieu determined by other genetic loci. The synthesis by Watkins and Morgan describes a portion of the chemical basis of interaction between the genetic loci responsible for the ABO, Lewis and secretor characters. The remarkable inferences of Ceppellini, referred to in the references of this paper and based upon Bateson's admonition to "treasure exceptions," reach similar conclusions on largely genetic grounds. Analogous complexities, and at once a more complete understanding, can be expected for other aspects of human variation, normal and aberrant, and, one can be certain will depend, as here, upon a complementary clinical, genetic and biochemical endeavor. Very often the beginning lies in the demonstration of simple inheritance.

Investigations on the chemical nature of the water-soluble substances associated with A, B, H and Le^a blood group specificities have shown these substances to be extremely complex and labile materials, and our knowledge of their detailed structure is still far from complete. The data at present available however, on the general chemical, physical and immunological properties of the blood group materials, and the structures within the macromolecules which confer on them their serological specificity seems to have reached a stage when it is possible and even advantageous, to speculate

* Reprinted by senior author's and publisher's permission from Vox Sang. 1959. **4:** 97-119.

on the relationships between the various substances and their possible mode of synthesis within the body. Any genetical scheme for the biosynthesis of the blood group substances proposed at the present time will, without doubt, be an over-simplification, but if the suggested steps are open to a measure of experimental proof, they can provide a basis for further biochemical investigations of these important gene products. It is proposed here to review briefly the biochemical facts about the blood group substances which must be taken into consideration in any such genetical scheme and then to outline a possible biosynthetic pathway which we believe might account for these findings.

CHEMICAL SIMILARITIES OF BLOOD GROUP SUBSTANCES

One of the most striking facts to emerge from the early biochemical studies on the water-soluble substances associated with the ABO blood group system was the identity in qualitative chemical composition of the serologically specific materials irrespective of the blood group of the individual from whom they were derived (see *Morgan* 1954/55; *Kabat* 1956). Thus the A and B substances were each found to contain the same four sugars—L-fucose, D-galactose, N-acetylglucosamine and N-acetylgalactosamine and the same eleven amino acids. The material present in the secretions of group O individuals, originally considered to be the product of the *O* gene but subsequently called H-substance because of its occurrence even in those individuals who do not possess an *O* gene, also proved to be qualitatively identical in composition with the A and B substances. Even more surprisingly, the product found in the secretions of the majority of ABH non-secretors, that is, the Lewis Le[a] substance, was shown to contain the same sugars and amino acids as the A, B and H substances although the Lewis system is genetically independent of the ABO system. The general properties and behaviour of all these substances established them as mucopolysaccharides which are complex macromolecules containing carbohydrate units and amino acid residues joined together by primary chemical bonds.

The lability of mucopolysaccharides precludes the use of drastic methods of purification and this has led to considerable difficulties in obtaining blood group substances in a form in which they can be considered as essentially free from contamination with materials of closely similar composition. Variations in quantitative chemical composition are, therefore, not always easy to interpret and cannot necessarily be associated with differences in specificity because small but significant variations in the amount of any one component are frequently observed among preparations obtained from individuals of the same blood group. Certain inter-group differences in quantitative composition of the materials are, however, observed fairly consistently and a typical set of analytical values for preparations of human blood group substances derived from ovarian cyst fluids are given in Table I.

Thus it will be seen that Le^a substance has a lower fucose content than the A, B, H or AB substances; several Le^a preparations contain 12-14% of fucose whereas A, B and H preparations usually contain 18-22%. The figures for a cyst preparation from an individual who was a non-secretor of A, B, H and a non-secretor of Le^a and Le^b ("Inactive substance, Fl.") in Table I, make it clear that this material, although remarkably similar in composition to the active substances, differs strikingly in possessing a very low fucose value.

Table I. ANALYTICAL FIGURES (TYPICAL VALUES) FOR PREPARATIONS OF THE HUMAN BLOOD GROUP SUBSTANCES

	Nitrogen	Fucose	Acetyl	Hexos-amine	Reduc-tion
	%	%	%	%	%
A-substance.............	5.4	19	9.0	29	54
H-substance............	5.3	18	8.6	28	50
Le^a-substance...........	5.0	14	9.9	32	56
B-substance.............	5.6	16	7.0	24	52
AB-substance...........	5.6	17	—	26	54
"Inactive substance, Fl."..	5.4	1.6	—	28	49

COMMON SPECIFICITIES SHOWN BY THE BLOOD GROUP MUCOPOLYSACCHARIDES

Beeson and Goebel (1939) followed up earlier observations that human erythrocytes are agglutinated by Type XIV antipneumococcus horse serum with the demonstration that blood group A substance obtained from commercial pepsin precipitated with the Type XIV antiserum. Subsequent studies showed that blood group substances isolated from hog gastric mucin, human saliva and human stomachs by peptic digestion cross react with anti-Type XIV serum (*Kabat, Bendich, Bezer and Knaub*, 1948). Human blood group A, B or H substances isolated from ovarian cyst fluids by the phenol extraction method frequently do not precipitate to any appreciable extent in this system; after mild hydrolysis with acid or by treatment with certain specific enzymes, however, all the substances have the capacity to cross react with the Type XIV antiserum. Le^a specific preparations usually cross react even in the undegraded state and even more marked is the capacity of the untreated "Inactive substance, Fl." to precipitate with the Type XIV antipneumococcus serum. These results suggest that all the blood group preparations, and the mucopolysaccharide material which has no demonstrable blood group activity, possess common or closely related chemical structures responsible for the reaction in the Type XIV system but that in the undegraded state these structures in the A, B and H substances are masked or overshadowed, in such a way that they are not available for reaction with the antibody.

Further evidence for the existence of similar structural units in A, B and H substances has been obtained from enzyme degradation experiments. *Iseki and Masaki* (1953) reported that an enzyme from *Clostridium tertium* specifically decomposed A substance with the disappearance of A specificity and the appearance of O (H) specificity. Subsequently it was found that when specific B-decomposing enzymes from *Bacillus cereus* (*Iseki and Ikeda* 1956) or *Trichomonas foetus* (*Watkins*, 1956) acted on B active preparations, which were initially devoid of H activity, the destruction of B serological properties was accompanied by the development of H specificity. Chromatographic examination of the material diffusible through a cellophane membrane after enzyme action showed that galactose was the sugar liberated in greatest amount by the B enzyme from *T. foetus*. It appears, therefore, that both A and B substances have underlying structures closely similar to, or identical with, the specific determinant groupings in H substance.

SEROLOGICALLY ACTIVE STRUCTURES WITHIN THE SPECIFIC MUCOPOLYSACCHARIDES

The similarity in general chemical composition of the blood group substances, the rapid loss of serological activity by hydrolysis methods which cause very little demonstrable change in the macromolecules, and the development of new specificities after mild degradation have all combined to suggest that only part of the mucopolysaccharide molecules determines their characteristic serological specificity. Studies in recent years have therefore been directed towards the determination of the simplest structure within each group-specific macromolecule which is responsible for its remarkable immunological specificity.

Antibody and enzyme inhibition experiments with simple sugars and oligosaccharides of known structure have now established fairly conclusively that the specificity of the blood group substances resides in the carbohydrate moiety of the mucopolysaccharide molecules and that in each substance one of the component sugars plays a more dominant role in serological specificity than do the others. The first indication that one of the component sugars of human H-substance is more closely involved in specificity than are the others was obtained when it was found that L-fucose inhibited the agglutination of O cells by an eel anti-H serum (*Watkins and Morgan*, 1952) and an anti-H reagent of plant origin, namely an extract of *Lotus tetragonolobus* seeds (*Morgan and Watkins*, 1953). Examination of the inhibiting capacity of the methyl L-fuco-pyranosides and furanosides showed that an α-L-fuco-pyranosyl structure had the greatest effect on both the eel and *Lotus* reagents. The enzymic decomposition of H substance by preparations from *Clostridium welchii* or *T. foetus* was also shown to be specifically inhibited by L-fucose and not by the other sugars present in the blood group substances (*Watkins and Morgan*, 1955).

Evidence that *N*-acetylgalactosamine plays a definite part in the chemical structure responsible for A specificity was obtained when it was shown to inhibit the agglutination of group A cells by extracts of *Vicia cracca* seeds and Lima beans (*Morgan and Watkins*, 1953); α-methyl *N*-acetylgalactosaminide was even more effective. By means of the quantitative precipitation inhibition technique *Kabat and Leskowitz* (1955) likewise demonstrated that *N*-acetylgalactosamine partially inhibited the precipitation of A-substance by human anti-A serum. Moreover, an enzyme obtained from *T. foetus* which destroyed the serological activity of A substance was specifically inhibited by *N*-acetylgalactosamine and its methyl glycoside (*Watkins and Morgan*, 1955). Subsequently, the isolation of a disaccharide, *O*-α-*N*-acetyl-D-galactosaminoyl-(1 → 3)-galactose, from A substance (*Côté and Morgan*, 1956) which was considerably more active in agglutination inhibition tests than *N*-acetylgalactosamine, or its methyl glycoside, confirmed the importance of the acetylamino sugar in the specific determinant of A substance and suggested that the unit represented by the disaccharide is a structure more closely associated with A-specificity than any so far identified.

By precipitation inhibition *Kabat and Leskowitz* (1955) showed that galactose was the only one of the four sugars in the blood group substance which inhibited B-anti-B precipitation and that compounds containing α-D-galactosyl structures were better inhibitors than simple galactose. Independent evidence for the part played by D-galactose in B specificity was provided by the specific inhibition by this sugar of the enzymic hydrolysis of B substance (*Watkins and Morgan*, 1955). More recently, by a combination of the enzyme and antibody inhibition techniques it has been possible to show that

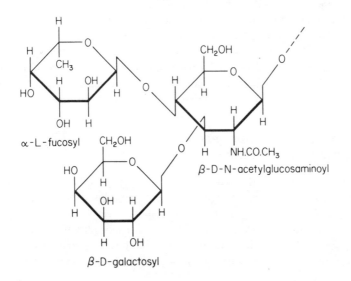

α-L-fucosyl

β-D-N-acetylglucosaminoyl

β-D-galactosyl

L-fucose plays an important role in Le^a specificity (*Watkins and Morgan*, 1957). In this instance, more detailed information about the probable structure responsible for Le^a serological reactivity is known than for any of the other blood group specificities because a pentasaccharide of known structure Lacto-N-fucopentaose II (*Kuhn, Baer and Gauhe*, 1958) isolated from human milk, was found to give considerable inhibition in the Le^a system. It can be postulated that the activity of the pentaose II resides in the specific spatial pattern given by the structure [See bottom of page 63] and that a branched trisaccharide unit formed by two non-reducing end units, α-L-fucosyl- and β-D-galactosyl attached to N-acetyl-D-glucosamine functions as the specific determinant grouping in Le^a serological reactions.

Partial acid hydrolysis of group A substance yielded six N-containing disaccharides (*Côté and Morgan*, 1956, and unpublished work) of which only the one mentioned above inhibited A agglutination. A second of these disaccharides, however, namely O-β-D-galactosyl-$(1 \rightarrow 4)$-N-acetyl-D-glucosamine, was found to inhibit strongly the precipitation of slightly degraded blood group substances by Type XIV pneumococcus anti-serum thus suggesting that this cross reactivity is attributable, at least in part, to the presence in these substances of units similar to the disaccharide (*Watkins and Morgan*, 1956). Quantitative precipitation inhibition experiments also implicated β-linked galactose residues in Type XIV cross reactivity (*Kabat*, 1957) and recent work on the structure of the Type XIV polysaccharide has shown the presence of β-$(1 \rightarrow 4)$ galactosyl-N-acetylglucosamine units in this material (*Barker, Heidelberger, Stacey and Tipper*, 1958).

In addition to the common specificities revealed by slight degradation of the blood group substances, it has been shown that the materials which are non-dialysable after mild acid hydrolysis of A and B substances each develop a new and independent specificity (*Allen and Kabat*, 1957). These materials are still antigenic in man and are able to induce antibody formation even in individuals of the same blood group as those from whom the original material was derived. The new specific precipitability which is developed by B substance after the original specificity has been destroyed by mild acid hydrolysis is also inhibited by α-methyl galactoside, indicating that different α-D-galactosyl structures have been exposed by the acid treatment.

MULTIPLE BLOOD GROUP SPECIFICITIES
OF MUCOPOLYSACCHARIDES

The results discussed in the preceding section have shown that, in terms of blood group specificity, the bulk of the mucopolysaccharide molecule can be regarded merely as a carrier for the specific serological structures. The question therefore arises whether in secretions displaying more than one specific serological activity each of the specificities is associated with a different molecular entity or whether individual mucopolysaccharide molecules carry more than one specificity. Whether, for example, the A and B serological activities of the secretions of AB "secretor" persons are due to a mixture of A and B specific mucopolysaccharides, or to a single new type of mucopolysaccharide which has both serologically reactive structures. The usual chemical fractionation procedures and electrophoretic and ultra-centrifugal methods cannot separate the A, B, H and Le^a substances from each other completely because of their close chemical and physical similarity. The method used to obtain evidence for the existence of mucopolysaccharide molecules with single or multiple specificities, therefore, was that of serological precipitation with selected mono-specific antisera. When a precipitating anti-A reagent, which was completely free from anti-B precipitins, was added to an artificial mixture of A and B substances the A activity, as measured by agglutination inhibition tests, was carried down in the precipitate leaving a supernatant solution which was free from A activity but which had the same inhibition titre against anti-B as the original mixture. The washed and redissolved precipitate possessed only A activity thus demonstrating that with the anti-A reagent used, it is possible to completely separate an artificial mixture of A and B substances. When this method was applied to cyst substances and salivas from individuals belonging to group A$_1$B or A$_2$B, however, it was found that after removal of the precipitate the supernatant solution showed almost complete loss of B activity as well as A, and the precipitate possessed both A and B activities in the same ratio as the original solution. These experiments, therefore, indicated that in the tissue fiuids and secretions of secretors belonging to group AB most, if not all, the macromolecules with blood group specificity have both A and B properties (*Morgan and Watkins*, 1956). This result is consistently obtained when the specifically precipitated material is repeatedly dissolved and reprecipitated with the same reagent or when it is precipitated first with anti-A and then, after re-solution, with anti-B serum.

The second application of this technique was to the secretions of group A$_2$ secretors with both A and H serological activity (*Watkins and Morgan*, 1956/57). Again, it was found possible using an anti-A precipitating reagent, to separate an artificial mixture of A and H substances whereas the precipitate obtained from group A$_2$ individuals had both A and H activity suggesting that the macromolecules carry both specificities. The supernatant solutions from the A$_2$ secretions after the removal of the precipitate usually had some H activity although the A activity had been completely removed. It would, therefore, appear that there are some free H specific molecules as well as those possessing both A and H activity. More recently, this technique was extended to secretions with Lewis Le^a specificity as well as A specificity and revealed the existence of molecules which possess both A and Le^a specificity as well as molecules with only Le^a activity.

The preceding results have demonstrated the existence of mucopolysaccharide molecules carrying two different specificities. It seems highly probable, however, and indeed we have some preliminary results to support this, that in fact molecules with multiple (i.e., more than two) specificities occur in secretions. In the tissue fluids and secretions of a group A_2B individual who also secreted Le^a substance, for example, one could postulate the existence of molecules each of which carried A, B, H and Le^a specificity. Owing to the lack of suitable sera it has not been possible to determine whether the Le^b serological character occurs on the same molecule as the other specific serological characters with which it is found in secretions; but the similarity in general chemical composition of H materials showing a high Le^b activity and those showing little or no Le^b activity (*Gibbons, Morgan and Gibbons*, 1955) suggests that the Le^b substance is also a mucopolysaccharide and it therefore seems highly probable that the Le^b specific groupings will be found to occur in association with other characters on the same molecule.

The biochemical facts which we believe must be reconciled in any genetical scheme put forward to account for the biosynthesis of the blood group mucopolysaccharides can be summarised as follows:

(1) The striking similarity in qualitative chemical composition of the blood group materials irrespective of the blood group of the individual from whom they were derived.

(2) The common Type XIV cross reactivity shown by the untreated "Inactive substance, Fl." and Le^a substance and by the A, B and H substances after mild degradation.

(3) The appearance of H activity in A and B substances after enzymic inactivation.

(4) The chemical nature of the structures responsible in each substance for its characteristic specificity and

(5) The multiple specificities which occur on the same mucopolysaccharide molecule.

SEROLOGICAL AND GENETICAL CONSIDERATIONS

The theory of inheritance of the ABO groups now generally accepted is that advanced by *Bernstein* (1924) according to which the blood group of an individual depends on the presence of any two of three allelic genes *A*, *B* and *O*. This scheme was later extended to include the subgroups A_1 and A_2 (*Thomsen, Friedenreich and Worsaae*, 1930). This theory has been amply supported by family studies carried out in all parts of the world in the three decades since it was first proposed and there can be little doubt that the A and B serological characters result from the action of allelic genes. The discovery (*Schiff*, 1927) of a serum which preferentially agglutinated O and A_2 cells, and of a substance in the saliva of group O individuals which inhibited this agglutination, was taken at first to indicate that the *O* gene gave rise to a product analogous to the products of the A and B genes. The authenticity of the sera which agglutinate O cells preferentially as reagents detecting the products of *Bernstein's* O gene, however, was soon questioned (*Hirschfeld*, 1934; *Moureau*, 1935). The strongest evidence that the so-called O-substance is not a product of the O gene consists in the fact that individuals of the genotype A_1B who, according to *Bernstein's* hypothesis, cannot possess an O gene, can secrete this O substance in addition to A and B substances; this led *Witebsky and Klendshoj* (1941) to suggest that the O-substance is a basic mucoid on which genes A and B superimpose the A and B reactive structures. *Morgan and Watkins* (1948) proposed that the substance secreted by group O secretors should be renamed H-substance to indicate the heterogenetic or ubiquitous origin of the material and to avoid the confusion implicit in the earlier nomenclature. The undoubted influence of the A, B and O genes on the quantitative manifestations of the H character of erythrocytes and on the amount of water soluble H substance in secretions led these authors to suggest a modification of the theory of *Hirschfeld and Amzel* (1940), namely that the genes A, B and O are formed as the result of mutation from a basic or primary gene H which engenders the formation of a basic or primary substance H, a precursor of the products of the A, B and O genes. Certain sera which agglutinated O and A_2 cells preferentially were not inhibited by H substance and it was assumed that these sera were detecting the true product of the O gene (*Boorman, Dodd and Gilbey*, 1948; *Morgan and Watkins*, 1948). This assumption was not substantiated by subsequent studies and the existence of a product of the O gene once more became questionable. It was, therefore, suggested that in place of a series of genes giving rise directly to varying amounts of A and H, or B and H, characters there exists a series of A and B genes which vary in their degree of effectiveness in converting the basic substrate H; it was also postulated the O gene does not compete for this basic substance (*Watkins and Morgan*, 1955; 1956/57). Thus large quantities of unconverted H substance would be expected in the secretions and on the red cells of group O individuals and the strong H reactivity of the secretions and red cells of A_2 individuals could be explained on the assumption that the A_2 gene is less effective than the A_1 gene in bringing about the conversion of the precursor H substance into A substance than is the A_1 gene.

The finding that serological characters resulting from the activity of different genes can occur on the same mucopolysaccharide molecules is consistent with the view that each blood group gene is responsible not for the complete synthesis of the group specific mucopolysaccharide but rather for the final stages only; that is, for the development of the special structures responsible for the strict immunological specificity of the ultimate mucopolysaccharide molecule. In man, few examples of the interaction of genes have been worked out in biochemical terms. *Filliti-Wurmser, Aubel-Lesure and Wurmser* (1953) found that the molecular weights of the β-agglutinins in OO,

A_1A_1, and A_1O individuals were 170,000, 300,000 and 500,000 respectively, thus indicating that the heterozygote produces a product which differs from that produced by either of the genes in the homozygous condition. More recently, it has been found that the two genes at the haptoglobin locus give rise to three, and possibly more, closely related proteins some of which can be distinguished ultracentrifugally. One of these products appears to be confined to the heterozygote and to be intermediate in its properties between those produced by either homozygote (*Bearn and Franklin*, 1958). Both these examples, however, are concerned with the interaction of allelic genes. The first observations on the multiple specificities of the blood group mucopolysaccharides, which showed that A and B structures occur together on the same molecule in group AB persons, were similarly interpreted as resulting from the interaction of allelic genes. It seemed improbable, however, that a similar interpretation could be applied to the observation that both A and H serologically reactive sites can occur on the same molecule and the subsequent demonstration that A and Le^a specificities could co-exist on the same molecule clearly showed that the resultant mucopolysaccharide molecules in secretions can arise from the action of genes situated at different loci.

The genetics of the Lewis groups are still not completely understood; especially obscure is the mode of inheritance of the Le^b character and its relationship to the ABO and Le^a groups (see *Race and Sanger*, 1958). The early work on the Lewis system showed that the Le^a character is inherited independently of the *ABO* genes but a relationship between the two systems was established when *Grubb* (1948) observed that all persons whose red cells were $Le(a+)$ were non-secretors of A, B or H substances. Later, *Grubb* (1950) suggested that the Lewis antigens are primarily water-soluble substances rather than red cell antigens and the observations of *Sneath and Sneath* (1955) and *Mäkelä and Mäkelä* (1956) showing that red cells passively acquire Lewis antigens from the plasma, appear to have confirmed this suggestion. On the basis of the secretion of the Lewis substances in saliva *Ceppellini* (1955) considers that individuals can be divided into four main groups:

(1) Secretors of A, B or H, Le^a and Le^b substances.
(2) Non-secretors of A, B or H, non-secretors of Le^b but secretors of Le^a.
(3) Secretors of A, B or H but not Le^b or Le^a substances, and
(4) Non-secretors of A, B or H, Le^b or Le^a substances.

In order to explain these results *Ceppellini* (1955) proposed a theory of inheritance (Table II) based on two pairs of alleles, S and s, L and l. These gene pairs are believed to segregate independently but to interact in some of their phenotypic effects. Le^b specificity, for example, is considered as the product of interaction of the genes S and L. *Grubb* (1951) had reported the existence of a fifth saliva group made up of individuals who were secretors of ABH and of Le^b but who lacked Le^a substance. This result, however, is considered by *Ceppellini* to be due to the use of an anti-Le^b serum which cross reacted with H substance.

Table II. Scheme of the Lewis System and Secretion of ABH
(After Ceppellini, 1955)

Genotypes	Saliva			Red cells
	ABH	Le^a	Le^b	
SSLL *SSLl* *SsLL* *SsLl*	+	+	+	Le (a−b+)
ssLL *ssLl*	−	+	−	Le (a+b−)
SSll *Ssll*	+	−	−	Le (a−b−)
ssll	−	−	−	Le (a−b−)

SUGGESTED PATHWAYS FOR THE BIOSYNTHESIS OF
THE BLOOD GROUP MUCOPOLYSACCHARIDES[2]

On the basis of the biochemical and serological data outlined above we propose two possible pathways for the later stages of the biosynthesis of the blood group mucopolysaccharides. For reasons discussed below, it is improbable that the scheme shown in Fig. 1 is completely acceptable, but it is presented here first because it is based largely on biochemical data; modifications introduced on genetical grounds resulted in the second scheme (Fig. 2).

It is suggested that the appearance of the ABH and Le^a substances in the secretions depends on the operation of three independent gene systems L' and l', S' and s', and the *ABO* genes. The symbols S and s used by Schiff for secretion have been retained because we think that the appearance of the water-soluble A, B and H substances in secretions is dependent on the possession by an individual of the S gene but the superscript has been added because the genes are considered also to be transforming genes determining a step in the biosynthesis of the mucopolysaccharides; the function normally attributed to the gene S is that of allowing the conversion of the ABH substances to a water-soluble form. Similarly, the symbols L and l used by *Ceppellini* for the presence or absence of the Le^a substance in secretions have been retained, but again the superscript has been added because a somewhat different function for these genes from that proposed by *Ceppellini* is envisaged. The genes L', S', A and B are considered to be transforming genes effecting certain stages in the conversion of a common precursor substance to the specific product which appears in the secretion. We suggest that the genes l', s' and O play no part in the conversion of the mucopolysaccharide materials

[2] Based on a paper given by Dr. *W. M. Watkins* at the 7th International Congress of Blood Transfusion, Rome, September 1958.

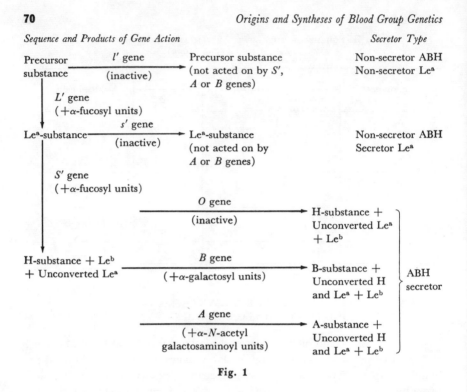

Fig. 1

i.e., as far as their part in the scheme is concerned they may be considered as inactive genes or amorphs. The scheme given in Fig. 1 also requires that the transformations brought about by the genes can take place only in the sequence shown and that no further change in the material can occur in the absence of one of the conversion steps.

The precursor substance which is believed to form the common core constituting the bulk of all the water-soluble blood group substances is thought to be the mucopolysaccharide material found in the secretions of individuals belonging to the group who secrete neither ABH substances nor Le^a or Le^b substances ("Inactive substance, Fl." Table I). The only serological reactivity of this material so far demonstrated is the capacity to cross react with anti-Type XIV pneumococcus serum and it is therefore suggested that the precursor material has prominent β-galactosyl-N-acetyl glucosaminoyl structures, most probably joined glycosidically by 1:4 linkages, which confer upon it this cross reactivity. These structures are responsible for the Type XIV reactivity developed by the A, B and H substances after mild degradation. The action of the gene L' is to bring about the conversion of the precursor substance to Le^a substance and, since fucose plays an important part in Le^a specificity, it is envisaged that this step involves, at least in part, the addition of non-reducing α-L-fucosyl units to the precursor material. This synthesis is brought about by the gene combinations $L'L'$ and $L'l'$. The

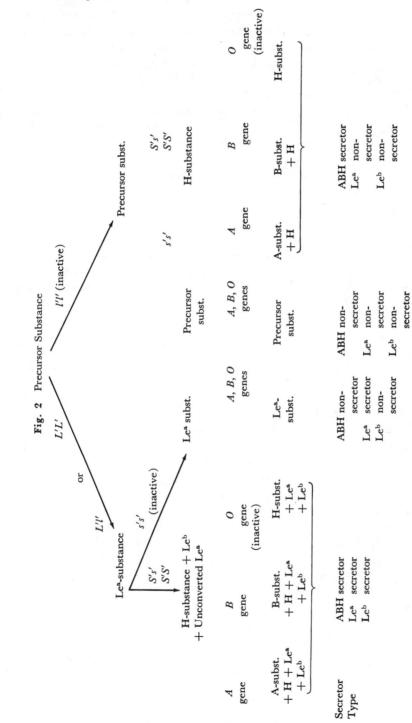

Fig. 2 Precursor Substance

very low fucose content of the "Inactive substance, Fl." and the substantially higher fucose content of typical Le^a preparations would be in agreement with the suggested biochemical function of the L' gene. In individuals homozygous for the gene l' the conversion of the precursor substance to Le^a substance cannot take place and, since in the absence of the conversion step effected by the L' gene the subsequent transformations brought about by the S', A or B genes cannot occur, the unchanged precursor substance appears in secretions. Individuals of the genotype $l'l'$ would therefore correspond to the small group who are non-secretors of ABH and Lewis substances.

The gene S', in single or double dose is considered to control the conversion of Le^a substance to H substance and, as fucose also plays a role in H specificity, this transformation step is believed to involve the addition of further α-fucosyl units, probably through different linkages and to different sugars from the changes effected by the L' gene. It is probable that this conversion is frequently incomplete so that the product retains some residual Le^a specificity in addition to its newly acquired H specificity. This could arise either because some molecules remain completely unchanged (and occur thereafter as free Le^a molecules) or through the molecules which have been converted to H retaining some residual Le^a structures in a condition in which they are available for reactivity with anti-Le^a sera. Though, for reasons mentioned above, it is not possible to put too much emphasis on small differences in the amounts of any one of the component sugars in preparations of blood group substances with different specificities the lower fucose content of the Le^a substances compared with most H preparations (Table I) would be compatible with the proposed action of the S' gene in adding on more fucosyl residues. In the absence of more precise information about the serological and genetical relationship of the Le^b character to the ABO system, or of its chemical nature, it is not easy to speculate on the origin of the Le^b serological structures. However, in its serological properties Le^b seems to be closely related to the H character and it might be that the S' gene converts Le^a to both H and Le^b-reacting substances. Preliminary observations on the inhibition by simple carbohydrates of the agglutination of Le (b+) cells by human anti-Le^b serum showed that two oligosaccharides containing fucose which had been isolated from human milk, namely Lacto-N-difucohexaose (*Kuhn*, 1957) and Lacto-difucotetraose (*Kuhn and Gauhe*, 1958) gave definite although weak inhibition (*Watkins and Morgan*, 1957). The constitutions of these two compounds are as follows:

1) Lacto–N–difucohexaose

β–D–galactosyl–(1→3)–β–D–N–acetylglucosaminoyl–(1→3)–β–D–galactosyl–

(1→4)–D–glucose

| (1→2) | (1→4)

α–L–fucosyl α–L–fucosyl

2) *Lacto-difucotetraose*

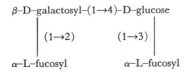

and it will be seen that both these compounds have α-fucosyl units joined to each of two adjacent sugars. It is reasonable, therefore, to suppose that the enzyme elaborated by the S' gene could form both H and Le^b reactive structures by the addition of either one or two fucose units respectively to different sugars or side chains in the Le^a macromolecule.

Individuals with an L' gene but who are homozygous for the inactive genes $s's'$ have Le^a substance which can undergo no further change because the A and B genes, even when present, require H substance as a substrate and cannot act directly on Le^a substance. These individuals therefore correspond to the group of ABH non-secretors who nevertheless contain large quantities of Le^a substance in their secretions.

We consider that the A gene, in either double or single dose, converts the preformed H substance to A substance by the addition of non-reducing α-N-acetylgalactosaminoyl units since there is definite experimental evidence to show that this unit is involved in A specificity. Any residual Le^a specificity remaining with the H substance will appear in the secretions together with the A substance and unchanged H and Le^b substance. The A_2 gene is believed to bring about the same conversion as the A_1 gene but to do so less effectively so that more H specific structures remain untransformed and are therefore available for reactivity with anti-H sera. The B gene in either single or double dose is thought to direct the addition of non-reducing α-galactosyl units to H-substance, since galactose has been shown to play an important part in B specificity, to give a B substance which, according to the extent of the conversion, contains residual H and Le^a specificities. In heterozygous AB individuals the A and B genes both act on the H substrate to convert it to an AB substance and individuals of this genotype would therefore be expected to retain very little residual H specificity as indeed is found experimentally. The O gene is regarded as inactive, and therefore, in individuals homozygous for this gene large quantities of unchanged H substance are found in the secretions together with free or combined residual Le^a and Le^b specificities. A combination of the genes L' and S' together with an A, B or O gene therefore gives rise to the group of ABH secretors who also secrete both Le^a and Le^b substances. The fourth secretor group which constitutes some 10% of the population i.e., secretors of ABH, non-secretors of Le^a (and possibly Le^b) could also be accommodated in this scheme if it were assumed that different S' genes, possibly alleles related to each other in the same way as A_1 and A_2 genes are related, can bring about varying degrees of conversion of Le^a to H.

In the presence of very effective genes no residual Le^a structures would remain and, therefore, the final product found in the secretions after the action of the *A*, *B* or *O* genes would be devoid of Le^a activity.

The scheme outlined in Fig. 1 therefore fits well with many of the biochemical facts which are known about the water-soluble human blood group mucopolysaccharides. However, with the sequence of gene action suggested in this scheme, a mating of an ABH non-secretor, Le^a non-secretor, i.e., an individual of the genotype *l'l'S'S'* or *l'l'S's'* with an ABH non-secretor, secretor of Le^a, i.e., an individual of the genotype *L'L's's'* or *L'l's's'* could give rise to an ABH secretor (genotype *L'l'S's'*). This combination would presumably occur fairly infrequently, but exceptions to the rule that non-secretors of ABH cannot give rise to secretors do not seem to have been recorded (see *Race and Sanger*, 1958). For this reason a modification of the scheme (Fig. 2) has been introduced which overcomes this objection. The concept that the genes can act only in a given sequence and that in the absence of one conversion step the succeeding steps cannot take place, has been modified to allow the gene *S'* to control the conversion of either Le^a substance or the unchanged precursor substance to H substance. When the *S'* gene acts on Le^a substance, Le^b specific structures are produced in addition to H whereas H structures alone arise as the result of the action of *S'* on the precursor substance. The four types of secretor groups could therefore be accounted for by this scheme without postulating the existence of *S'* genes of differing effectiveness.

The possible combination of the genes *L'l'S'* and *s'* for this second scheme are the same as those postulated for the genes *L*, *l*, *S* and *s* on *Ceppellini's* theory; the distribution and frequency of secretor types predicted on this theory fit well with the family data available (*Ceppellini*, 1955a, 1955b), (*Ceppellini and Siniscalco*, 1955). The scheme, largely based on biochemical observations on the blood group mucopolysaccharides, will thus be seen to be in very close agreement with the genetical ideas elaborated by *Ceppellini* on the basis of serological results on family material.

The feasibility of the scheme from the point of view of the mechanism of biosynthesis of mucopolysaccharides is difficult to assess at present because very little is known concerning the biogenesis of such materials. Hyaluronic acid is the only mucopolysaccharide whose biosynthesis has been examined in detail (see *Whistler and Olson*, 1957); (*Dorfman and Cifonelli*, 1958) and even for this substance the present knowledge is almost entirely limited to the mechanism of synthesis of the monosaccharide units, N-acetylglucosamine and glucuronic acid, which are subsequently built up into the macromolecule. Recent work on the biosynthesis of proteins is consistent with the view that proteins are built up directly and completely from free amino acid units without the incorporation of preformed precursors; it should perhaps be emphasised however, that the material called precursor substance in the scheme outlined above is considered as a macromolecular mucopolysaccharide with all the peptide chains completely synthesised and with most of the carbohydrate chains already integrated in the molecule. The suggested synthetic steps are considered as contributing only relatively small changes to the mucopolysaccharide precursor. Studies on the biosynthesis of poly-saccharides have been largely restricted to those containing only one type of sugar unit but the results for these compounds show that the most common method of synthesis involves the transfer of a glycosyl unit, derived from a donor substrate, to the non-reducing chain ends of an acceptor substrate (see *Whelan* 1956/57). The suggested function of the genes in mediating the addition of non-reducing glycosyl units would not, therefore, be inconsistent with the present state of knowledge regarding polysaccharide synthesis. It is not suggested, however, that this is the only function of the genes; the action of the genes might be to determine the complete sequence of sugars which constitute the specific determinant structures or even to effect changes in parts of the molecule not directly concerned in specificity. The observations of *Allen and Kabat* (1957) that after acid hydrolysis of A, B and H substances each develops a new and independent specificity demonstrate that the sub-stances differ by more than those terminal non-reducing sugars which play a dominant role in specificity. The exact nature of the changes brought about by the acid treatment is, however, not known and the new specificities could have arisen either through partial hydrolysis of the original specific determinant structures, thereby revealing a new terminal unit which could induce the formation of antibodies of a different specificity from the intact determinant structure, or through exposure of new structures in other parts of the molecule.

The schemes which we have suggested contain a number of steps for which it should be possible to obtain some biochemical evidence. For example, by mild hydrolytic procedures, especially with enzymes if the appropriate specific reagents can be obtained, it should be possible to determine whether H substances contain any underlying Le^a specific structures as would be expected for the products derived via the pathway outlined on the left-hand side in Fig. 2. Secretors of H who are non-secretors of Le^a and Le^b, on the other hand, should not, if the scheme is correct, possess Le^a groupings at any level in the molecule. Examination of further samples of mucopolysaccharide from individuals whose secretions possess neither A, B, H, Le^a nor Le^b specific character will demonstrate whether the analytical figures given for the single preparation in Table I ("Inactive substance, Fl.") are consistently obtained and whether cross reactivity with Type XIV anti-pneumococcus serum is a constant property of these materials. Experiments along the lines carried out by *Allen and Kabat* (1957) might also give further evidence of the degree of similarity or dissimilarity of the blood group muco-polysaccharides derived from individuals of different blood groups.

In conclusion, the remark made at the beginning of this article, namely that any scheme for the biosynthesis of the blood group substances proposed at the present time will, without doubt, be an oversimplification, should perhaps be restated. The suggested pathways accord well with the biochemical data available at present, but further experimental results may show one, or several, of the steps to be incorrect. If, however, the ideas formulated provide a stimulus for further investigations on these important gene products they will have served a useful purpose.

REFERENCES

(1) P. Z. Allen and E. A. Kabat. 1957. Immunochemical studies on partially hydrolysed blood group, A, B and O (H) substances. Fed. Proc. **16:** 404.

(2) S. A. Barker, M. Heidelberger, M. Stacey and D. J. Tipper. 1958. Immunopolysaccharides. Part X. The structure of the immunologically specific polysaccharide of pneumoccocus type XIV. J. Chem. Soc.: 3468.

(3) A. G. Bearn and E. C. Franklin. 1958. Some genetical implications of physical studies of human haptoglobins. Science. **128:** 596.

(4) P. B. Beeson and W. F. Goebel. 1939. The immunological relationship of the capsular polysaccharide of type XIV pneumococcus to the blood group A specific substance. J. Exp. Med. **70:** 239.

(5) F. Bernstein. 1924. Ergebnisse einer biostatischen zusammenfassenden Betrachtung über die erblichen Blutstrukturen des Menschen. Klin. Wschr. **3:** 1495.

(6) K. E. Boorman, B. E. Dodd and B. E. Gilbey. 1948. A serum which demonstrates the co-dominance of the blood group gene *O* with *A* and *B*. Ann. Eugen., London. **14:** 201.

(7) R. Ceppellini. 1955a. On the genetics of secretor and Lewis characters: a family study. Proc. V. Int. Cong. of Blood Transfusion, Paris: 207.

(8) R. Ceppellini. 1956. Nuova interpretazione sulla genetica dei caratteri Lewis eritrocitari e salivari derivante dall'analisi di 87 famiglie. Suppl. Ric. Sci. Mem. **25:** 3.

(9) R. Ceppellini and M. Siniscalco. 1955. Una nuova ipotesi genetica per il sistema Lewis secretore e suoi riflessi nei riguardi di alcune evidenze di linkage con altri loci. Riv. Ist. sieroter. Ital. **30:** 431.

(10) R. H. Côté and W. T. J. Morgan. 1956. Some nitrogen containing disaccharides isolated from human blood group A substance. Nature, London. **178:** 1171.

(11) A. Dorfman and J. A. Cifonelli. 1958. Biosynthesis of mucopolysaccharides. The uridine nucleotides of group A streptococci. Ciba Foundation Symposium, Chemistry and Biology of Mucopolysaccharides. J. and A. Churchill, Ltd., London: 64.

(12) S. Filliti-Wurmser, G. Aubel-Lesure and R. Wurmser. 1953. Constantes de sédimentation des iso-agglutinines $\beta(A_1O)$, $\beta(OO)$ and $\beta(A_1A_1)$. J. Chem. Phys. **50:** 236.

(13) R. A. Gibbons, W. T. J. Morgan and M. Gibbons. 1955. The isolation of blood group active mucoids from ovarian cyst fluids. Biochem. J. **60:** 428.

(14) R. Grubb. 1948. Correlation between Lewis blood group and secretor character in man. Nature, London. **162**: 933.

(15) R. Grubb. 1950. Quelques aspects de la complexité des groupes ABO. Rev. Hémat. **5**: 269.

(16) R. Grubb. 1951. Observations on the human blood group system Lewis. Acta. Path. Microbiol. Scand. **28**: 61.

(17) L. Hirschfeld and R. Amzel. 1940. Sur les pleiades «isosériques» du sang. 1. Contribution a l'étude des sous-groupes sanguins. Ann. Inst. Pasteur. **65**: 251, 386.

(18) L. Hirschfeld. 1934. Hauptprobleme der Blutgruppenforschung in den Jahren 1927 bis 1933. Ergebn. Hyg. **15**: 54.

(19) S. Iseki and S. Masaki. 1953. Transformation of blood group substance by bacterial enzyme. Proc. Imp. Acad., Japan. **29**: 460.

(20) S. Iseki and T. Ikeda. 1956. On bacterial enzyme specifically decomposing group B substance. Proc. Imp. Acad., Japan. **32**: 201.

(21) E. A. Kabat. 1956. Blood group substances. Academic Press, Inc., New York.

(22) E. A. Kabat. 1958. Immunochemical approaches to polysaccharide and mucopolysaccharide structure. Ciba Foundation Symposium, Chemistry and Biology of Mucopolysaccharides. J. and A. Churchill Ltd., London: 42.

(23) E. A. Kabat, A. Bendich, A. E. Bezer and V. Knaub. 1948. Immunochemical studies of blood groups VI. The cross reaction between type XIV antipneumococcal horse serum and purified blood group A, B and O substances from dog and human sources. J. Exp. Med. **87**: 295.

(24) E. A. Kabat and S. Leskowitz. 1955. Immunochemical studies on blood groups XVII. Structural units involved in blood group A and B specificity. J. Am. Chem. Soc. **77**: 5159.

(25) R. Kuhn. 1957. Aminozucker. Angew. Chem. **60**: 23.

(26) R. Kuhn, H. H. Baer and A. Gauhe. 1958. Die Konstitution der Lacto-N-fucopentaose II. Chem. Ber: **91**: 364.

(27) R. Kuhn and A. Gauhe. 1958. Über die Lacto-difucotetraose der Frauenmilch. Liebigs Ann. **611**: 249.

(28) O. Mäkelä and P. Mäkelä. 1956. Le[b] antigen. Studies on its occurrence in red cells, plasma and saliva. Ann. Med. Exp. Fenn. **34**: 157.

(29) W. T. J. Morgan. 1954-1955. The chemical basis of blood group specificity in man. Lectures on the Scientific Basis of Medicine. **4**: 92.

(30) W. T. J. Morgan and W. M. Watkins. 1948. The detection of a product of the blood group O gene and the relationship of the so-called O substance to the agglutinogens A and B. Brit. J. Exp. Path. **29**: 159.

(31) W. T. J. Morgan and W. M. Watkins. 1953. The inhibition of the haemagglutinins in plant seeds by human blood group substances and simple sugars. Brit. J. Exp. Path. **34**: 94.

(32) W. T. J. Morgan and W. M. Watkins. 1956. The product of the human blood group *A* and *B* genes in individuals belonging to group AB. Nature, London. **177**: 521.

(33) P. Moureau. 1937. Antigène O et antigène humain spécifique. C. R. Soc. Biol., Paris. **125**: 366.

(34) R. R. Race and R. Sanger. 1958. Blood groups in man, 3rd ed. Blackwell, Oxford.

(35) F. Schiff. 1927. Über den serologischen Nachweis der Blutgruppeneigenschaft O. Klin. Wschr. **6**: 303.

(36) J. S. Sneath and P. H. A. Sneath. 1955. Transformation of the Lewis groups of human red cells. Nature, London. **176**: 172.

(37) O. Thomsen, V. Friedenreich and E. Worsaae. 1930. Über die Möglichkeit der Existenz zweier neuer Blutgruppen; auch ein Beitrag zur Beleuchtung sogenannter Untergruppen. Acta Path. Microbiol. Scand. **7**: 157.

(38) W. M. Watkins. 1956. The appearance of H specificity following the enzymic inactivation of blood group B substance. Biochem. J. **64**: 21 P.

(39) W. M. Watkins and W. T. J. Morgan. 1952. Neutralisation of the anti-H agglutinin in eel serum by simple sugars. Nature, London. **169**: 825.

(40) W. M. Watkins and W. T. J. Morgan. 1955a. Inhibition by simple sugars of enzymes which decompose the blood-group substances. Nature, London. **175**: 676.

(41) W. M. Watkins and W. T. J. Morgan. 1955b. Some observations on the O and H characters of human blood and secretions. Vox Sang. **5**: 1.

(42) W. M. Watkins and W. T. J. Morgan. 1956. Role of O-β-D-galactopyranosyl-$(1\rightarrow4)$-N-acetyl-D-glucosamine as inhibitor of the precipitation of blood group substances by anti-type XIV pneumococcus serum. Nature, London. **178**: 1289.

(43) W. M. Watkins and W. T. J. Morgan. 1956/1957. The A and H character of the blood group substances secreted by persons belonging to group A_2. Acta Genet. **6**: 521.

(44) W. M. Watkins and W. T. J. Morgan. 1957. Specific inhibition studies relating to the Lewis blood group system. Nature, London. **180**: 1038.

(45) W. J. Whelan. 1956/57. The synthesis and degradation of polysaccharides. Lectures on the Scientific Basis of Medicine. **6**: 233.

(46) R. L. Whistler and E. J. Olson. 1957. The biosynthesis of hyaluronic acid. Advanc. Carbohyd. Chem. **12**: 299.

(47) E. Witebsky and N. C. Klendshoj. 1941. The isolation of an O specific substance from gastric juice of secretors and carbohydrate—like substances from gastric juice of non-secretors. J. Exp. Med. **73**: 655.

Biochemical Genetics: The Enzymatic Defects

Part Three—Section One

As contributions to the understanding of normal and disturbed metabolism this paper and the Croonian lectures which succeeded it (1) endure today. Paramountly Garrod recognized that there are many inherited variations in chemical behavior and that a portion of such individuality may be expressed as disease. Forty years later these concepts came to fruition with the recognition by Beadle and Tatum (2) that genes direct the formation of enzymes and specifically that one gene controls only one enzyme. The importance of this one gene-one enzyme formulation, whose roots are in Garrod's paper, was recognized by the Nobel Prize in Medicine and Physiology in 1958.

(1) Archibald E. Garrod. 1908. The inborn errors of metabolism. Lancet. **2**: 1-7, 73-79, 142-148. See also A. E. Garrod. 1923. Inborn errors of metabolism. London: Oxford University Press. A contemporary review of alkaptonuria is presented by W. E. Knox. 1958. American Journal Human Genetics. **10**: 95-124.

(2) G. W. Beadle. 1945. Biochemical Genetics. Chemical Reviews. **37**: 15-96.

The Incidence of Alkaptonuria: A Study in Chemical Individuality*

ARCHIBALD E. GARROD

Physician to the Hospital for Sick Children, Great Ormondstreet; Demonstrator of Chemical Pathology at St. Bartholomew's Hospital

All the more recent work on alkaptonuria has tended to show that the constant feature of that condition is the excretion of homogentisic acid, to the presence of which substance the special properties of alkapton urine, the darkening with alkalies and on exposure to air, the power of staining fabrics deeply, and that of reducing metallic salts, are alike due. In every case which has been fully investigated since Wolkow and Baumann[1] first isolated and described this acid its presence has been demonstrated and re-examination of the material from some of the earlier cases also has led to its detection. The second allied alkapton acid, uroleucic, has hitherto only been found in the cases investigated by Kirk and in them in association with larger amounts of homogentisic acid.[2] By the kindness of Dr. R. Kirk I have recently been enabled to examine fresh specimens of the urines of his patients who have now reached manhood and was able to satisfy myself that at the present time even they are no longer excreting uroleucic acid. After as much of the homogentisic acid as possible had been allowed to separate out as the lead salt the small residue of alkapton acid was converted into the ethyl ester by a method recently described by Erich Meyer[3] and the crystalline product obtained had the melting point of ethyl homogentisate (120° C.). Further observations, and especially those of Mittelbach,[4] have also strengthened the belief that the homogentisic acid excreted is derived from tyrosin, but why al-

* Reprinted by publisher's permission from Lancet. 1902. ii: 1616-1620.

[1] Wolkow and Baumann. 1891. Z. physiol. Chemie. XV: 228.

[2] R. Kirk. 1889. Journal of Anatomy and Physiology. XXIII: 69; Huppert. 1897. Zeitschrift für Physiologische Chemie. XXIII: 412.

[3] E. Meyer. 1901. Deutsches Archiv für Klinische Medicin. LXX: 443.

[4] Mittelbach. 1901. *Ibid.* LXXI: 50.

kaptonuric individuals pass the benzene ring of their tyrosin unbroken and how and where the peculiar chemical change from tyrosin to homogentisic acid is brought about, remain unsolved problems.

There are good reasons for thinking that alkaptonuria is not the manifestation of a disease but is rather of the nature of an alternative course of metabolism, harmless and usually congenital and lifelong. Witness is borne to its harmlessness by those who have manifested the peculiarity without any apparent detriment to health from infancy on into adult and even advanced life, as also by the observations of Erich Meyer who has shown that in the quantities ordinarily excreted by such persons homogentisic acid neither acts as an aromatic poison nor causes acid intoxication, for it is not excreted as an aromatic sulphate as aromatic poisons are, nor is its presence in the urine attended by any excessive output of ammonia. However, regarded as an alternative course of metabolism the alkaptonuric must be looked upon as somewhat inferior to the ordinary plan, inasmuch as the excretion of homogentisic acid in place of the ordinary end products involves a certain slight waste of potential energy. In this connexion it is also interesting to note that, as far as our knowledge goes, an individual is either frankly alkaptonuric or conforms to the normal type, that is to say, excretes several grammes of homogentisic acid per diem or none at all. Its appearance in traces, or in gradually increasing or diminishing quantities, has never yet been observed, even in the few recorded temporary or intermittent cases. In cases in which estimations have been carried out the daily output has been found to lie within limits which, considering the great influence of proteid food upon the excretion of homogentisic acid and allowing for differences of sex and age, may be described as narrow. This is well illustrated by Table I, in which the cases are arranged in order of age.

The information available as to the incidence of alkaptonuria is of great

Table I. SHOWING THE AVERAGE EXCRETION OF HOMOGENTISIC ACID

No.	Sex	Age	Average excretion of homogentisic acid per 24 hours on ordinary mixed diet	Name of observers
1	M	2½ years	3.2 grams	Erich Meyer
2	M	3½ years	2.6 grams	A. E. Garrod
3	M	8 years	2.7 grams	Ewald Stier
4	M	18 years	5.9 grams	P. Stange
5	M	44 years	4.6 grams	Mittelbach
6	M	45 years	4.7 grams	H. Ogden
7	M	60 years	5.3 grams	Hammarsten
8	F	60 years	3.2 grams	H. Emlslen
9	M	68 years	4.8 grams	Wolkow and Baumann

interest in connexion with the above view of its nature. That the peculiarity is in the great majority of instances congenital cannot be doubted. The staining property of the urine allows of its being readily traced back to early infancy. This has been repeatedly done and in one of my cases[5] the staining of the napkins was conspicuous 57 hours after the birth of the child. The abnormality is apt to make its appearance in two or more brothers and sisters whose parents are normal and among whose forefathers there is no record of its having occurred, a peculiar mode of incidence which is well known in connexion with some other conditions. Thus of 32 known examples, which were presumably congenital, no less than 19 have occurred in seven families. One family contained four alkaptonurics, three others contained three, and the remaining three two each. The proportion of alkaptonuric to normal members is of some interest and Table II embodies such definite knowledge upon this point as is at present available regarding congenital cases.

Table II. Showing the Proportion of Alkaptonuric Members
to Normal Members in 9 Families

No.	Total number of family (brothers and sisters)	Number of alkaptonuric members	Number of normal members	Observers
1	14	4	10	Pavy
2	4	3	1	Kirk
3	7	3	4	Winternitz
4	2	1	1	Ewald Stier
5	2	2	0	Baumann, Embden
6	1	1	0	Erich Meyer
7	10	1	9	Noccioli and Domenici
8	5	2	3	A. E. Garrod
9	3	2	1	W. Smith, Garrod
Totals	48	19	29	—

The preponderance of males is very conspicuous. Thus, of the 40 subjects whose cases have hitherto been recorded 29 have been males and only 11 females.

In a paper read before the Royal Medical and Chirurgical Society in 1901 the present writer pointed out that of four British families in which 11 were congenitally alkaptonuric members no less than three were the offspring of marriages of first cousins who did not themselves exhibit this anomaly. This fact has such interesting bearings upon the etiology of

[5] A. E. Garrod. November 30, 1901. Lancet: 1481; 1902. Transactions of the Royal Medical and Chirurgical Society. **LXXXV**: 69.

alkaptonuria that it seemed desirable to obtain further information about as many as possible of the other recorded cases and especially of those which were presumably congenital. My inquiries of a number of investigators who have recorded such cases met with a most kindly response, and although the number of examples about which information could still be obtained proved to be very limited, some valuable facts previously unknown have been brought to light and indications are afforded of points which may be inquired into with advantage regarding cases which may come under observation in the future. In a number of instances the patients have been lost sight of, or for various reasons information can no longer be obtained concerning them. To those who have tried to help me with regard to such cases, and have in some instances been at great trouble in vain, my hearty thanks are no less due than to those who have been able to furnish fresh information.[6]

The following is a brief summary of the fresh information collected. Dr. Erich Meyer,[7] who mentioned in his paper that the parents of his patient were related, informs me that as a matter of fact they are first cousins. Dr. H. Ogden[8] states that his patient is the seventh of a family of eight members and that his parents were first cousins. The three eldest children died in infancy; the fifth, a female, has three children, but neither is she nor are they alkaptonuric. There is no record of any other examples in the family. The patient, whose wife is not a blood relation, has three children none of whom are alkaptonuric. Professor Hammarsten[9] states that the parents of an alkaptonuric man, whose case he recently described, were first cousins. The patient, aged 61 years, has three brothers and the only brother whose urine has been seen is not alkaptonuric. I have learned from Professor Noccioli[10] that the parents of the woman whose case he investigated with Dr. Domenici were not blood relations. The patient, a twin, who is one of two survivors of a family of ten, states that none of her relations have exhibited the condition. Dr. Ewald Stier[11] informs me that the parents of his patient were not related and it is mentioned in his paper that they were not alkaptonuric. Professor Ebstein[12] states that the parents of the child with "pyro-

[6] To Hofrath Professor Huppert and to Professor Osler my very special thanks are due for invaluable aid in collecting information, and I would also express my most sincere gratitude to Professor Hammarsten, Geheimrath Professor Ebstein, Geheimrath Professor Fürbringer, Geheimrath Professor Erb, Professor Noccioli, and Professor Denigès, as also to Dr. F. W. Pavy, Dr. Kirk, Dr. Maguire, Dr. Futcher, Dr. Erich Meyer, Dr. H. Ogden, Dr. H. Embden, Dr. Mittelbach, Dr. Ewald Stier, Dr. Grassi, Dr. Carl Hirsch, and Dr. Winternitz, all of whom have been kind enough to help the inquiry in various ways.

[7] E. Meyer. *Loc. cit.*

[8] H. Ogden. 1895. Z. physiol. Chemie. **XX**: 289.

[9] Hammarsten. 1901. Upsala Läkareförenings Förhandlingar. **VII**: 26.

[10] Noccioli e Domenici. 1898. Gazetta degli Ospedali. **XIX**: 303.

[11] Ewald Stier. 1898. Berliner klinische Wochenschrift. **XXXV**: 185.

[12] Ebstein and Müller. 1875. Virchow's Archiv. **LXII**: 554.

catechinuria" whose case was investigated by him in conjunction with Dr. Müller in 1875 were not related, but I gather that he would not regard this as an ordinary case of alkaptonuria, the abnormal substance in the urine having been identified as pyrocatechin. Lastly, Professor Osler supplies the very interesting information that of two sons of the alkaptonuric man previously described by Dr. Futcher[13] one is alkaptonuric. This is the first known instance of direct transmission of the peculiarity. The parents of the father, who has an alkaptonuric brother whose case was recorded by Marshall,[14] were not blood relations. The above particulars are embodied with those of the congenital British cases previously recorded in the following tabular epitome (Table III).

It will be seen that the results of further inquiries on the continent of Europe and in America confirm the impression derived from the British cases that of alkaptonuric individuals a very large proportion are children of first cousins. The above table includes 19 cases in all out of a total of 40 recorded examples of the condition, and there is little chance of obtaining any further information on the point until fresh cases shall come under observation. It will be noticed that among the families of parents who do not themselves exhibit the anomaly a proportion corresponding to 60 per cent are the offspring of marriages of first cousins. In order to appreciate how high this proportion is it is necessary to form some idea of the total proportion of the children of such unions to the community at large. Professor G. Darwin,[15] as the outcome of an elaborate statistical investigation, arrived at the conclusion that in England some 4 per cent of all marriages among the aristocracy and gentry are between first cousins; that in the country and smaller towns the proportion is between 2 and 3 per cent, whereas in London it is perhaps as low as 1.5 per cent. He suggests 3 per cent as a probable superior limit for the whole population. Assuming, although this is, perhaps, not the case, that the same proportion of these as of all marriages are fruitful, similar percentages will hold good for families, and assuming further that the average number of children results from such marriages they will hold good for individuals also. A very limited number of observations which I have made among hospital patients in London gave results which are quite compatible with the above figures. Thus, among 50 patients simultaneously inmates of St. Bartholomew's Hospital there was one whose parents were first cousins. On another occasion one such was found among 100 patients, and there was one child of first cousins among 100 children admitted to my ward at the Hospital for Sick Children. It is evident, on the one hand, that the proportion of alkaptonuric families and individuals who are the offspring of first cousins is remarkably high, and, on the other hand, it is equally clear that only a minute proportion of the children of such unions are alkaptonuric.

[13] Futcher. 1898. New York Medical Journal. **LXVII:** 69.
[14] Marshall. 1887. Medical News, Philadelphia. **L:** 35.
[15] G. Darwin. 1875. Journal of the Statistical Society. **XXXVIII:** 153.

Table III. SHOWING THE LARGE PROPORTION OF ALKAPTONURICS WHO ARE THE OFFSPRING OF MARRIAGE OF FIRST COUSINS

A

Families the offspring of marriages of first cousins.

No.	Total number of family	Number of known alkaptonuric members	Observers
1	14	4	Pavy
2	4	3	R. Kirk
3	5	2	A. E. Garrod
4	1	1	Erich Meyer
5	8	1	H. Ogden
6	4	1	Hammarsten
Total..........	36	12	—

B

Families whose parents were not related and not alkaptonuric.

No.	Total number of family	Number of known alkaptonuric members	Observers
1	3	2	Armstrong, Walter Smith, and Garrod
2	2	1	Ewald Stier
3	10	1	Noccioli and Domenici
4*	?	2	Marshall and Futcher
Total..........		6	—

C

Family in which alkaptonuria was directly inherited from a parent.

No.	Total number of family	Number of known alkaptonuric members	Observers
1*	?	1	Osler and Futcher
Total..........	—	1	—

* B 4 and C 1 refer to two generations of one family. No information is forthcoming as to the absence of alkaptonuria in previous generations. Ebstein and Müller's case, which is not included in the table for reasons given above, would raise the number of families in list B to 5.

Even if such persons form only 1 per cent of the community their numbers in London alone should exceed 50,000, and of this multitude only six are known to be alkaptonuric. Doubtless there are others, but that the peculiarity is extremely rare is hardly open to question. A careful look-out maintained for several years at two large hospitals has convinced me of this, and although the subject has recently attracted much more attention than formerly the roll of recorded examples increases but slowly.

The question of the liability of children of consanguineous marriages to exhibit certain abnormalities or to develop certain diseases has been much discussed, but seldom in a strictly scientific spirit. Those who have written on the subject have too often aimed at demonstrating the deleterious results of such unions on the one hand, or their harmlessness on the other, questions which do not here concern us at all. There is no reason to suppose that mere consanguinity of parents can originate such a condition as alkaptonuria in their offspring, and we must rather seek an explanation in some peculiarity of the parents, which may remain latent for generations, but which has the best chance of asserting itself in the offspring of the union of two members of a family in which it is transmitted. This applies equally to other examples of that peculiar form of heredity which has long been a puzzle to investigators of such subjects, which results in the appearance in several collateral members of a family of a peculiarity which has not been manifested at least in recent preceding generations.

It has recently been pointed out by Bateson[16] that the law of heredity discovered by Mendel offers a reasonable account of such phenomena. It asserts that as regards two mutually exclusive characters, one of which tends to be dominant and the other recessive, cross-bred organisms will produce germinal cells (gametes) each of which, as regards the characters in question, conforms to one or other of the pure ancestral types and is therefore incapable of transmitting the opposite character. When a recessive gamete meets one of the dominant type the resulting organism (the zygote) will usually exhibit the dominant character, whereas when two recessive gametes meet the recessive character will necessarily be manifested in the zygote. In the case of a rare recessive characteristic we may easily imagine that many generations may pass before the union of two recessive gametes takes place. The application of this to the case in question is further pointed out by Bateson, who, commenting upon the above observations on the incidence of alkaptonuria, writes as follows:[17] "Now there may be other accounts possible, but we note that the mating of first cousins gives exactly the conditions most likely to enable a rare, and usually recessive, character to show itself. If the bearers of such a gamete mate with individuals not bearing it the character will hardly

---

[16] W. Bateson. 1902. Mendel's Principles of Heredity, Cambridge.

[17] W. Bateson and Miss E. R. Saunders. 1902. Report to the Evolution Committee of the Royal Society. (1): 133*n*.

ever be seen; but first cousins will frequently be the bearers of similar gametes, which may in such unions meet each other and thus lead to the manifestation of the peculiar recessive characters in the zygote." Such an explanation removes the question altogether out of the range of prejudice, for, if it be the true account of the matter, it is not the mating of first cousins in general but of those who come of particular stocks that tends to induce the development of alkaptonuria in the offspring. For example, if a man inherits the tendency on his father's side his union with one of his maternal first cousins will be no more liable to result in alkaptonuric offspring than his marriage with one who is in no way related to him by blood. On the other hand, if members of two families who both inherit the strain should intermarry the liability to alkaptonuria in the offspring will be as great as from the union of two members of either family, and it is only to be expected that the peculiarity will also manifest itself in the children of parents who are not related. Whether the Mendelian explanation be the true one or not, there seems to be little room for doubt that the peculiarities of the incidence of alkaptonuria and of conditions which appear in a similar way are best explained by supposing that, leaving aside exceptional cases in which the character, usually recessive, assumes dominance, a peculiarity of the gametes of *both* parents is necessary for its production.

Hitherto nothing has been recorded about the children of alkaptonuric parents, and the information supplied by Professor Osler and Dr. Ogden on this point has therefore a very special interest. Whereas Professor Osler's case shows that the condition may be directly inherited from a parent Dr. Ogden's case demonstrates that none of the children of such a parent need share his peculiarity. As the matter now stands, of five children of two alkaptonuric fathers whose condition is known only one is himself alkaptonuric. It will be interesting to learn whether this low proportion is maintained when larger numbers of cases shall be available. That it will be so is rendered highly probable by the undoubted fact that a very small proportion of alkaptonurics are the offspring of parents either of whom exhibits the anomaly. It would also be extremely interesting to have further examples of second marriages of the parents of alkaptonurics. In the case of the family observed by Dr. Kirk the only child of the second marriage of the father, not consanguineous, is a girl who does not exhibit the abnormality. The only other available example is recorded by Embden. The two alkaptonurics studied by Professor Baumann and himself were a brother and sister born out of wedlock, and as far as could be ascertained the condition was not present in the children of the subsequent marriages which both parents contracted. The patient of Noccioli and Domenici was a twin, and I gather from Professor Noccioli's kind letter that the other twin was also a female, did not survive, and was not alkaptonuric. Further particulars are wanting, and the information was derived from the patient herself, who is described as a woman of limited intelligence but who was aware that in her own case the condition had existed from infancy. It is difficult to imagine that of twins developed from a single ovum one should be alkaptonuric and the other normal, but this does not necessarily apply to twins developed from separate ova.

It may be objected to the view that alkaptonuria is merely an alternative mode of metabolism and not a morbid condition, that in a few instances, not included in the above tables, it appears not to have been congenital and continuous but temporary or intermittent. In some of the cases referred to the evidence available is not altogether conclusive, and it is obvious that for the proof of a point of so much importance to the theory of alkaptonuria nothing can be regarded as wholly satisfactory which falls short of a complete demonstration of the presence of homogentisic acid in the urine at one time and its absence at another. The degree and rate of darkening of the urine vary at different periods apart from any conspicuous fluctuations in the quantity of homogentisic acid which it contains. The staining of linen in infancy is a much more reliable indication, especially if the mother of the child has had previous experience of alkaptonuric staining. In Geyger's case[18] of a diabetic man the intermittent appearance in the urine of an acid which he identified with the glycosuric acid of Marshall was established beyond all doubt, and the melting point and proportion of lead in the lead salt render it almost certain that he was dealing with homogentisic acid. In Carl Hirsch's case[19] a girl, aged 17 years, with febrile gastro-intestinal catarrh, passed dark urine which gave the indican reaction for three days. Professor Siegfried extracted by shaking with ether an acid which gave the reactions of homogentisic acid and formed a sparingly soluble lead salt. Neither the melting point of the acid nor any analytical figures are given. After three days the urine resumed its natural colour and reactions.

Von Moraczewski[20] also records a case of a woman, aged 43 years, who shortly before her death passed increasingly dark urine, rich in indican, from which he extracted an acid which had the melting point and reactions of homogentisic acid. Such increasing darkening of the urine as was here observed not infrequently occurs with urines rich in indoxyl-sulphate, as Baumann and Brieger first pointed out, and this was probably a contributory factor in the production of the colour which first called attention to the condition. Stange[21] has described a case in which the presence of homogentisic acid was very fully established, but he clearly does not regard the mother's evidence as to the intermittent character of the condition as con-

[18] A. Geyger. 1892. Pharmazeutische Zeitung: 488.
[19] C. Hirsch. 1897. Berliner klinische Wochenschrift. **XXXIV**: 866.
[20] W. von Moraczewski. 1896. Centralblatt für die Innere Medizin. **XVII**: 177.
[21] P. Stange. 1896. Virchow's Archiv. **CXLVI**: 86.

clusive. Zimnicki's[22] case of intermittent excretion of homogentisic acid by a man with hypertrophic biliary cirrhosis is published in a Russian journal which is inaccessible to me, and having only seen abstracts of his paper I am unacquainted with the details. Of hearsay evidence the most convincing is afforded in Winternitz's cases.[23] The mother of seven children, three of whom are alkaptonuric, was convinced that whereas two of her children had been alkaptonuric from the earliest days of life this had not been so with the youngest child in whom she had only noticed the peculiarity from the age of five years. This is specially interesting as supplying a link between the temporary and congenital cases. In a somewhat similar case described by Maguire[24] the evidence of a late onset is not so conclusive. Slosse's case[25] in which, as in von Moraczewski's, the condition apparently developed in the last stages of a fatal illness, completes the list of those falling into the temporary class. Evidently we have still much to learn about temporary or intermittent alkaptonuria, but it appears reasonable to suppose that those who exhibit the phenomenon are in a state of unstable equilibrium in this respect, and that they excrete homogentisic acid under the influence of causes which do not bring about this result in normal individuals. There is reason to believe that a similar instability plays a not unimportant part in determining the incidence of certain forms of *disease* in which derangements of metabolism are the most conspicuous features. Thus von Noorden,[26] after mentioning that diabetes occasionally develops at an early age in brothers and sisters and comparatively seldom occurs in the children of diabetic parents, adds that in three instances he has met with this disease in the off-spring of marriages of first cousins. In one such family two out of six children, in another two out of three, and in the third the only two children became diabetic at ages between one and four years.

The view that alkaptonuria is a "sport" or an alternative mode of metabolism will obviously gain considerably in weight if it can be shown that it is not an isolated example of such a chemical abnormality, but that there are other conditions which may reasonably be placed in the same category. In the phenomenon of albinism we have an abnormality which may be looked upon as chemical in its basis, being due rather to a failure to produce the pigments of the melanin group which play so conspicuous a part in animal colouration than to any defect of development of the parts in which in normal individuals such pigments are laid down. When we study the

[22] Zimnicki. 1900. Jeschenedelnik. Abstract, Centralblatt für Stoffwechsel und Verdauungs-Krankheiten. I(4): 348.

[23] Winternitz. 1899. Münchener Medizinische Wochenschrift. **XLVI:** 749.

[24] R. Maguire. 1884. Brit. Med. J. **II:** 808.

[25] A. Slosse. 1895. Annales de la Société Royale des Sciences Médicales et Naturelles, Bruxelles. **IV:** 89.

[26] Von Noorden. 1901. Die Zuckerkrankheit. 3, Aufgabe: 47.

incidence of albinism in man we find that it shows a striking resemblance to that of alkaptonuria. It, too, is commoner in males than in females, and tends to occur in brothers and sisters of families in which it has not previously appeared, at least in recent generations. Moreover, there is reason to believe that an undue proportion of albinos are the offspring of marriages of first cousins. Albinism is mentioned by most authors who have discussed the effects of such marriages and Arcoleo,[27] who gives some statistics of albinism in Sicily, states that of 24 families in which there were 62 albino members five were the offspring of parents related to each other in the second canonical degree. On the other hand, Bemiss[28] found that of 191 children of 34 marriages of first or second cousins five were albinos. In a remarkable instance recorded by Devay[29] two brothers married two sisters, their first cousins. There were no known instances of albinism in their families, but the two children of the one marriage and the five children of the other were all albinos. After the death of his wife the father of the second family married again and none of the four children of his second marriage were albinos. Again, albinism is occasionally directly inherited from a parent, as in one instance quoted by Arcoleo, but this appears to be an exceptional occurrence. The resemblance between the modes of incidence of the two conditions is so striking that it is hardly possible to doubt that whatever laws control the incidence of the one control that of the other also.

A third condition which suggests itself as being probably another chemical "sport" is cystinuria. Our knowledge of its incidence is far more incomplete and at first sight direct inheritance appears to play here a more prominent part. However, when more information is forthcoming it may turn out that it is controlled by similar laws. In this connexion a most interesting family described by Pfeiffer[30] is very suggestive. Both parents were normal, but all their four children, two daughters and two sons, were cystinuric. The elder daughter had two children neither of whom was cystinuric. A number of other examples of cystinuria in brothers and sisters are recorded, but information about the parents is wanting, except in the cases of direct transmission. In some of the earlier cases such transmission through three generations was thought to be probable, but the presence of cystin in the urine of parent and child has only been actually demonstrated in two instances. In Joel's[31] often-quoted case it was only shown that the mother's urine contained excess of neutral sulphur. E. Pfeiffer[32] found cystin

[27] G. Arcoleo. 1871. Sull' Albinismo in Sicilia. See notice in Archivio per l'Anthropologia. I: 367.

[28] Bemiss. 1857. J. of Psychol. Med. X: 368.

[29] Devay. 1857. Du Danger des Mariages Consanguins, &c., Paris.

[30] E. Pfeiffer. 1894. Centralblatt für Krankheiten der Harn-und Sexual-Organe. V: 187.

[31] Joel. 1855. Annalen der Chemie und Pharmacologie: 247.

[32] E. Pfeiffer. 1897. Centralblatt für Krankheiten der Harn-und Sexual-Organe. VIII: 173.

in the urine of a father and son and in a family observed by Cohn[33] the mother and six of her children shared the peculiarity. As more than 100 cases are on record the proportion of cases of direct inheritance has not hitherto been shown to be at all high and Pfeiffer's first case shows that, as with alkaptonuria, the children of a cystinuric parent may escape. A large majority of the recorded cystinurics have been males. There is as yet no evidence of any influence of consanguinity of parents and in the only two cases about which I have information the parents were not related. Neither has it yet been shown that cystinuria is a congenital anomaly, although in one case, at any rate, it has been traced back to the first year of life. Observations upon children of cystinuric parents from their earliest infancy or upon newly-born brothers or sisters of cystinurics would be of great interest and should in time settle this question. Lastly, it seems certain that, like alkaptonuria, this peculiarity of metabolism is occasionally temporary or intermittent. The so frequent association with cystinuria of the excretion of cadaverine and putrescine adds to the difficulty of the problem of its nature and upon it is based the infective theory of its causation. However, it is possible that, as C. E. Simon[34] has suggested, these diamines may themselves be products of abnormal metabolism. Unlike alkaptonuria and albinism cystinuria is a distinctly harmful condition, but its ill effects are secondary to its deposition in crystalline form and the readiness with which it forms concretions. Its appearance in the urine is not associated with any primary morbid symptoms. All three conditions referred to above are extremely rare and all tend to advertise their presence in conspicuous manners. An albino cannot escape observation; the staining of clothing and the colour of the urine of alkaptonurics seldom fail to attract attention, and the calculous troubles and the cystitis to which cystinurics are so liable usually bring them under observation sooner or later. May it not well be that there are other such chemical abnormalities which are attended by no obvious peculiarities and which could only be revealed by chemical analysis? If such exist and are equally rare with the above they may well have wholly eluded notice up till now. A deliberate search for such, without some guiding indications, appears as hopeless an undertaking as the proverbial search for a needle in a haystack.

If it be, indeed, the case that in alkaptonuria and the other conditions mentioned we are dealing with individualities of metabolism and not with the results of morbid processes the thought naturally presents itself that these are merely extreme examples of variations of chemical behaviour which are probably everywhere present in minor degrees and that just as no two individuals of a species are absolutely identical in bodily structure neither are their chemical processes carried out on exactly the same lines. Such minor chemical differences will obviously be far more subtle than those of form, for whereas the latter are evident to any careful observer the former will only

---

[33] J. Cohn. 1899. Berliner klinische Wochenschrift. **XXXVI**: 503.
[34] C. E. Simon. 1890. Am. J. Med. Sci. **CXIX**: 39.

be revealed by elaborate chemical methods, including painstaking comparisons of the intake and output of the organism. This view that there is no rigid uniformity of chemical processes in the individual members of a species, probable as it is *a priori*, may also be arrived at by a wholly different line of argument. There can be no question that between the families, genera and species both of the animal and vegetable kingdoms, differences exist both of chemical composition and of metabolic processes. The evidences for this are admirably set forth in a most suggestive address delivered by Professor Huppert[35] in 1895. In it he points out that we find evidence of chemical specificity of important constituents of the body, such as the hæmoglobins of different animals, as well as in their secretory and excretory products such as the bile acids and the cynuric acid of the urine of dogs. Again, in their behaviour to different drugs and infecting organisms the members of the various genera and species manifest peculiarities which presumably have a chemical basis, as the more recent researches of Ehrlich tend still further to show. To the above examples may be added the results of F. G. Hopkins's[36] well-known researches on the pigments of the pieridæ and the recent observations of the precipitation of the blood proteids of one kind of animal by the serum of another. From the vegetable kingdom examples of such generic and specific chemical differences might be multiplied to an almost indefinite extent. Nor are instances wanting of the influence of natural selection upon chemical processes, as for example, in the production of such protective materials as the sepia of the cuttlefish and the odorous secretion of the skunk, not to mention the innumerable modifications of surface pigmentation. If, then, the several genera and species thus differ in their chemistry we can hardly imagine that within the species, when once it is established, a rigid chemical uniformity exists. Such a conception is at variance with all that is known of the origin of species. Nor are direct evidences wanting of such minor chemical diversities as we have supposed to exist within the species. Such slight peculiarities of metabolism will necessarily be hard to trace by methods of direct analysis and will readily be masked by the influences of diet and of disease, but the results of observations on metabolism reveal differences which are apparently independent of such causes, as for example, in the excretion of uric acid by different human individuals. The phenomena of obesity and the various tints of hair, skin, and eyes point in the same direction, and if we pass to differences presumably chemical in their basis idiosyncrasies as regards drugs and the various degrees of natural immunity against infections are only less marked in individual human beings and in the several races of mankind than in distinct genera and species of animals.

If it be a correct inference from the available facts that the individuals of a species do not conform to an absolutely rigid standard of metabolism, but

[35] Huppert. 1896. Üeber die Erhaltung der Arteigenschaften, Prague.

[36] F. G. Hopkins. 1895. Philosophical Transactions of the Royal Society. **CLXXXVI** (B):661.

differ slightly in their chemistry as they do in their structure, it is no more surprising that they should occasionally exhibit conspicuous deviations from the specific type of metabolism than that we should meet with such wide departures from the structural uniformity of the species as the presence of supernumerary digits or transposition of the viscera.

Über Ausscheidung von Phenylbrenztraubensäure in dem Harn als Stoffwechselanomalie in Verbindung mit Imbezillität*
(The Excretion of Phenylpyruvic Acid (ppa) in the Urine, an Anomaly of Metabolism in Connection with Imbecility)

ASBJÖRN FÖLLING

Medical genetics is predicated on the belief that exact knowledge of a gene and its product can lead to successful treatment of a disease. The discovery of phenylketonuria by Fölling, reprinted here, provides a striking illustration of this concept and, at the same time, becomes an excellent example of the individuality of metabolism described by Garrod. The many investigations (1) which followed Fölling's report established that the disorder is simply inherited (2), that affected individuals lack the enzyme phenylalanine hydroxylase (3) and consequently are unable to convert phenylalanine into tyrosine. All clinical and chemical manifestations stem from this single metabolic block. The finding that reduction of dietary phenylalanine, if begun early in life, can prevent the consequences of enzymatic deficiency (4) is of paramount importance and emphasizes the interdependence between a gene and the environment in which it acts.

(1) Q. v., the summary by W. E. Knox. Phenylketonuria. J. B. Stanbury, J. B. Wyngaarden and D. S. Fredrickson (editors). 1960. The metabolic basis of inherited disease. McGraw-Hill Book Co., Inc., New York: 321-382.

(2) G. A. Jervis. 1939. The genetics of phenylpyruvic oligophrenia. J. Mental Science. 85: 719-762.

* Hoppe-Seyler's Zeitschrift für physiologische Chemie. 1934. 227: 169-176.

(3) G. A. Jervis. 1953. Phenylpyruvic oligophrenia: deficiency of phenylalanine oxidizing system. Proc. Soc. Exper. Biol. Med. **82:** 514-515.

(4) H. Bickel, J. Gerrard and E. M. Hickmans. 1954. The influence of phenylalanine intake on the chemistry and behaviour of a phenylketonuric child. Acta Paediat. **43:** 64-77.

Investigations of children affected with feeble-mindedness have shown an anomaly of metabolism which has never before been described in human beings. The anomaly is defined by an excretion of ppa in the urine and there seems to be a connection between this anomaly and imbecility. Until now, I found 10 patients excreting ppa; 9 of these patients are doubtlessly affected with feeble-mindedness, whereas the tenth is still so young that no conclusion can be drawn concerning his present psychic behavior. First, I shall give a short description of the clinical material.

1. L.E., female, born 6/14/27. The patient is the older of two children. Parents in good health; no relationship between them. A maternal aunt of the father suffered from dementia praecox. Normal birth weight; breast-fed 8-9 months; normal teething. Started to walk at 22 months. No vomiting, no spasms. No disease other than angina. Normal physical development. 31 kgs, 131 cm, circumference of the skull 51 cm. Normal natural functions, very alert. Expresses herself in single words to communicate with her surroundings. She likes to play and likes music (the family shows a musical disposition from the paternal side). She feeds herself. She fixes the eyes, but is a bit confused. No nystagmus. Normal tongue, thyroid of normal size, good teeth, no rachitis. Skin, especially on the extension side of the extremities, rough, with small white papules. All reflexes normal. Slight rigidity of all muscles. Normal physical findings.

2. D.E., male, born 4/22/30. Brother of No. 1. Normal delivery, normal birth weight. Slight icterus neonatorum. Breast-fed for 7 months. Teething at normal age. No spasms. Sporadic vomiting at beginning of meals. No disease during childhood. Repeated cystopyelitis; hospitalized for treatment of this disease in June 1933. Temperature 39.7. An X-ray showed a coral shaped stone in the right kidney pelvis. Treatment with tablets of thyroid during 9 months in 1933, without any success other than slight loss of weight. 14 kgs, 105 cm, circumference of the skull 47.5 cm. Cannot walk, hardly sits without support. Head is held sideways. Cannot speak, but utters inarticulate sounds, screams, laughs, likes to play and is social. Cannot feed himself. Cannot chew solid food; has to be fed with liquids. Is absolutely unclean. Cannot fix the eyes. Rapid horizontal nystagmus. Athetotic movements of arms,

fingers and legs. Extended spasms. Normal tongue. Thyroid hardly palpable. Good teeth. Small cavity of the sternum; besides this, no rachitis. Skin slightly rough. Retentio testis. Plantar and patellar reflexes probably normal. Normal physical findings.

3. S.H., female (communicated by Dr. Salomonsen), born 10/29/29. Normal delivery, birth weight 3,250 grams. During the first weeks a large flat, subcutaneous hemorrhage appeared above the parting of the hair; this disappeared spontaneously. Received mixed feeding during the first months, later food. Began to walk at 2 years of age. Suffered from severe obstipation. Does not speak. After having been separated from the parents for 1 month, she did not recognize them any more. Treatment with thyroid without any success. Normal physical findings.

4. N.H., male (communicated by Dr. Salomonsen), brother of No. 3, born 1/27/33. Quick delivery with forceps, birth weight 3,680 grams. The day after birth slight bleedings from the navel. On the third day large subcutaneous hemorrhage in the neck and in the groin. Intramuscular bleedings occurred on the fourth and fifth days. Afterwards no more bleedings and good development. No jaundice. During the first months, mixed food of breast milk and cow milk. Physically normal. Can now walk with support (1 1/2 years old). Speaks a little. No certain conclusions may be drawn at this moment from his mental behavior. No relationship between the parents. The maternal aunt suffers from dementia praecox. Apart from this, there is no case of mental disease or idiocy in the family.

5. S.E., female, pupil of the school for feeble-mindedness, Oslo. Born 4/28/23. Youngest child of 6. Father is said to be an alcoholic; among the relatives of the mother there are also alcoholics. A cousin of the mother suffers from feeble-mindedness (not investigated). A brother of the patient is an idiot (No. 6). The four other children are normal, good pupils. There is no ppa in their urine. Birth weight unknown, normal delivery. Breast-feeding during the first months, started to walk at the age of 2. Cramps were observed once at the age of 2. Normal physical development. 36.2 kgs, 138.5 cm. Skull circumference 52 cm. The skin is dry and rough. Slight cyanosis of the lower extremities. Thyroid normal. Tongue normal, bad teeth. Normal reflexes, normal chest and abdomen. Slightly flat-footed. Slight rigidity of the muscles. Gives the appearance of being anxious. Speaks coherently, but the words are sometimes confused. Slow apprehension and expression. Confused and without interest. Difficulties in reading and arithmetic. Writes neatly. She is always clean, but often acts strangely.

6. H.E., male, born 3/13/13. Brother of No. 5, the third of the children. Normal delivery. Started to walk at the age of 2, and to speak at the age of 5-6. Clean since the age of 9. Has never suffered from cramps. Suffered from eczema during his whole life. Examination is difficult

or impossible because of his shyness. Relatively small and thin. Speaks only one-syllable words. Was dismissed from a school for feeble-minded and mentally retarded children several years ago.

7.   E.B., female, pupil of the school for mentally retarded children, Oslo. Born 6/15/20, the second of 6 children, the oldest of them was born in 1918. Parents are healthy, mother indolent, no relationship between parents. The mother of the father suffered from chorea. A cousin of the patient, 14 years old, is also mentally retarded. The urine of this cousin is free of ppa. No other cases of mental retardation known in the family. All children normal, pupils of average intelligence, no ppa in their urine. Normal delivery, no signs of asphyxia. Breast feeding for 2 months. No specific diseases in early childhood. Suffered occasionally from pavor nocturnus. No cramps. Started to walk at 1 year, to speak at the age of 3 years. Was hospitalized at the State Hospital from 6/13 to 7/5/1934, for investigation of her metabolism. Physically tall, well developed. Length 156 cm, 64 kgs, skull circumference 55 cm. Slightly spastic walk with adduction of the thighs. Tongue and skin normal. Slight, diffused enlargement of the thyroid. Beginning of the development of pubes. Mammae well developed. Normal physical findings. Speaks coherently and replies to questions. Has a sweet personality, good-natured and clean; however, appears to be lazy, indolent and mentally slow. Is able to add 2 and 2, but not 3 and 4. Does not know year and dates and names of month and days. Is able to perform simple manual jobs. Pirquet positive, basal metabolism 100% and 96%. X-ray of arms, hands, pelvis and skull normal.

8.   R.M., female nursing patient of the Nursing Home for mentally retarded children operated by Mrs. Hjorths. Born 11/4/20. Never attended school. It was impossible to teach her. She learned some simple songs and sounds from other patients and sings those while performing stereotype movements of the body. She can repeat one or more words said to her, can reply yes or no, but very often without sense. However she is able to give words their right meaning, for instance, during the examination she always exclaims "dangerous." She is a sweet person and clean, but during the last 1½ years, she has become more and more negativistic and also unclean. Very often, she vomits after the meals. Very anxious, screams loud and does not permit thorough examination. 145 cm. 41.5 kgs. The skin of the lower extremities bears white papules. Tongue and thyroid normal. Normal reaction of the pupils, plantar reflex downwards. Significant rigidity of the muscles. Her walk is clearly spastic, halfway on her toes. Beginning of the development of pubes. Normal development of mammae.

9.   P.L., male, nursing patient of the Nursing Home for mentally retarded children operated by Mrs. Hjorths. Born 11/4/20. Gives the appearance of being asocial. Replies correctly yes and no. Is able to speak co-

herently, but never does so spontaneously. Is usually obedient, but when irritated, he can be in a rage. Enuresis nocturna, but is clean during the day. Thin. 145.5 cm, 35 kgs, skull circumference 32 cm. Hunchback, with protruding scapulae. Torticollis spastica. Remains standing the way he was put down, but no other signs of catatonia. Slight rigidity of the muscles. Normal tongue. Small thyroid. Normal reflexes and normal chest organs.

10. K.L., female, nursing patient of the Nursing Home for mentally retarded children operated by Mrs. Hjorths. Born 2/6/1907. Gives the appearance of being catatonic, does not change positions or places when standing still. Stands inclined forward with curved arms and inverted thumbs. She has to be led by her hand to all places always. She is a sweet person and clean. She utters a few inarticulate sounds and is not able to reply yes or no. 150.5 cm, 48 kgs. Skull circumference 51 cm. The skin is sore and scaly. Swelling of the calves. Tongue normal. Thyroid not palpable. Defective teeth. Normal reflexes of the pupils. No patellar reflexes. Plantar reflex downwards. Pubes poorly developed and rudimentary mammae. Normal chest organs.

I was not able to get any data on the families of the last 3 patients. The parents of the first seven patients are all alive and the urine of those was examined. None gave a positive reaction to the ppa-test. Nothing was found, either in the patients or in their parents, which could lead to the diagnosis of syphilis.

The clinical analysis of the material presents several difficulties. The described cases do not form a group physically as well defined as the cretins and the mongoloid idiots. However there are single traits which are to a certain degree common to all these patients. If I exclude patients 3 and 4, whom I did not examine myself, I find in most of the patients more or less expressed skin diseases. Only one (No. 7) seems to have a normal skin. All of them show either a slight (No. 5 and No. 7) or a more expressed (No. 8) rigidity of the muscles. All showed a forward leaning position; most of them also show a large width of the shoulders. Common to all of them, without any doubt, is a feeble-mindedness of different degrees and the excretion of ppa in the urine. The ppa may be detected chemically in the urine very easily as the urine turns to a deep green with the addition of iron chloride. This phenomenon led me to further investigation of the urine.

The substance, in the beginning unknown, was extracted in a pure form in the following way: the urine was saturated with sodium chloride, acidified with concentrated hydrochloric acid until positive to Congo Red. Then the urine was 3 times extracted with ether. The ether extracts had to be shaken again, first with addition of a few milliliters of water, then twice with sodium bicarbonate solution, whereby organic acids were transferred quantitatively into the bicarbonate layer whereas the phenols remain in the ether.

The bicarbonate solution was acidified with hydrochloric acid until positive to Congo Red and again shaken with ether. The ether solution was fairly brown colored, due to impurities which could lead to difficulties during crystallization. By means of shaking 2 or 3 times with a few millimeters of concentrated hydrochloric acid, these impurities were partly removed and the excess of hydrochloric acid was removed with a little water. The ether solution was then dried with water-free sodium sulfate, and the ether was expelled in the water bath by continuous adding of nitrogen. The last remains were removed by evaporation over sulfuric acid. The material can now be crystallized from chloroform or benzene, the best is a mixture of both with just enough benzene added to cause the crystals to sediment. Since the material is destroyed and turns black in the presence of air, all these operations are performed under a nitrogen atmosphere. The material crystallizes from benzene into long thin needles, from chloroform into long small tables with 6 angles. After crystallizing the material 6 times, the melting point is constant $= 155°$. It melts with liberation of carbonic acid. The material is easily soluble in the normal organic solutions and slightly soluble in water. The water solution turns Red Congo paper blue. The solutions do not rotate polarized light. The material contains only C, H, and O.

4,890; 4,437 mgs substance.[1] 11,775; 10,680 mgs CO_2. 2,130; 2,010 mgs H_2O. $C_9H_8O_3$ ber. C 65.83 H 4.92 gef. C 65.69, 65.67 H 4.87, 5.07.
The determination of the molecular weight after Rast $= 181$ and 182.
By titration
28.0 mgs of the acid consume 1.70 ml $n/10$ NaOH and
34.4 mgs of the acid consume 2.11 ml $n/10$ NaOH.
This is equivalent (under the assumption of a one normal acid) to a molecular weight of 164.7 and 164.4. Therefore the empiric formula of the substance is $C_9H_8O_3$, with a molecular weight of 164.06.

After solution in water and addition of iron chloride or other oxidative agents the substance gives a smell typical of benzaldehyde. An impure preparation spontaneously yields benzaldehyde after several days. To investigate this phenomenon, several milligrams of the substance were oxidized with potassium permanganate in an alkaline solution, whereafter the surplus of the oxidating agent is destroyed by hydrogen peroxide. In the reactive mixture, benzoic and oxalic acids were found, the first by sublimation and determination of the melting point, the latter by reaction with calcium salt.

This mode of reaction suggests that the substance consists of a benzol ring with a side chain of at least 3 carbon atoms. With regard to the empiric composition and the strong acid character of the substance, the structural formula will probably be the following: $C_6H_5 \cdot CH_2 \cdot CO \cdot COOH$, that means phenyl pyruvic acid. Therefore, a few milligrams of the substance were mixed to equal parts with synthetic ppa. The melting point was not changed during

---

[1] Editor's note: Duplicate determinations.

this procedure and the identity of the substance is therefore established.

After Bougault and Hammerle it seems that free acids exist mostly as enols, whereas salts exist mostly as ketones. The enol form

$$C_6H_5 \cdot CH = C \cdot COOH$$
$$| $$
$$OH$$

explains the easy transition to benzaldehyde, as well as the coloration with iron chloride.

Therefore, there has been found, in some imbecile patients, an anomaly of metabolism which is defined by excretion of ppa. And, as I have never found ppa in the urine of normal persons, it seems probable that there is a relationship between this anomaly of the metabolism and imbecility. It is true that I had investigated only a few normal persons with regard to the present work, but as ppa is easy to detect and as it would be detected in each performance of Gerhardt's reaction in acetic acid, it would have been detected a long time ago, if it occurred in normal persons. Furthermore, ppa has, in the past, never been found in human beings. I therefore believe that I have detected an anomaly of metabolism, so far unknown, and that this anomaly is related to imbecility. One could name this pathologic condition "imbecillitas phenylpyruvica." opa is closely related to phenylalanine and could be created by means of an oxidative deamination of the latter amino acid. In 1922, Kotake, Masai and Mori were able to detect small amounts of ppa in the urine of rabbits after oral administration of huge amounts of phenylalanine. These experiments with rabbits were successfully repeated by Shambaugh, Lewis and Tourtelotte in 1931, and by Chandler and Lewis in 1932. In an experiment with one of my patients (No. 7), which shall be published later, I was also able to demonstrate an increase of the excretion of ppa after moderate administration of dl-phenylalanine, whereby the excretion varied also with the amount of protein contained in food. It seems that in the case of phenylalanine a direct oxidative deamination is not the normal pathway. In this connection, it is interesting to see that Embden and Baldes were able to demonstrate a liberation of acetic acid from phenylalanine after perfusion of the liver. This could not be demonstrated with ppa. They therefore concluded that the primary alteration in the breakdown of phenylalanine must be another one, perhaps an oxidation to tyrosine which then will be deaminated secondarily. This was highly probable as the experiment has shown. Also the possibility of a hydrolytic deamination of the phenylalanine was proven by experiments. On the other hand, there are investigations showing that ppa administered to a normal organism is transferred completely to carbonic acid and water.

Therefore, it seems to be probable that in my patients there is an anomaly of the deamination of phenylalanine as well as of the oxidation of ppa. However, as these patients are alive and growing up nearly normally, they must be able to use phenylalanine for an anabolic synthesis in the body.

With regard to the extent of my material, I have to add that approximately 430 patients affected with feeble-mindedness, mostly children, were investigated. In addition to my original material (No. 1 and 2), which revealed the condition, I investigated 123 people in the public school for mentally retarded children in Oslo, and 250 patients in the nursing home of Mrs. Hjorths at Bärum. Furthermore, I received about 50 urine samples from different physicians and from the pediatric department of the State Hospital. It would be wrong to calculate the frequency of this condition in mentally retarded patients from these figures. The first 2 patients have come for examination to me by mere chance and No. 4 and No. 6 have been looked for and examined deliberately after having obtained proof of the disease in their sisters. A better rate of frequency will be obtained when the material of the public school and of the nursing home of Mrs. Hjorths are selected as basis for the investigation.

LITERATURE

(1) C. r. Acad. Sci. **160:** 100. Cited after Beilstein.

(2) This journal. 1922. **122: 195.**

(3) J. Biol. Chem. 1931. **92:** 499.

(4) J. Biol. Chem. 1932. **96:** 619.

(5) Biochem. Z. 1913. **60:** 301.

(6) Biochem. Z. 1933. **262:** 300.

(7) H. D. Dakin. 1912. Oxidations and reductions in the animal body: 71.

(8) H. H. Mitchell and T. S. Hamilton. 1929. The biochemistry of the amino acids: 403.

Galactosemia, a Congenital Defect in a Nucleotide Transferase: A Preliminary Report*

HERMAN M. KALCKAR

ELIZABETH P. ANDERSON

KURT J. ISSELBACHER

National Institute of Arthritis and Metabolic Diseases, National Institutes of Health, United States Public Health Service, Bethesda, Maryland

Communicated by Gerty T. Cori, December 22, 1955

One of the principal goals of biochemical genetics is the characterization of gene products. The pursuit of such products, in any organism, ultimately proceeds through biochemistry. This report of Kalckar and his colleagues is one of several exemplary papers which describes the manner in which a specific product, in this case the enzyme P-Gal-transferase, is identified as deficient in galactosemia. Such investigation of an inborn error of metabolism increases our understanding of normal as well as abnormal metabolism and is thus "Garrod revisited."

Galactosemia is a disease of childhood which manifests itself biochemically as a disorder in the metabolism of galactose (cf. Hartmann[1]) as well as of α-galactose-1-phosphate (Gal-1-P).[2] The latter ester has recently been shown to accumulate in the blood of galactosemic infants after the administration of galactose.[2]

According to Leloir,[3] the conversion of Gal-1-P to α-glucose-1-phosphate (G-1-P) involves the following steps, in which a nucleotide, uridinediphospho-glucose (UDPG) is required:

---

* Reprinted by senior author's and publisher's permission from Proceedings of the National Academy of Sciences. 1956. **42**: 49-51.

[1] A. Hartmann. 1955. J. Pediat. **47**: 537.

[2] V. Schwartz, L. Goldberg, G. M. Komrower and A. Holzel. 1955. Biochem. J. **59**: xxii.

[3] L. F. Leloir. 1951. In W. D. McElroy and B. Glass (editors). Phosphorus metabolism. Johns Hopkins University Press, Baltimore. **1**: 67.

$$\text{Gal-1-P} + \text{UDPG} \rightleftharpoons \text{G-1-P} + \text{UDPGal}, \tag{1}$$

$$\text{UDPGal} \rightleftharpoons \text{UDPG}. \tag{2}$$

Step (2) is catalyzed by an enzyme discovered by Leloir[4] in 1951 and called "galacto-waldenase." Step (1) was found to be catalyzed by an enzyme which has been found in galactose-adapted yeast[5] and mammalian liver.[6] We call this enzyme "PGal-transferase." It has been postulated at various times that galactosemia is a defect due to a block in the synthesis of galacto-waldenase. The fact that Gal-1-P accumulates in the erythrocytes of galacto-semic subjects when galactose is administered, together with the fact that the clinical symptoms completely disappear if the patients are put on a galactose-free diet, would be compatible with a block in step (1), i.e., PGal-transferase, rather than with a block in step (2) catalyzed by galacto-waldenase.

METHODS AND MATERIALS

Hemolyzates were used as the enzyme source. The incubation time was 30 minutes. One sample was incubated with Gal-1-P alone and the second with UDPG alone. The missing substrate was added after deproteinization. The third sample was incubated with both substrates. For the determination of Gal-1-P, UDPG, and UDPGal specific enzymatic methods were used. The indicator in these methods is one of the pyridine nucleotides (TPN or DPN), both of which upon reduction develop an increase in absorption at 340 mμ. The Gal-1-P was determined by means of its liberation of G-1-P from UDPG, using purified PGal transferase and a TPN indicator system.[7]

UDPG was determined by means of a specific, purified UDPG dehydrogenase,[8] using DPN as indicator. UDPGal was determined by the same principle, except that galacto-waldenase (fractionated from liver[6]) was also added.[9] Alpha Gal-1-P was kindly made available to us through Drs. Hewitt G. Fletcher, Jr., and Elizabeth Maxwell. UDPG was a commercial product from the Sigma Chemical Company, St. Louis, Missouri. UDPGal was prepared by enzymatic techniques.[6]

RESULTS

We have confirmed and extended the observation of Schwartz *et al.*[2] that galactose added to erythrocytes from galactosemic children gives rise to accumulation of Gal-1-P. The erythrocytes were incubated in vitro with

[4] L. F. Leloir. 1951. Arch. Biochem. Biophys. **33**: 186.

[5] H. M. Kalckar, B. Braganca and A. Munch-Petersen. 1953. Nature. **172**: 1039.

[6] E. Maxwell, H. M. Kalckar and R. Burton. 1955. Biochem et Biophys. Acta. **18**: 389.

[7] A. Munch-Petersen, H. M. Kalckar and E. E. B. Smith. 1955. Kgl Videnskab. selskab Biol. Medd. **22**(7).

[8] J. L. Strominger, E. Maxwell and H. M. Kalckar. 1956. S. P. Colowick and N. O. Kaplan (editors). Academic Press, New York. Methods in enzymology. **3**.

[9] H. M. Kalckar and E. P. Anderson. 1956. Biochim. et Biophys. Acta.

galactose for three hours at 37° and the Gal-1-P determined enzymatically.[7] Blood from normal children showed no accumulation of Gal-1-P under these conditions (less than 0.01 μM per milliliter of red blood cells per hour), whereas, in three cases of galactosemia, about 0.1 μM of Gal-1-P accumulated per milliliter of red blood cells per hour.

The presence of PGal transferase was studied by means of incubating Gal-1-P and UDPG together with hemolyzates and subsequently measuring by enzymatic techniques the conversion of UDPG to UDPGal.[8,9]

In order to insure that the hemolyzates were not fortuitously varying in activity with respect to this class of enzymes, another nucleotide transferase, which we call "PP transferase,"[10] was also measured by the same type of method and at the same time as the PGal transferase. The PP transferase catalyzes the following reaction, which involves inorganic pyrophosphate (PP) and uridine triphosphate (UTP): $G\text{-}1\text{-}P + UTP \rightleftharpoons PP + UDPG$. The PP transferase does not play a direct role in the metabolism of Gal-1-P.[7] It brings about a conversion of G-1-P to UDPG, which by subsequent enzymatic dehydrogenation is converted to UDP-glucuronic acid,[11] or, alternatively, without oxidation can be converted into UDPGal by the above-mentioned enzyme, galacto-waldenase.[4]

In Table 1, average values of PGal and PP transferases for three groups

Table 1. Average Rates for PGal and PP Transferases in Human Hemolyzates from Nongalactosemic and Galactosemic Subjects

Number of cases	Types of cases	Diet	μM UDPG exchanged per milliliter red blood cells per hour	
			PGal transf.	PP transf.
11	Normal	Ordinary	0.75	1.10
3	Milk allergies	Galactose-free	0.88	1.35
8	Galactosemic	Galactose-free	<0.02	1.85

of subjects are presented. The first group comprises normal subjects of various ages (male and female); the second group deals with individuals on galactose-free diets on account of milk allergy (three cases); and the third group deals with galactosemic subjects (eight cases). It can be seen that blood from the galactosemic subjects is devoid of PGal transferase (less than 3 per cent, which means essentially undetectable). The PP transferase, however, is constantly present not only in the group of normal and milk-allergy subjects but also in the galactosemic subjects.

[10] A. Munch-Petersen, H. M. Kalckar and E. E. B. Smith. 1953. Nature. **172:** 1036.
[11] J. L. Strominger, H. M. Kalckar, J. Axelrod and E. Maxwell. 1954. J. Am. Chem. Soc. **76:** 6411.

We therefore propose that galactosemia is an inborn defect, presumably of genetic origin,[12] in the production of PGal transferase.

SUMMARY

Galactosemia seems to furnish an example of a congenital human metabolic disease in which a specific enzyme is missing. The enzyme which catalyzes the exchange of α-galactose-1-phosphate with uridinediphospho-glucose, forming α-glucose-1-phosphate and uridinediphospho-galactose, is absent in blood from galactosemic subjects. It is known that this enzymatic exchange is an important step reaction by which administered galactose is used in general carbohydrate metabolism. Several of the metabolic manifestations of the disease might readily be explained on the basis of this enzymatic defect.

Our thanks are due to Drs. G. T. Cori, V. O'Donnell, J. Kety, H. H. Mason, R. Harris, and A. Hartmann for their kind help in obtaining the galactosemic cases, and to Miss Bodil Waage-Jensen, who rendered valuable assistance as a trainee under the Scandinavian-American Foundation through a grant-in-aid generously made available to one of us (H. M. K.) by the Eli Lilly Laboratories.

[12] A. Holzel and G. M. Komrower. 1955. Arch. Disease Childhood. 30: 155.

Biochemical Genetics: The Hemoglobin-opathies

Part Three—Section Two

The delineation of the hemoglobinopathies represents one of the great accomplishments of the life sciences. The papers reprinted in this section provide an outline of the manner in which this advance has proceeded.

Requisite to the understanding of any genetic system is its manner of inheritance. In the paper by Neel as well as in a report by Beet (1), traditional methods of family analysis are applied to the in vitro *sickling phenomenon which is established as present in the heterozygous or carrier individuals as well as in those with sickle cell disease. In contrast sickle cell disease is shown to be recessively inherited. It is thus evident on genetic grounds alone that there are three classes of individuals: normal, those with* in vitro *sickling without anemia, and those with* in vitro *sickling with anemia. These examples clearly indicate that the terms dominance and recessivity are purely operational definitions which relate to characters and not to the genes responsible for the characters.*

(1) E. A. Beet. 1949. The genetics of the sickle-cell trait in a Bantu tribe. Ann. Eugen. **14:** 279-284.

The Inheritance of Sickle Cell Anemia*[1]

JAMES V. NEEL
Heredity Clinic, Laboratory of Vertebrate Biology, University of Michigan

If a drop of blood is collected from each member of a randomly assembled series of American Negroes and sealed under a cover slip with vaseline, to be observed at intervals up to 72 hours, in the case of about 8 per cent of the individuals composing the series a high proportion of the erythrocytes will be observed to assume various bizarre oat, sickle, or holly leaf shapes. This ability of the erythrocytes to "sickle," as the phenomenon is commonly described, appears to be attended by no pathological consequences in the majority of these individuals, and they are spoken of as having sicklemia, or the sickle cell trait. However, a certain proportion of the individuals who sickle are the victims of a severe, chronic, hemolytic type of anemia known as sickle cell anemia. This proportion has been variously estimated at between 1:1.4 (8) and 1:40 (4). The essential difference between sicklemia and sickle cell anemia appears at present to depend at least in part upon the relative ease with which sickling takes place. In sickle cell anemia the erythrocytes may frequently sickle under the conditions encountered in the circulating blood, whereas in sicklemia sickling does not usually occur under these conditions (12). This difference has been attributed to a greater tendency of the erythrocytes of sickle cell anemia to sickle when the O_2-tension is reduced, although recently this viewpoint has been challenged (13). Perhaps because of this difference—although there may be other factors

* Reprinted by author's and publisher's permission from Science. 1949. **110**: 64-66.
[1] This investigation was supported in part by a grant from the U. S. Public Health Service. The study has been possible only through the generous cooperation of the Anemia Clinic of the Children's Hospital of Michigan, Detroit, Michigan, The University Hospital of the University of Michigan, Ann Arbor, Michigan, and the Wayne County General Hospital and Infirmary, Eloise, Michigan; all three institutions have made their case records of sickle cell anemia freely available. It is a pleasure to acknowledge my indebtedness to Mrs. Marion Weyrauch for technical assistance, and to Mrs. Laura Williams for case work.

involved, such as the aniso- and poikilocytosis to be observed in some individuals with the disease, and a greater resistance to hemolysis of trait cells when sickled than sickle cell anemia cells when sickled—the erythrocytes of a patient with sickle cell anemia have a greatly shortened life span, both in the individuals with the disease and in normal persons who have been transfused with the cells of sickle cell anemia patients, whereas sicklemia erythrocytes have a normal life span (3, 14).

The ability of the red cells to sickle was observed to have a genetic basis not long after sickle cell anemia was recognized as a clinical entity (5). On the basis of a study of one large family, Taliaferro and Huck (15) postulated that the ability to sickle was due to a single dominant gene. At that time the clinical distinction between sicklemia and sickle cell anemia had not been clearly drawn, and the inference was that this gene was more strongly expressed in some individuals (sickle cell anemia) than in others (sicklemia). This has remained the accepted hypothesis up to the present time. Several years ago the author, in a review on the clinical detection of the genetic carriers of inherited disease (9), was led to suggest an alternative hypothesis—namely, that there existed in Negro populations a gene which in heterozygous condition results in sicklemia, and in homozygous condition in sickle cell anemia. This hypothesis has a counterpart in the relationship which has been demonstrated to exist between thalassemia major and minor (10, 16). Recently the opportunity has arisen to give this hypothesis a thorough test.

There exist a number of arguments permitting a critical decision between the two hypotheses. The present preliminary note will consider only one of these arguments. If the homozygous-heterozygous hypothesis is correct, then both the parents of any patient with sickle cell anemia should always sickle (barring the occasional role of mutation; see below). If, on the other hand, the disease is due to a dominant gene with variable expression, only one parent need sickle, although occasionally, due to the chance marriage of two sicklers, both parents may sickle. In calculating the exact proportion of sicklemia to be expected among the parents of individuals with sickle cell anemia according to the dominant hypothesis, certain assumptions must be made. To the best of the author's knowledge, the question of the phenotype of the homozygote has never been raised by those who have accepted the variable dominant hypothesis of sickle cell anemia. For purposes of calculation we shall assume that under the variable dominant hypothesis all homozygotes have sickle cell anemia—alternative assumptions, such as intra-uterine lethality, are possible. We shall further assume that one in fifty heterozygotes also develops sickle cell anemia. Finally, we shall assume on the basis of the clinical data that the fertility of those with sickle cell anemia approximates 20 percent of normal, with the result that only a few individuals with this disease—so few that they may be disregarded in so rough a calculation—have one or both parents who are likewise affected. With these assumptions we may calculate, as shown in Table 1, that the

Table 1. Calculation of the Proportion of Sickling to Be Expected Among the Parents of Individuals with Sickle Cell Anemia According to the Variable Dominant Hypothesis*

Type of marriage	Frequency of marriage	Frequency of offspring of the indicated genotype			Sickle cell anemia patients	
		Sk Sk	Sk sk	sk sk	Proportion in general population	Proportion among total anemia patients
One sickler parent (Sk sk × sk sk)	2 × 0.08 × 0.92 = 0.1472	—	0.0736	0.0736	0.02 × 0.0736 = 0.001472	0.4693
Two sickler parents (Sk sk × Sk sk)	0.08 × 0.08 = 0.0064	0.0016	0.0032	0.0016	0.0016 + (0.02 × 0.0032) = 0.001664	0.5307
Total					0.003136	1.0000

* The assumption is made that all individuals homozygous for the sickling gene (Sk) develop sickle cell anemia, as do 1 in 50 persons heterozygous for the gene, and further that individuals with sickle cell anemia reproduce so infrequently that no significant error is introduced by their omission.

Expected proportion of sickling parents = (proportion of patients having *one* parent sickler) × (proportion of sicklers among these parents) + (proportion of patients having *both* parents sicklers) × (proportion of sicklers among these parents) = 0.4693 × ½ + 0.5307 × 1 = 0.765.

proportion of sickling among the parents of individuals with sickle cell anemia should be 0.765. If one assumes that more than one in fifty of the heterozygotes develop sickle cell anemia, or that the homozygote is lethal, then the proportion of sickling parents should be even lower.

Thus far we have tested 42 parents of 29 patients with sickle cell anemia for the occurrence of sickling. In 13 instances both parents were studied and in 16, only one. Tests have been conducted in a variety of ways; especial reliance has been placed on a combination of the techniques described by Scriver and Waugh (11) and Hansen-Pruss (7), whereby a tourniquet is applied to a finger for 3-5 minutes, and then a drop of static blood from the finger is placed on a slide to which a small amount of Janus green or methylene blue has been added, and it is quickly covered with a cover slip which is sealed with vaseline. Observations are made at intervals up to 72 hours. Five preparations have been made for each individual. Every parent tested to date has sickled. This is the result expected from the homozygous-heterozygous hypothesis outlined above. On the other hand, the probability of the occurrence of such a number of positive parents under the variable dominant hypothesis is $(0.765)^{42}$, or 0.000013.

There are to be found in the literature a number of reports where one or both parents of a child with sickle cell anemia have been tested and found not to sickle (review in reference 9). The results of tests for the sickling phenomenon are known to be variable; it is felt that the experience quoted may be explained in terms of lack of familiarity with the techniques necessary to elicit sickling.

The approximate frequency of the gene responsible for sickling in the American Negro (p) may be determined from the equation $2p(1 - p) = 0.08$. Solution of this equation yields a p value of 0.042, from which the incidence at birth of this chronic, disabling, and fatal disease among American Negroes may be placed at $(0.042)^2 = 1.8$ per 1000.[2] The ratio among Negro births in the United States of those with sicklemia to those who will develop sickle cell anemia should therefore be approximately $80:1.8 = 44:1$; in the Negro population as a whole the ratio of sicklemia : sickle cell anemia is significantly higher because of the greater mortality among those with sickle cell anemia. In Africa, the incidence of sickling has been reported to vary from approximately 12 percent in Northern Rhodesia (1) to 17 percent in the Gold Coast Negroes and 19 percent in natives of Nigeria and the Camaroons (6). This would correspond to a gene frequency of approximately 0.064-0.106, and a frequency of the homozygote of 4.1-11.2/1000. The complex and fascinating problems in gene dynamics raised by frequencies of this order will be dealt with in another paper.

In a genetic situation such as appears to obtain here, where the heterozygote, who may be termed the genetic carrier of the disease, may be readily distinguished from normal and from the homozygote, it is possible to predict with a high degree of accuracy which marriages should result in homozygous individuals—in this case, children with sickle cell anemia. Since (homozygous) individuals with sickle cell anemia either die young or, if they reach maturity, have a greatly lowered fertility, the vast majority of cases of the disease are the issue of marriages between two (heterozygous) persons with the sickle cell trait. In the absence of marriage between individuals whose erythrocytes exhibit the sickling phenomenon, the frequency of the homozygote would greatly decrease, and sickle cell anemia would tend to disappear, with only a very rare case arising as a result of mutation in a normal individual married to a person homozygous or heterozygous for the sickling gene.

---

[2] The correct formula is $y = ap + (1 - a)p^2$, where a = the mean coefficient of inbreeding. The value of a for the American Negro is unknown, but probably quite small, in the neighborhood of 0.0005. For present purposes the value of p^2 is a sufficiently close approximation to y.

REFERENCES

(1) E. A. Beet. 1946; 1947. E. Afr. Med. J. **23**: 75; **24**: 212.

(2) *Ibid.* 1947. **24**: 212.

(3) S. T. E. Callender *et al.* 1948. J. Lab. Clin. Med. **34**: 90.

(4) L. W. Diggs, C. F. Ahmann and J. Bibb. 1933. Ann. Int. Med. **7**: 769.

(5) V. E. Emmel. 1917. Arch. Int. Med. **20**: 586.

(6) R. W. Evans. 1914. Trans. Roy. Soc. Trop. Med. Hyg. **37**: 281.

(7) O. G. Hansen-Pruss. 1936. J. Lab. Clin. Med. **22**: 311.

(8) B. Mera. 1943. Bol. Of. Sanit. Panam. **22**: 680.

(9) J. V. Neel. 1947. Medicine. **26**: 115.

(10) J. V. Neel and W. N. Valentine. 1947. Genetics. **32**: 38.

(11) J. B. Scriver and T. R. Waught. 1930. Canad. Med. Ass. J. **23**: 375.

(12) I. J. Sherman. 1940. Bull. Johns Hopkins Hosp. **67**: 309.

(13) K. Singer and S. Robin. 1948. J. Am. Med. Soc. **136**: 1021.

(14) K. Singer *et al.* 1948. J. Lab. Clin. Med. **33**: 975.

(15) W. H. Taliaferro and J. G. Huck. 1923. Genetics. **8**: 594.

(16) W. N. Valentine and J. V. Neel. 1944. Arch. Int. Med. **74**: 185.

Sickle Cell Anemia, a Molecular Disease[*][1]

LINUS PAULING,

HARVEY A. ITANO,[2]

S. J. SINGER,[2]

IBERT C. WELLS[3]

Gates and Crellin Laboratories of Chemistry, California Institute of Technology, Pasadena, Cal.[4]

The demonstration that sickle cell hemoglobin differs in electrophoretic mobility from normal hemoglobin led to the entitled inference: "Sickle cell anemia, a molecular disease." This astonishingly simple concept is of fundamental importance to medicine for the ultimate understanding of the origins of sickness, and to biology for the insight into what genes do. In the author's words, "This investigation . . . reveals a clear case of a change produced in a protein molecule by an allelic change in a single gene involved in synthesis."

The erythrocytes of certain individuals possess the capacity to undergo reversible changes in shape in response to changes in the partial pressure of oxygen. When the oxygen pressure is lowered, these cells change their forms from the normal biconcave disk to crescent, holly wreath, and other forms.

[*] Reprinted by senior author's and publisher's permission from Science. 1949. **110:** 543-548.

[1] This research was carried out with the aid of a grant from the United States Public Health Service. The authors are grateful to Professor Ray D. Owen, of the Biology Division of this Institute, for his helpful suggestions. We are indebted to Dr. Edward R. Evans, of Pasadena, Dr. Travis Winsor, of Los Angeles, and Dr. G. E. Burch, of the Tulane University School of Medicine, New Orleans, for their aid in obtaining the blood used in these experiments.

[2] U. S. Public Health Service postdoctoral fellow of the National Institutes of Health.

[3] Postdoctoral fellow of the Division of Medical Sciences of the National Research Council.

[4] Contribution No. 1333.

This process is known as sickling. About 8 percent of American Negroes possess this characteristic; usually they exhibit no pathological consequences ascribable to it. These people are said to have sicklemia, or sickle cell trait. However, about 1 in 40 (4) of these individuals whose cells are capable of sickling suffer from a severe chronic anemia resulting from excessive destruction of their erythrocytes; the term sickle cell anemia is applied to their condition.

The main observable difference between the erythrocytes of sickle cell trait and sickle cell anemia has been that a considerably greater reduction in the partial pressure of oxygen is required for a major fraction of the trait cells to sickle than for the anemia cells (11). Tests *in vivo* have demonstrated that between 30 and 60 percent of the erythrocytes in the venous circulation of sickle cell anemic individuals, but less than 1 percent of those in the venous circulation of sicklemic individuals, are normally sickled. Experiments *in vitro* indicate that under sufficiently low oxygen pressure, however, all the cells of both types assume the sickled form.

The evidence available at the time that our investigation was begun indicated that the process of sickling might be intimately associated with the state and the nature of the hemoglobin within the erythrocyte. Sickle cell erythrocytes in which the hemoglobin is combined with oxygen or carbon monoxide have the biconcave disk contour and are indistinguishable in that form from normal erythrocytes. In this condition they are termed promeniscocytes. The hemoglobin appears to be uniformly distributed and randomly oriented within normal cells and promeniscocytes, and no birefringence is observed. Both types of cells are very flexible. If the oxygen or carbon monoxide is removed, however, transforming the hemoglobin to the uncombined state, the promeniscocytes undergo sickling. The hemoglobin within the sickled cells appears to aggregate into one or more foci, and the cell membranes collapse. The cells become birefringent (11) and quite rigid. The addition of oxygen or carbon monoxide to these cells reverses these phenomena. Thus the physical effects just described depend on the state of combination of the hemoglobin, and only secondarily, if at all, on the cell membrane. This conclusion is supported by the observation that sickled cells when lysed with water produce discoidal, rather than sickle-shaped, ghosts (10).

It was decided, therefore, to examine the physical and chemical properties of the hemoglobins of individuals with sicklemia and sickle cell anemia, and to compare them with the hemoglobin of normal individuals to determine whether any significant differences might be observed.

EXPERIMENTAL METHODS

The experimental work reported in this paper deals largely with an electrophoretic study of these hemoglobins. In the first phase of the investigation, which concerned the comparison of normal and sickle cell anemia hemoglobins, three types of experiments were performed: 1) with carbon-monoxyhemoglobins; 2) with uncombined ferrohemoglobins in the presence of dithionite ion, to prevent oxidation to methemoglobins; and 3) with carbonmonoxyhemoglobins in the presence of dithionite ion. The experiments of type 3 were performed and compared with those of type 1 in order to ascertain whether the dithionite ion itself causes any specific electrophoretic effect.

Samples of blood were obtained from sickle cell anemic individuals who had not been transfused within three months prior to the time of sampling. Stroma-free concentrated solutions of human adult hemoglobin were prepared by the method used by Drabkin (3). These solutions were diluted just before use with the appropriate buffer until the hemoglobin concentrations were close to 0.5 grams per 100 milliliters, and then were dialyzed against large volumes of these buffers for 12 to 24 hours at 4° C. The buffers for the experiments of types 2 and 3 were prepared by adding 300 ml of 0.1 ionic strength sodium dithionite solution to 3.5 liters of 0.1 ionic strength buffer. About 100 ml of 0.1 molar NaOH was then added to bring the pH of the buffer back to its original value. Ferrohemoglobin solutions were prepared by diluting the concentrated solutions with this dithionite-containing buffer and dialyzing against it under a nitrogen atmosphere. The hemoglobin solutions for the experiments of type 3 were made up similarly, except that they were saturated with carbon monoxide after dilution and were dialyzed under a carbon monoxide atmosphere. The dialysis bags were kept in continuous motion in the buffers by means of a stirrer with a mercury seal to prevent the escape of the nitrogen and carbon monoxide gases.

The experiments were carried out in the modified Tiselius electrophoresis apparatus described by Swingle (14). Potential gradients of 4.8 to 8.4 volts per centimeter were employed, and the duration of the runs varied from 6 to 20 hours. The pH values of the buffers were measured after dialysis on samples which had come to room temperature.

RESULTS

The results indicate that a significant difference exists between the electrophoretic mobilities of hemoglobin derived from erythrocytes of normal individuals and from those of sickle cell anemic individuals. The two types of hemoglobin are particularly easily distinguished as the carbonmonoxy compounds at pH 6.9 in phosphate buffer of 0.1 ionic strength. In this buffer the sickle cell anemia carbonmonoxyhemoglobin moves as a positive ion, while the normal compound moves as a negative ion, and there is no detectable amount of one type present in the other.[5] The hemoglobin derived

[5] Occasionally small amounts (less than 5 percent of the total protein) of material with mobilities different from that of either kind of hemoglobin were observed in these uncrys-

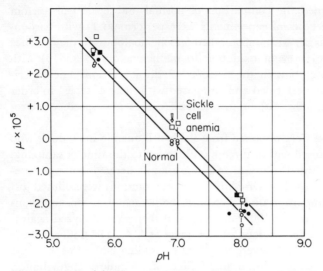

Fig. 1. Mobility (μ)-pH curves for carbonmonoxyhemoglobins in phosphate buffers of 0.1 ionic strength. The black circles and black squares denote the data for experiments performed with buffers containing dithionite ion. The open square designated by the arrow represents an average value of 10 experiments on the hemoglobin of different individuals with sickle cell anemia. The mobilities recorded in this graph are averages of the mobilities in the ascending and descending limbs.

from erythrocytes of individuals with sicklemia, however, appears to be a mixture of the normal hemoglobin and sickle cell anemia hemoglobin in roughly equal proportions. Up to the present time the hemoglobins of 15 persons with sickle cell anemia, 8 persons with sicklemia, and 7 normal adults have been examined. The hemoglobins of normal adult white and Negro individuals were found to be indistinguishable.

The mobility data obtained in phosphate buffers of 0.1 ionic strength and various values of pH are summarized in Figs. 1 and 2.[6]

---

tallized hemoglobin preparations. According to the observations of Stern, Reiner, and Silber (12) a small amount of a component with a mobility smaller than that of oxyhemoglobin is present in human erythrocyte hemolyzates.

[6] The results obtained with carbonmonoxyhemoglobins with and without dithionite ion in the buffers indicate that the dithionite ion plays no significant role in the electrophoretic properties of the proteins. It is therefore of interest that ferrohemoglobin was found to have a lower isoelectric point in phosphate buffer than carbonmonoxyhemoglobin. Titration studies have indicated (5, 6) that oxyhemoglobin (similar in electrophoretic properties to the carbonmonoxy compound) has a lower isoelectric point than ferrohemoglobin in the absence of other ions. These results might be reconciled by assuming that the ferrous iron of ferrohemoglobin forms complexes with phosphate ions which cannot be formed when the iron is combined with oxygen or carbon monoxide. We propose to continue the study of this phenomenon.

The isoelectric points are listed in Table 1. These results prove that the electrophoretic difference between normal hemoglobin and sickle cell anemia hemoglobin exists in both ferrohemoglobin and carbonmonoxyhemoglobin.

Table 1. ISOELECTRIC POINTS IN PHOSPHATE BUFFER, $\mu = 0.1$.

Compound	Normal	Sickle cell anemia	Difference
Carbonmonoxyhemoglobin.....	6.87	7.09	0.22
Ferrohemoglobin..............	6.87	7.09	0.22

We have also performed several experiments in a buffer of 0.1 ionic strength and pH 6.52 containing 0.08 M NaCl, 0.02 M sodium cacodylate, and 0.0083 M cacodylic acid. In this buffer the average mobility of sickle cell anemia carbonmonoxyhemoglobin is 2.63×10^{-5}, and that of normal carbonmonoxyhemoglobin is 2.23×10^{-5} cm/sec per volt/cm.[7] These experiments with a buffer quite different from phosphate buffer demonstrate that the difference between the hemoglobins is essentially independent of the buffer ions.

Typical Longsworth scanning diagrams of experiments with normal,

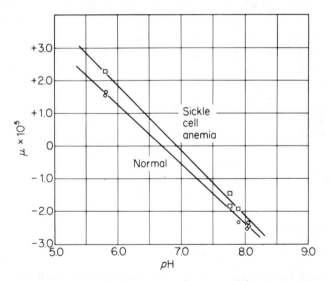

Fig. 2. Mobility (μ)-pH curves for ferrohemoglobins in phosphate buffers of 0.1 ionic strength containing dithionite ion. The mobilities recorded in the graph are averages of the mobilities in the ascending and descending limbs.

[7] The mobility data show that in 0.1 ionic strength cacodylate buffers the isoelectric points of the hemoglobins are increased about 0.5 pH unit over their values in 0.1 ionic strength phosphate buffers. This effect is similar to that observed by Longsworth in his study of ovalbumin (7).

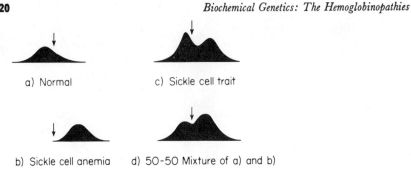

a) Normal   c) Sickle cell trait

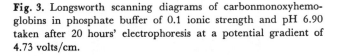

b) Sickle cell anemia   d) 50-50 Mixture of a) and b)

Fig. 3. Longsworth scanning diagrams of carbonmonoxyhemoglobins in phosphate buffer of 0.1 ionic strength and pH 6.90
taken after 20 hours' electrophoresis at a potential gradient of
4.73 volts/cm.

sickle cell anemia, and sicklemia carbonmonoxyhemoglobins, and with a
mixture of the first two compounds, all in phosphate buffer of pH 6.90 and
ionic strength 0.1, are reproduced in Fig. 3. It is apparent from this figure
that the sicklemia material contains less than 50 percent of the anemia component. In order to determine this quantity accurately some experiments at
a total protein concentration of 1 percent were performed with known
mixtures of sickle cell anemia and normal carbonmonoxyhemoglobins in the
cacodylate-sodium chloride buffer of 0.1 ionic strength and pH 6.52 described above. This buffer was chosen in order to minimize the anomalous
electrophoretic effects observed in phosphate buffers (7). Since the two
hemoglobins were incompletely resolved after 15 hours of electrophoresis
under a potential gradient of 2.79 volts/cm, the method of Tiselius and
Kabat (16) was employed to allocate the areas under the peaks in the electrophoresis diagrams to the two components. In Fig. 4 there is plotted the
per cent of the anemia component calculated from the areas so obtained
against the per cent of that component in the known mixtures. Similar
experiments were performed with a solution in which the hemoglobins of
5 sicklemic individuals were pooled. The relative concentrations of the two
hemoglobins were calculated from the electrophoresis diagrams, and the
actual proportions were then determined from the plot of Fig. 4. A value of
39 percent for the amount of the sickle cell anemia component in the
sicklemia hemoglobin was arrived at in this manner. From the experiments
we have performed thus far it appears that this value does not vary greatly
from one sicklemic individual to another, but a more extensive study of this
point is required.

·Up to this stage we have assumed that one of the two components of
sicklemia hemoglobin is identical with sickle cell anemia hemoglobin and the
other is identical with the normal compound. Aside from the genetic evidence
which makes this assumption very probable (see the discussion section),
electrophoresis experiments afford direct evidence that the assumption is

valid. The experiments on the pooled sicklemia carbonmonoxyhemoglobin and the mixture containing 40 percent sickle cell anemia carbonmonoxy-hemoglobin and 60 percent normal carbonmonoxyhemoglobin in the cacodylate-sodium chloride buffer described above were compared, and it was found that the mobilities of the respective components were essentially identical.[8] Furthermore, we have performed experiments in which normal hemoglobin was added to a sicklemia preparation and the mixture was then subjected to electrophoretic analysis. Upon examining the Longsworth scanning diagrams we found that the area under the peak corresponding to the normal component had increased by the amount expected, and that no indication of a new component could be discerned. Similar experiments on mixtures of sickle cell anemia hemoglobin and sicklemia preparations yielded similar results. These sensitive tests reveal that, at least electrophoretically, the two components in sicklemia hemoglobin are identifiable with sickle cell anemia hemoglobin and normal hemoglobin.

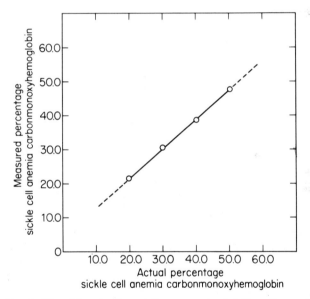

Fig. 4. The determination of the per cent of sickle cell anemia carbonmonoxyhemoglobin in known mixtures of the protein with normal carbonmonoxyhemoglobin by means of electrophoretic analysis. The experiments were performed in a cacodylate sodium chloride buffer described in the text.

[8] The patterns were very slightly different in that the known mixture contained 1 per cent more of the sickle cell anemia component than did the sickle cell trait material.

DISCUSSION

(1) ON THE NATURE OF THE DIFFERENCE BETWEEN SICKLE
CELL ANEMIA HEMOGLOBIN AND NORMAL HEMOGLOBIN

Having found that the electrophoretic mobilities of sickle cell anemia hemoglobin and normal hemoglobin differ, we are left with the considerable problem of locating the cause of the difference. It is impossible to ascribe the difference to dissimilarities in the particle weights or shapes of the two hemoglobins in solution: a purely frictional effect would cause one species to move more slowly than the other throughout the entire pH range and would not produce a shift in the isoelectric point. Moreover, preliminary velocity ultracentrifuge[9] and free diffusion measurements indicate that the two hemoglobins have the same sedimentation and diffusion constants.

The most plausible hypothesis is that there is a difference in the number or kind of ionizable groups in the two hemoglobins. Let us assume that the only groups capable of forming ions which are present in carbonmonoxyhemoglobin are the carboxyl groups in the heme, and the carboxyl, imidazole, amino, phenolic hydroxyl, and guanidino groups in the globin. The number of ions nonspecifically adsorbed on the two proteins should be the same for the two hemoglobins under comparable conditions, and they may be neglected for our purposes. Our experiments indicate that the net number of positive charges (the total number of cationic groups minus the number of anionic groups) is greater for sickle cell anemia hemoglobin than for normal hemoglobin in the pH region near their isoelectric points.

According to titration data obtained by us, the acid-base titration curve of normal human carbonmonoxyhemoglobin is nearly linear in the neighborhood of the isoelectric point of the protein, and a change of one pH unit in the hemoglobin solution in this region is associated with a change in net charge on the hemoglobin molecule of about 13 charges per molecule. The same value was obtained by German and Wyman (5) with horse oxyhemoglobin. The difference in isoelectric points of the two hemoglobins under the conditions of our experiment is 0.23 for ferrohemoglobin and 0.22 for the carbonmonoxy compound. This difference corresponds to about 3 charges per molecule. With consideration of our experimental error, sickle cell anemia hemoglobin therefore has 2-4 more net positive charges per molecule than normal hemoglobin.

Studies have been initiated to elucidate the nature of this charge difference more precisely. Samples of porphyrin dimethyl esters have been prepared from normal hemoglobin and sickle cell anemia hemoglobin. These samples were shown to be identical by their x-ray powder photographs and by identity of their melting points and mixed melting point. A sample made

[9] We are indebted to Dr. M. Moskowitz, of the Chemistry Department, University of California at Berkeley, for performing the ultracentrifuge experiments for us.

from sicklemia hemoglobin was also found to have the same melting point. It is accordingly probable that normal and sickle cell anemia hemoglobin have different globins. Titration studies and amino acid analyses on the hemoglobins are also in progress.

(2) ON THE NATURE OF THE SICKLING PROCESS

In the introductory paragraphs we outlined the evidence which suggested that the hemoglobins in sickle cell anemia and sicklemia erythrocytes might be responsible for the sickling process. The fact that the hemoglobins in these cells have now been found to be different from that present in normal red blood cells makes it appear very probable that this is indeed so.

We can picture the mechanism of the sickling process in the following way. It is likely that it is the globins rather than the hemes of the two hemoglobins that are different. Let us propose that there is a surface region on the globin of the sickle cell anemia, hemoglobin molecule which is absent in the normal molecule and which has a configuration complementary to a different region of the surface of the hemoglobin molecule. This situation would be somewhat analogous to that which very probably exists in antigen-antibody reactions (9). The fact that sickling occurs only when the partial pressures of oxygen and carbon monoxide are low suggests that one of these sites is very near to the iron atom of one or more of the hemes, and that when the iron atom is combined with either one of these gases, the complementariness of the two structures is considerably diminished. Under the appropriate conditions, then, the sickle cell anemia hemoglobin molecules might be capable of interacting with one another at these sites sufficiently to cause at least a partial alignment of the molecules within the cell, resulting in the erythrocyte's becoming birefringent, and the cell membrane's being distorted to accommodate the now relatively rigid structures within its confines. The addition of oxygen or carbon monoxide to the cell might reverse these effects by disrupting some of the weak bonds between the hemoglobin molecules in favor of the bonds formed between gas molecules and iron atoms of the hemes.

Since all sicklemia erythrocytes behave more or less similarly, and all sickle at a sufficiently low oxygen pressure (11), it appears quite certain that normal hemoglobin and sickle cell anemia hemoglobin coexist within each sicklemia cell; otherwise there would be a mixture of normal and sickle cell anemia erythrocytes in sicklemia blood. We might expect that the normal hemoglobin molecules, lacking at least one type of complementary site present on the sickle cell anemia molecules, and so being incapable of entering into the chains or three-dimensional frameworks formed by the latter, would interfere with the alignment of these molecules within the sicklemia erythrocyte. Lower oxygen pressures, freeing more of the complementary sites near the hemes, might be required before sufficiently large aggregates of sickle cell anemia hemoglobin molecules could form to cause sickling of the erythrocytes.

This is in accord with the observations of Sherman (11), which were mentioned in the introduction, that a large proportion of erythrocytes in the venous circulation of persons with sickle cell anemia are sickled, but that very few have assumed the sickle forms in the venous circulation of individuals with sicklemia. Presumably, then, the sickled cells in the blood of persons with sickle cell anemia cause thromboses, and their increased fragility exposes them to the action of reticulo-endothelial cells which break them down, resulting in the anemia (1).

It appears, therefore, that while some of the details of this picture of the sickling process are as yet conjectural, the proposed mechanism is consistent with experimental observations at hand and offers a chemical and physical basis for many of them. Furthermore, if it is correct, it supplies a direct link between the existence of "defective" hemoglobin molecules and the pathological consequences of sickle cell disease.

(3) ON THE GENETICS OF SICKLE CELL DISEASE

A genetic basis for the capacity of erythrocytes to sickle was recognized early in the study of this disease (4). Taliaferro and Huck (15) suggested that a single dominant gene was involved, but the distinction between sicklemia and sickle cell anemia was not clearly understood at the time. The literature contains conflicting statements concerning the nature of the genetic mechanisms involved, but recently Neel (8) has reported an investigation which strongly indicates that the gene responsible for the sickling characteristic is in heterozygous condition in individuals with sicklemia, and homozygous in those with sickle cell anemia.

Our results had caused us to draw this inference before Neel's paper was published. The existence of normal hemoglobin and sickle cell anemia hemoglobin in roughly equal proportions in sicklemia hemoglobin preparations is obviously in complete accord with this hypothesis. In fact, if the mechanism proposed above to account for the sickling process is correct, we can identify the gene responsible for the sickling process with one of an alternative pair of alleles capable through some series of reactions of introducing the modification into the hemoglobin molecule that distinguishes sickle cell anemia hemoglobin from the normal protein.

The results of our investigation are compatible with a direct quantitative effect of this gene pair; in the chromosomes of a single nucleus of a normal adult somatic cell there is a complete absence of the sickle cell gene, while two doses of its allele are present; in the sicklemia somatic cell there exists one dose of each allele; and in the sickle cell anemia somatic cell there are two doses of the sickle cell gene, and a complete absence of its normal allele. Correspondingly, the erythrocytes of these individuals contain 100 per cent normal hemoglobin, 40 per cent sickle cell anemia hemoglobin and 60 per cent normal hemoglobin, and 100 per cent sickle cell anemia hemoglobin, respectively. This investigation reveals, therefore, a clear case of a change produced in a protein molecule by an allelic change in a single gene involved in synthesis.

The fact that sicklemia erythrocytes contain the two hemoglobins in the ratio 40:60 rather than 50:50 might be accounted for by a number of hypothetical schemes. For example, the two genes might compete for a common substrate in the synthesis of two different enzymes essential to the production of the two different hemoglobins. In this reaction, the sickle cell gene would be less efficient than its normal allele. Or, competition for a common substrate might occur at some later stage in the series of reactions leading to the synthesis of the two hemoglobins. Mechanisms of this sort are discussed in more elaborate detail by Stern (13).

The results obtained in the present study suggest that the erythrocytes of other hereditary hemolytic anemias be examined for the presence of abnormal hemoglobins. This we propose to do.

Based on a paper presented at the meeting of the National Academy of Sciences in Washington, D. C., in April, 1949, and at the meeting of the American Society of Biological Chemists in Detroit in April, 1949.

REFERENCES

(1) W. Boyd. 1938. Textbook of pathology, 3rd ed. Lea and Febiger, Philadelphia: 864.

(2) L. W. Diggs, C. F. Ahmann and J. Bibb. 1933. Ann. Int. Med. **7**: 769.

(3) D. L. Drabkin. 1946. J. Biol. Chem. **164**: 703.

(4) V. E. Emmel. 1917. Arch. Int. Med. **20**: 586.

(5) B. German and J. Wyman, Jr. 1937. J. Biol. Chem. **117**: 533.

(6) A. B. Hastings *et al.* 1924. J. Biol. Chem. **60**: 89.

(7) L. G. Longsworth. 1941. Ann. N. Y. Acad. Sci. **41**: 276.

(8) J. V. Neel. 1940. Science. **110**: 64.

(9) L. Pauling, D. Pressman and D. Campbell. 1943. Physiol. Rev. **23**: 203.

(10) E. Ponder. 1947. Ann. N. Y. Acad. Sci. **48**: 579.

(11) I. J. Sherman. 1940. Bull. Johns Hopkins Hosp. **67**: 309.

(12) K. G. Stern, M. Reiner and R. H. Sibler. 1945. J. Biol. Chem. **161**: 731.

(13) C. Stern. 1948. Science. **108**: 615.

(14) S. M. Swingle. 1947. Rev. Sci. Inst. **18**: 128.

(15) W. H. Taliaferro and J. G. Huck. 1923. Genetics. **8**: 594.

(16) A. Tiselius and E. Kabat. 1939. J. Exp. Med. **69**: 119.

C14-Hybrids of Human Hemoglobins. II. The Identification of the Aberrant Chain in Human Hemoglobin S†

The continuing electrophoretic analysis of human hemoglobins has provided many additional examples of molecular variation. Indeed, the western alphabet has proved inadequate to designate the number of different hemoglobins observed. Such findings have been complemented by a chemical and genetic dissection of the hemoglobin molecule. The next three reprinted papers describe different aspects of this dissection. For purposes of synthesis these three reports are best considered together.

Rhinesmith, Schroeder and Pauling established that the human hemoglobin molecule contains two each of two types of polypeptide chains, designated α and β. Subsequently in the note, reprinted below, hemoglobin S was identified as a β chain abnormality.

A parallel development was the ingenious approach adopted by Itano and Singer. They demonstrated that the four polypeptide chains of hemoglobin could be asymmetrically dissociated into α_2 and β_2 sub-units and subsequently reassociated or "recombined" into whole four chain molecules which could thus be abbreviated $\alpha_2\beta_2$. This comparatively simple technique provides a means of identifying the polypeptide chain aberrant in a particular abnormal hemoglobin. Of greater interest is the inference embodied in the reprinted paper by Itano and Robinson, that the α and β polypeptide chains of hemoglobin have genetically independent control.

The genetic proof of Itano's inference lay in the family with Hopkins-2, sickle and adult hemoglobins described by Smith and Torbert and reprinted in this series. An expanded study of this family corroborates their conclusion (1). Moreover Itano's (2) study of this family indicates that Hopkins-2 hemoglobin, like hemoglobin I, contains an α chain abnormality.

The sum of these three papers establishes that one gene controls the formation of one kind of polypeptide chain. A corollary of this conclusion is that a protein molecule composed of several different types

† Reprinted by senior author's and publisher's permission from J. Am. Chem. Soc. 1959. **81:** 3168-3169.

of polypeptide chains is, like the hemoglobin molecule, controlled by several genetic loci. The manner in which this synthesis was reached emphasizes once again the interdependence of genetics, biochemistry, and medicine.

(1) T. B. Bradley, Jr., S. H. Boyer, and F. H. Allen, Jr. 1961. Hopkins-2 hemoglobin: a revised pedigree with blood and serum group data. Bull. Johns Hopkins Hosp. **108**: 75-79.

(2) Harvey A. Itano and Elizabeth A. Robinson. 1960. Genetic control of the α- and β-chains of hemoglobin. Proc. U. S. Nat. Acad. Sci. **46**: 1492-1500.

Sir:

Both normal adult human hemoglobin and sickle cell hemoglobin (HbA and HbS) contain two each of two kinds of polypeptide chains.[1] The two α chains have the N-terminal sequence, val-leu, and the β chains the sequence val-his-leu.[2] In HbS, a valyl residue has been substituted in one kind of chain for a glutamyl residue in HbA.[3] We wish to report that substitution is in the β chain.

Both hemoglobins may be dissociated into two equal or nearly equal molecules by change in pH.[4,5,6,7] When a mixture of HbA and S is first taken to a dissociating pH and then returned to a non-dissociating pH, the lack of new species, either electrophoretically[7] or chromatographically,[8] suggests two possibilities: that heterologous recombination does not occur or that dissociation is asymmetric[7] $\alpha_2\beta_2 \rightleftarrows \alpha_2 + \beta_2$. According to Itano dissociation in acid solution is asymmetric and the expected hybrids do form.[9] When labelled and unlabelled hemoglobins are hybridized,[8] the hybrids contain both labelled and unlabelled chains and any peptide may be assigned to the proper chain. In the experiments to be described, the N-terminal peptides have been used to define the aberrant chain in HbS.

[1] H. S. Rhinesmith, W. A. Schroeder and L. Pauling. 1957. This Journal. **79**: 4682, and unpublished data.

[2] H. S. Rhinesmith, W. A. Schroeder and N. Martin. 1958. *Ibid.* **80**: 3358. 1956; 1957.

[3] V. M. Ingram. 1956; 1957. *Nature.* **178**: 792; **180**: 326.

[4] E. O. Field and J. R. P. O'Brien. 1955. *Biochem. J.*, **60**: 656.

[5] U. Hasserodt and J. Vinograd, paper presented at the meeting of the American Chemical Society, New York, September 8-13, 1957. Hutchinson, M. S. Thesis, California Institute of Technology, Pasadena, 1957.

[6] U. Hasserodt and J. Vinograd. 1959. *Proc. U. S. Nat. Acad. Sci.* **45**: 12.

[7] S. J. Singer and H. A. Itano. 1958. *Ibid.* **44**: 522.

[8] J. R. Vinograd and W. D. Hutchinson. July 16, 1960. Carbon-14 Labelled Hybrids of Hemglobin. Nature. **187**: 216-218.

[9] H. A. Itano, paper presented at the meeting of the American Chemical Society, Chicago, Ill., September 7-12, 1958.

HbA* (7,000 c.p.m./mg.) and HbS* (2,600 c.p.m./mg.) were prepared by incubating the appropriate reticulocyte-rich bloods with uniformly C^{14}-labelled L-leucine.[8,10]

As required, both radioactive or non-radioactive hemoglobins were purified chromatographically[11] to prevent interference from minor hemoglobin components.

In Experiment I, oxyhemoglobin A* diluted 1:1 with HbA was mixed with an equal amount of HbS. The solution was dialyzed at 3° against 0.1 M sodium acetate buffer at pH 5.0 for 24 hr. and further dialyzed for 24 hr. prior to chromatography with Developer No. 12 at pH 7.22. Chromatographic separation of 50 mg. of the mixture then was carried out with Developer No. 1. The main portion of the zone of HbS (now radioactive, 850 c.p.m./mg.) was taken, combined with 150 mg. of HbS as a carrier, and dinitrophenylated. In Experiment II, HbS* was hybridized with HbA at pH 11.0 in 0.05 M sodium phosphate, 0.15 M NaCl at 3° for 24 hours. The N-terminal peptides were isolated chromatographically, estimated spectrophotometrically,[1,2] and assayed for radioactivity with these results.

	Hybrid HbS* from HbS and HbA*		Hybrid HbA* from HbS* and HbA	
	c.p.m./μmole	μmoles	c.p.m./μmole	μmoles
DNP-val-leu	47.5[a]	2.21	32.2	2.33
di-DNP-val-his-leu	6.2	0.52	3.4	1.08
di-DNP-val-his	7.2	1.09	1.8	0.56
Dinitroaniline	0.6	2.79	0.2	5.36

[a] Contents of planchette rechromatographed and reassayed: DNP val-leu, 47 c.p.m./μmole.

Because the N-terminal dipeptide DNP-val-leu is radioactive and the N-tripeptide di-DNP-val-his-leu is substantially inactive, the α chains must have exchanged and are the chains common to both hemoglobins. The β chains differ and are aberrant in HbS.

Thus, sickle cell anemia is associated with a mutation of the gene which controls the synthesis of the β chains of hemoglobin.

We wish to thank Miss Joan Balog for isolating the N-terminal peptides.

[10] We wish to thank Dr. P. A. Sturgeon, Children's Hospital, Los Angeles, for supplying us with the blood samples and the hematological data. The blood for experiment I was obtained from an individual with an acquired hemolytic anemia. We wish to thank Professor H. M. Dintzis for aid in the preparation of the labelled hemoglobins.

[11] D. W. Allen, W. A. Schroeder and J. Balog. 1958. This Journal. **80**: 1628.

This investigation was supported in part by a grant (H-3394) from the National Institutes of Health, United States Public Health Service.

CONTRIBUTION NO. 2432
GATES AND CRELLIN LABORATORIES   J. R. VINOGRAD
  OF CHEMISTRY   W. D. HUTCHINSON
CALIFORNIA INSTITUTE OF TECHNOLOGY   W. A. SCHROEDER
PASADENA, CALIFORNIA
RECEIVED JANUARY 9, 1959

Formation of Normal and Doubly Abnormal Haemoglobins by Recombination of Haemoglobin I with S and C*

HARVEY A. ITANO

ELIZABETH ROBINSON

National Institute of Arthritis and Metabolic Diseases, National Institutes of Health, Public Health Service, U.S. Department of Health, Education, and Welfare, Bethesda, Maryland

A molecule of normal human adult haemoglobin (haemoglobin A) is symmetrical about a dyad axis[1] and is composed of four haem groups and four polypeptide chains, a pair of α-chains and a pair of β-chains.[2] Haemoglobins A, S, and C dissociate asymmetrically in acid into two unlike sub-units, each of which consists of a pair of identical chains and two haems.[3,4] Complete molecules are regenerated from these sub-units when an acidified solution is neutralized, and sub-units are exchanged when a mixture of a pair of unlike haemoglobins is dissociated and recombined. The chemical abnormalities of haemoglobins S and C occur at the same place in the β-chain.[5,6]

* Reprinted by senior author's and publisher's permission from Nature. 1959. **183:** 1799-1800.

[1] M. F. Perutz, A. M. Liquori and F. Eirich. 1951. Nature. **167:** 929.

[2] H. S. Rhinesmith, W. A. Schroeder and N. Martin. 1958. J. Am. Chem. Soc. **80:** 3358.

[3] H. A. Itano and S. J. Singer. 1958. Proc. U. S. Nat. Acad. Sci. **44:** 522.

[4] S. J. Singer and H. A. Itano. 1959. Proc. U. S. Nat. Acad. Sci. **45:** 174.

[5] J. A. Hunt and V. M. Ingram. 1958. Nature. **181:** 1062.

[6] J. R. Vinograd, W. D. Hutchinson and W. A. Schroeder. 1959. J. Am. Chem. Soc.

Haemoglobin I, on the other hand, is abnormal in the α-chain.[7] We wish to report evidence for the formation of haemoglobin A and a doubly abnormal molecule when haemoglobin I is recombined with haemoglobin S or C.

A mixture of haemoglobins A and I received from Dr. L. M. Tocantins was used.[8] The mixture, and mixtures of it with haemoglobin S and with haemoglobin C, were examined electrophoretically both before and after recombination. All samples were in the form of carbonmonoxyhaemoglobin. Recombined mixtures were prepared by dissociation in acetate-sodium chloride buffer of pH 4.7, $\Gamma/2$ 0.2 (ref. 4) for 4 hr. at 5° C. followed by dialysis against potassium phosphate buffer of pH 6.3, $\Gamma/2$ 0.02, for about 20 hr. at 5° C. The resulting samples were analysed by moving-boundary electrophoresis in the same buffer for 5 hr. at 3° C. with a potential gradient of 8.5 V. cm.$^{-1}$. Control electrophoretic analyses on undissociated aliquots of the same mixtures were carried out under identical conditions. Satisfactory resolution was obtained only in the ascending limb. When a mixture of carbonmonoxyhaemoglobins A, I and S was recombined, a new component appeared between A and I. At the same time the proportion of haemoglobin A increased and the proportions of I and S decreased. Recombination of carbonmonoxyhaemoglobins A, I and C produced no new electrophoretic component; however, the proportion of haemoglobin A increased with decrease of I and C. No new component or change in proportions occurred when carbonmonoxyhaemoglobins A and I were recombined. The results are shown in Fig. 1 and Table 1. The numerical values of Table 1 are directly proportional to the areas under the peaks of Fig. 1. These areas are probably anomalous because of low ionic strength of buffer. However, since aliquots

Table 1. Composition of Haemoglobin Mixtures Before and After Recombination

		Electrophoretic composition: per cent of total				
Mixture		$a_2i_2^{-4}$ (I)	$s_2i_2^{-2}$	a_2u_2 (A)	$s_2u_2^{+2}$ (S)	$c_2u_2^{+4}$ (C)
A + I	Control	53	—	47*	—	—
	Recombined	55	—	45*	—	—
A + I + S	Control	34	—	24*	42	—
	Recombined	23	11	32	34	—
A + I + C	Control	36	—	20	—	44*
	Recombined †	22	—	42‡	—	36*

* Includes 3-4 per cent of trailing shoulder.
† Re-run of original control; C peak too sharp in original for determination of area.
‡ Probably includes c_2i_2.

[7] V. M. Ingram, M. Murayama and V. M. Ingram. Nature (preceding communications).
[8] I. R. Schwartz, J. Atwater, E. Repplinger and L. M. Tocantins. 1957. Fed. Proc. **16:** 115.

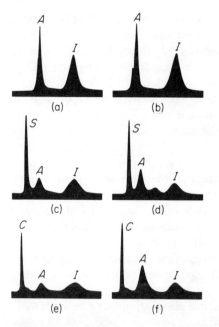

Fig. 1. Ascending boundary patterns from electrophoresis of 1.0 per cent carbonmonoxyhaemoglobin in phosphate buffer of pH 6.3, $\Gamma/2 = 0.02$. The direction of migration is from right to left. From left to right the components are: (a) A, I control; (b) A, I recombined; (c) S, A, I control; (d) S, A, I, recombined. Note the new component ($s_2i_2^{-2}$) between A and I and the increase in proportion of A; (e) C, A, I control; (f) C, A, I recombined. Note the increase in the proportion of A ($a_2u_2 + c_2i_2$).

of the same mixture were used in each pair of analyses, change in relative areas following recombination must reflect change in true composition.

A simplified nomenclature[3,4] is convenient for discussion of dissociation-recombination phenomena. The β-chains of haemoglobins A, S and C are a, s and c, respectively; and their common α-chain is u. The abnormal α-chain of haemoglobin I is i, and its β-chain, presumably normal, is a. The abnormalities in net charge of haemoglobins S and C are $+2$ and $+4$, respectively.[5] The mobility of haemoglobin I indicates an abnormality in net charge of close to -4. The net charge of the unaltered portions of the molecules may be omitted in the present discussion; accordingly carbon-monoxyhaemoglobins A, S, C and I may be written a_2u_2, $s_2u_2^{+2}$, $c_2u_2^{+4}$, and $a_2i_2^{-4}$, respectively. Asymmetric dissociation would result in the sub-units a_2, s_2^{+2}, c_2^{+4}, u_2, and i_2^{-4}.

We can now interpret our results with the assumption of asymmetrical dissociation and recombination. When a mixture of a_2u_2 and $a_2i_2^{-4}$ is recombined, exchange of a_2 sub-units can occur without effect on electrophoretic composition, in agreement with our observations on the mixture of carbonmonoxyhaemoglobins A and I. The situation is analogous to the exchange of u_2 sub-units when mixtures of carbonmonoxyhaemoglobins A, S and C were recombined. Recombined mixtures yielded the same electrophoretic patterns as corresponding untreated mixtures, and exchange was demonstrated by use of labelled molecules.[3,4] Since recombination of carbonmonoxyhaemoglobin A with S, C or I is not associated with change in composition, it appears that the effects observed in the mixture A, S and I, and in the mixture A, C and I, arise from recombination of S and C, respectively, with I. Asymmetrical recombination of $s_2 u_2^{+2}$ and $a_2 i_2^{-4}$ would result in a mixture of $a_2 u_2$, $s_2 i_2^{-2}$, and the original components. The net effect on the composition of a mixture of carbonmonoxyhaemoglobins A, S and I would be the appearance of a new component between A and I, increase in A and decrease in S and I. Asymmetrical recombination of $c_2 u_2^{+4}$ and $a_2 i_2^{-4}$ would produce a mixture of $a_2 u_2$, $c_2 i_2$, and the original components. Since $c_2 i_2$ has the same net charge as $a_2 u_2$, no new component would be detected. The effect on a mixture of carbonmonoxyhaemoglobins A, C and I would be an increase in the A component, which includes both $a_2 u_2$ and $c_2 i_2$, and decrease in C and I.

Thus our observations are consistent with the assumption of asymmetrical recombination between carbonmonoxyhaemoglobin I, which is abnormal in the α-chain, and carbomonoxyhaemoglobin S or C, which is abnormal in the β-chain, to produce carbonmonoxyhaemoglobin A and a carbonmonoxyhaemoglobin molecule composed of two different pairs of abnormal chains. According to these results, it is possible for an individual who is heterozygous for an abnormality in each chain to have four molecular species of adult haemoglobin in his red cells, provided the two types of chains are physically independent up to the time they associate to form complete molecules. If the abnormalities in net charge of the two abnormal chains are equal and opposite, the four species would appear as three electrophoretic components. In either circumstance one of the four species would be composed entirely of normal chains. Formation of a normal protein molecule by association of the normal components of two different abnormal molecules suggests one possible mechanism for extranuclear formation of a normal enzyme molecule by the co-operative action of two mutant strains of the same organism, neither of which produces active enzyme.[4]

Study of Two Abnormal Hemoglobins with Evidence for a New Genetic Locus for Hemoglobin Formation[1]

ERNEST W. SMITH[2]

JOHN V. TORBERT[3]

Department of Medicine, The Johns Hopkins University School of Medicine and Hospital. Received for publication September 20, 1957

Electrophoresis of hemoglobin is routinely performed in the study of Negro patients from the clinics of the Johns Hopkins Hospital, and abnormal hemoglobins are sometimes encountered in the absence of specific hematologic abnormalities. In two instances from a total of over 6,000 specimens, hemoglobins with an electrophoretic mobility greater than that of normal hemoglobin at pH 8.6 were discovered. The first of these hemoglobins has a mobility equal to that of hemoglobin I (1). This hemoglobin was subsequently discovered in other members of the family of the patient. In each of these the proportion of normal to fast-moving fractions was about 1:1. In the North Carolina family in which hemoglobin I was first encountered, the proportion of I to normal was approximately 1:3.

The second of the hemoglobins encountered in our clinic has a mobility at pH 8.6 which is less than that of hemoglobin I, and roughly comparable to that of hemoglobin J of Thorup (2) or to Liberian-2 hemoglobin (3). Erythrocytes of individuals with hemoglobin J contained approximately equal parts of A and J, but in the family to be described, the fast hemoglobin represents only 15 per cent of the total amount.

Family studies indicate that each of these abnormalities is inherited as a simple Mendelian dominant trait. The locus of the first mentioned hemoglobin cannot be ascertained, but the data available indicate clearly that the second abnormal hemoglobin is acting on a locus other than that for normal, sickle, C and D hemoglobins. Since it has not been possible to compare all of

[1] Reprinted by senior author's and publisher's permission from Bulletin of the Johns Hopkins Hospital. 1958. **101:** 38-45.

[2] Investigator of the Howard Hughes Medical Institute.

[3] Clinical Fellow of the American Cancer Society.

the chemical and physical properties of these hemoglobin abnormalities with the abnormal hemoglobins which have been encountered in other clinics, the custom which has been adopted by others of informally labeling hemoglobins with a tentative designation is being followed here. Thus, the first of these hemoglobins will be designated as Hopkins-1 and the second, or that hemoglobin acting at a locus apart from the A, S, C, D hemoglobin locus, will be designated as Hopkins-2 hemoglobin.

METHODS

The standard laboratory procedures of the Johns Hopkins Hospital were used for most of the hematologic and chemical determinations. Paper electrophoresis was performed by the method previously described from these laboratories (4).

(A) HOPKINS-1 HEMOGLOBIN

The propositus of this family was O. H. (JHH #720589). A 59 year old Negro male was admitted to the Johns Hopkins Hospital in October of 1955 in coma. He had been entirely well prior to the onset of convulsive seizures and left hemiparesis 6 days before admission to the hospital. At the time of admission to the hospital, he was stuporous. The blood pressure was 150/80 millimeters of mercury and he was dehydrated. There was left hemiparesis, and the eyes were deviated to the right. The liver and spleen were not palpable. A serologic test for syphilis was positive to 64 units. The hematocrit value was 44 per cent and the red cell indices were normal. The white cell count was 26,000 per mm^3. Erythrocyte fragility studies, coagulation studies, and erythrocyte survival as determined with Cr^{51} were normal. During the stay in the hospital, the patient developed a staphylococcus and proteus mirabilis septicemia with multiple abscesses in the skin and the subcutaneous tissues. The paresis was not relieved. Despite intensive therapy, he remained somewhat stuporous and died on the thirty-fourth hospital day.

Because of routine screening procedures in use at the time, the hemoglobin was subjected to electrophoresis at pH 8.6 and the pattern revealed 50 per cent normal hemoglobin and 50 per cent of a hemoglobin with a distinctly faster than normal mobility. This hemoglobin was designated as Hopkins-1 (Ho-1) hemoglobin. Other members of the family were studied in order to determine the genetic and clinical expressions of this abnormality. The kindred is shown in Figure 1. The propositus depicted as I-1 had nine siblings of whom seven remained alive, but of whom only three, listed as I-4, I-5 and I-9, have been studied. Of these, one sister, I-4, and one brother, I-9, had Hopkins-1 trait. I-4 had eight children, 13 grandchildren and 6 great-grandchildren. From this family, I-4, II-17, II-22, III-5, III-6 and III-7 had hemoglobin electrophoretic patterns which exhibited the abnormality in combination with normal hemoglobin and in concentrations of

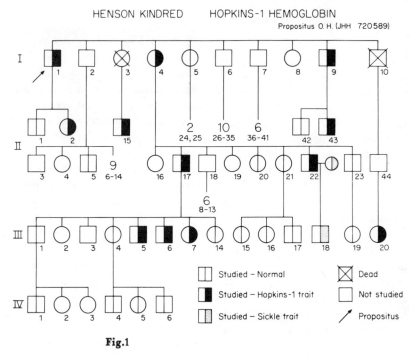

HENSON KINDRED   HOPKINS-1 HEMOGLOBIN
Propositus O. H. (JHH 720589)

Fig.1

approximately 50 per cent of each. I-3 was dead but her one child, II-15, had Hopkins-1 trait. One of two children of I-9, designated as II-43, also had the abnormality. The propositus had one child, II-1, who had only normal hemoglobin and one child, II-2, who had normal and Hopkins-1 hemoglobins. A sibling of the propositus, I-10, is deceased but a grandchild, III-20, has the Hopkins-1 trait. Those who were tested and found normal included I-5, II-1, II-5, II-20, II-21, II-23, II-42, III-1, III-4, III-14, III-15, III-16, III-17, III-19, IV-1, IV-4, IV-5 and IV-6. Excluding the propositus, seven members of the kindred with Hopkins-1 trait were males and four were females. In no instance was the abnormal hemoglobin present in a child when it was absent in the parent. One individual, II-22, with Hopkins-1 trait, married a woman with sickle trait. One child with sickle trait resulted from this union. It is impossible to conclude from these data that the genetic locus of Hopkins-1 hemoglobin is the same as that for normal sickle, C and D hemoglobins.

The data obtained are entirely compatible with the belief that the Hopkins-1 hemoglobin is inherited as a Mendelian dominant, not sex-linked or limited. It is not possible to conclude either that the responsible gene is an allele of normal (A) hemoglobin or that it is present at a different locus. From study of the 12 individuals in the kindred no associated hematologic abnormality was recognized.

(B) HOPKINS-2 HEMOGLOBIN

The propositus for this study was D. F., (JHH #A-97378), a 4 year old Negro male who was admitted to the Harriet Lane Home of the Johns Hopkins Hospital in November, 1956, with acute glomerulonephritis. His birth had been normal but chronic, generalized eczematous dermatitis persisted from age 4 months and asthmatic bronchitis had recurred repeatedly from age 18 months. Because of recurrent episodes of otitis media and secondary infection of the eczematous skin eruption, he had received many antibiotics. Among these, he had received penicillin to which he had demonstrated an urticarial reaction. An exacerbation of the eczema with secondary infection was treated with erythromycin. After two days of therapy he developed periorbital edema and hematuria. Upon admission to the hospital, the blood pressure was elevated to 135/110 millimeters of mercury. There was mild periorbital edema. There was generalized lymphadenopathy and widespread flexural eczematization and pustulation of the skin. Wheezes and fine rales were heard throughout the chest. The liver and spleen were easily palpable. The hematocrit value was 35 per cent. The white cell count was 16,000 per mm³ with a normal differential. No abnormalities of the red cells were seen on blood smears. Examination of the urine revealed gross hematuria, 4 plus albuminuria, and granular and cellular casts. The serum non-protein nitrogen was 80 milligrams per 100 ml. and the potassium 7.5 milliequivalents per liter. During his hospital stay, diuresis was brought about, the urine became normal and the azotemia disappeared.

As a routine hospital procedure, electrophoresis of the hemoglobin was performed and a component with a migration greater than that of normal, A, hemoglobin was revealed which amounted to approximately 15 per cent of the total hemoglobin concentration (Fig. 2). Erythrocyte fragility studies were normal. The electrophoretic composition of the hemoglobin did not change upon aging or repeated freezing and thawing. Subsequently, study of other members of the family revealed the presence of the fast component of hemoglobin designated as Hopkins-2 (Ho-2) hemoglobin. In some individuals sickle hemoglobin was also present.

Study of the Kindred. The mother of the propositus had been well throughout life, had married twice and had three children of whom the propositus was the youngest. Electrophoresis of her hemoglobin revealed the presence of three components. One with the mobility of S hemoglobin comprised 45 per cent of the total, the normal hemoglobin concentration was 45 per cent and 10 per cent was of a mobility faster than normal and equal in mobility to the fast component present in the propositus. Sickling preparations on this blood were positive. The hematocrit value, the white cell count, reticulocyte and platelet counts, osmotic and mechanical fragility of the erythrocytes were normal. The red cell indices and the appearance of the erythrocytes on blood smears were also normal. Hematologic studies including hemoglobin electro-

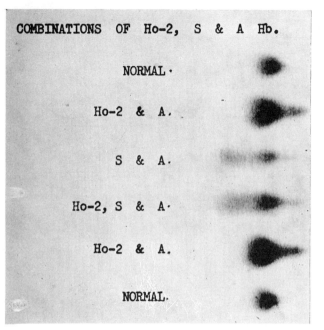

Fig. 2a

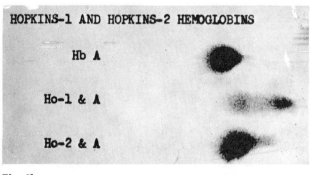

Fig. 2b

Fig. 2. Hemoglobin electrophoresis in Veronal pH 8.6, 0.6m.
(a) The mobility and relative concentrations of Ho-1 and Ho-2.
(b) The relative concentration of various combinations of Ho-2.

phoresis were performed on 15 other members of the family. In none was there significant alteration of the hematocrit value, white blood cell count, reticulocyte or platelet counts or of the appearance of the erythrocytes on smears. The fast-migrating hemoglobin was demonstrable in 11 of the 17 members and sickling could be produced in the 10 whose erythrocytes contained S hemoglobin.

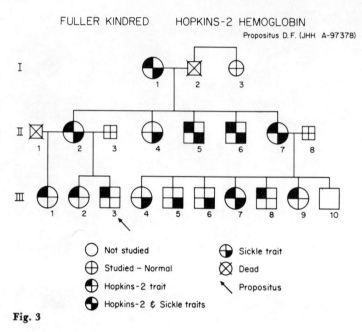

Fig. 3

In Figure 3 the pedigree has been charted. The propositus has been designated as III-3 in the chart and his mother is designated as II-2, six members, including at least one from each generation, had S, A and Hopkins-2 components in the erythrocytes. These members were I-1, II-2, II-5, II-6, II-7, and III-7. In each the proportions of approximately 45, 45 and 10 per cent for S, A and Hopkins-2 hemoglobin were represented. The combination of Hopkins-2 hemoglobin and A was present in 5 members of the third generation including III-1, III-2, III-3 and III-8 and III-9. In these individuals the Ho-2 represented 15 to 20 per cent of the total hemoglobin concentration. The combination of sickle and normal hemoglobins without Hopkins-2 was represented by 4 members including II-4, III-4, III-5, III-6. Normal hemoglobin alone was encountered in only the second spouse of the individual II-2 and in the spouse of II-7. One member of the pedigree, III-10, remains unstudied. Thus, in no instance of direct inheritance from I-1 was an individual encountered with only normal hemoglobin.

DISCUSSION

Several hemoglobins with an electrophoretic mobility which is greater than normal hemoglobin at pH 8.6 have been encountered by different workers. Time has not allowed their complete identification and designation as new forms of hemoglobin or as further instances of previously described hemoglobins. Those for which a designation has been established include the small component found in normal blood (5, 6), hemoglobin H (7), I, J and Liberian-2. The mobility of the Hopkins-2 hemoglobin is clearly greater than the fast hemoglobin which is present in the erythrocytes of all normal individuals. At pH 8.6 the mobility of Hopkins-2 is less than I. It is not precipitated from solution with time or freezing as is hemoglobin H, but it may prove to be identical to hemoglobin J or to Liberian-2 hemoglobin.

The inheritance of hemoglobins S and Hopkins-2 is observed in three matings within this pedigree. In two instances, the children of such matings include combinations of (a) sickle and normal, (b) Hopkins-2 and normal, and of (c) sickle, normal and Hopkins-2. The inheritance of sickle and Hopkins-2 from a single parent precludes the possibility that these hemoglobins are allelomorphs. The frequency with which one is inherited independently of the other makes a close chromosomal linkage unlikely. Furthermore, the Hopkins-2 hemoglobin cannot be transferred on the A hemoglobin gene since the Ho-2 hemoglobin may be inherited with sickle hemoglobin, a situation which would preclude the inheritance of the A gene from that parent. The segregation of these hemoglobins within the pedigree can be explained by localization of the Hopkins-2 gene on a chromosome other than that carrying the S, A, C, D gene. Offspring of an individual with A and S genes at one locus and Hopkins-2 on a different locus should include (a) 25 per cent with the combination sickle, Hopkins-2, and A hemoglobins (the A originating in this case from the second parent), (b) 25 per cent with Hopkins-2 and A (inheritance of A from both parents), (c) 25 per cent with sickle and A (A from the second parent) and (d) 25 per cent with only A hemoglobin. In this pedigree the expected number of normal individuals is 3.7. However, with 14 of the 15 offspring studied none with only A hemoglobin was encountered, a happening which could be due to chance.

No hematologic abnormality has been associated with the inheritance of Hopkins-2 hemoglobin in combination with A, or together with A and sickle. The concentration of Hopkins-2 hemoglobin in combination with sickle and normal is significantly less (10 per cent) than when it occurs with only A hemoglobin (15–20 per cent). It could be postulated that Hopkins-2 is formed at the expense of A hemoglobin, since the proportion of S remains approximately 45 per cent whether Hopkins-2 is present or absent.

The evidence has been brought forth that the abnormalities associated with the thalassemia syndromes are determined at a locus or at loci apart from the A, S, C, D locus (8, 9, 10). Schwartz and his associates (10) believe that hemoglobin G is determined at yet a third locus. Accepting the presence of the three loci, normal, thalassemia, and G and tentatively placing Hopkins-2 hemoglobin at a fourth locus, the genotype of an individual with the combinations of Hopkins-2 and A hemoglobins would be:

Hb₁A	Hb₁A	(S, A, C, D, locus)
Hb_tA	Hb_tA	(thalassemia locus)
Hb₃A	Hb₃A	(G locus)
Hb₄Ho-2	Hb₄A	(Ho-2 locus)

and the genotype for an individual with the combinations of sickle, normal and Hopkins-2 would be:

Hb₁S	Hb₁A
Hb_tA	Hb_tA
Hb₃A	Hb₃A
Hb₄Ho-2	Hb₄A

Since each of the hemoglobins, Ho-1 and Ho-2, occurred only once in routine testing of 6,000 individuals, the chance occurrence of this hemoglobin in combination with other abnormal forms seems small unless a geographic area of higher incidence for the abnormality is discovered.

SUMMARY

(1) Two hemoglobins are described, each with an electrophoretic mobility in veronal at pH 8.6 which is greater than the mobility of hemoglobin A.

(2) The inheritance of each seems to be as a Mendelian autosomal dominant. The locus of one, Hopkins-1 hemoglobin, is not determined. The locus of the other, Hopkins-2 hemoglobin, is shown to be on a different chromosome than is the A, S, C, D allele system.

REFERENCES

(1) W. N. Jensen, E. B. Page and D. L. Rucknagel. 1955. Hemoglobin H—an inherited hemoglobin abnormality. Clin. Res. Proc. **3**: 93.

(2) O. A. Thorup, H. A. Itano, M. Wheby and B. S. Leavell. 1956. Hemoglobin J. Science. **123**: 889.

(3) A. R. Robinson, W. W. Zuelzer, J. V. Neel, F. B. Livingstone and M. J. Miller. 1956. Two "Fast" hemoglobin components in Liberian blood samples. Blood. **11**: 902.

(4) E. W. Smith and C. L. Conley. 1953. Filter paper electrophoresis of human hemoglobins with special reference to the incidence and clinical significance of hemoglobin C. Bull. Johns Hopkins Hosp. **93**: 94.

(5) H. G. Kunkel and G. Wallenius. 1955. New hemoglobin in normal adult blood. Science. **122**: 288.

(6) M. Morrison and J. L. Cook. 1955. Chromatographic fractionation of normal adult oxy-hemoglobin. Science. **122**: 920.

(7) D. A. Rigas, R. D. Kiler and E. E. Osgood. 1956. Hemoglobin H: Clinical, laboratory, and genetic studies of a family with a previously undescribed hemoglobin. J. Lab. & Clin. Med. **47**: 5.

(8) E. Silvestroni and I. Bianco. 1952. Genetic aspects of sickle cell anemia and micro-drepanocytic disease. Blood. **7**: 429.

(9) K. Singer, A. P. Kraus, L. Singer, H. M. Rubenstein and S. R. Goldberg. 1954. Studies of abnormal hemoglobins; X. A new syndrome: Hemoglobin C—thalassemia disease. Blood. **9**: 1032.

(10) H. C. Schwartz, T. H. Spaet, W. W. Zuelzer, J. V. Neel, A. R. Robinson and S. F. Kaufman. 1957. Combinations of hemoglobin G, hemoglobin S and thalassemia occurring in one family. Blood. **12**: 238.

Gene Mutations in Human Haemoglobin: the Chemical Difference Between Normal and Sickle Cell Haemoglobin*

V. M. INGRAM

Medical Research Council Unit for the Study of the Molecular Structure of Biological Systems, Cavendish Laboratory, University of Cambridge

With this paper and the next two, the unravelling of the hemoglobin molecule advances into a penultimate stage. Ingram's experiments follow the principles earlier applied by Sanger to the exact description of the primary structure of insulin. However, the precise characterization of the comparatively large hemoglobin molecule only became possible with Ingram's invention of molecular "fingerprinting" which is described in the first of these papers. The proof that one gene causes the substitution of one kind of amino acid for another at one point in a protein is provided by Ingram. As a result the human hemoglobin variants have become the pre-eminent examples of the manner in which point mutations affect protein structure. It is perhaps ironic and at once prophetic that man, long regarded as a rather poor object for genetic exploration, should become, in at least one respect, the exemplary organism.

The final stage in our understanding of the hemoglobinopathies still remains unentered for we do not yet understand, for example, the manner in which the simple substitution of one amino acid for another results in a red cell that sickles. Moreover we do not yet know the means by which the amount of hemoglobin, normal and abnormal, is regulated.

* Reprinted by author's and publisher's permission from Nature. 1957. **180**: 326-328.

I reported recently[1] that the globins of normal and sickle cell anaemia human haemoglobins differed only in a small portion of their polypeptide chains. I have now found that out of nearly 300 amino-acids in the two proteins, only one is different; one of the glutamic acid residues of normal haemoglobin is replaced by a valine residue in sickle cell anaemia haemoglobin. The latter is an abnormal protein which is inherited in a strictly Mendelian manner; it is now possible to show, for the first time, the effect of a single gene mutation as a change in one amino-acid of the haemoglobin polypeptide chain for the manufacture of which that gene is responsible.

In previous experiments,[1] tryptic digests of the two proteins had been prepared; the resulting mixtures of small peptides were separated on a sheet of paper, using electrophoresis in one direction and partition chromatography in the other. These paper chromatograms derived from the two proteins, which I had called 'finger-prints,' showed all peptides to have identical electrophoretic and chromatographic properties, except for one spot, peptide No. 4. This occupied different positions in the 'finger-prints' of normal (Hb *A*) and sickle cell anaemia (Hb *S*) haemoglobins, indicating that the difference between the two proteins was located there. I have now determined the chemical constitution of these No. 4 peptides derived from both haemoglobin *A* and *S*.

The haemoglobin *A* No. 4 peptide was prepared by elution from the neutral fraction of many 'finger-prints,' followed by cooled paper electrophoresis in pyridine/acetic acid/water (pH 3.6)[2] on Whatman No. 3 *MM* paper at 30 V./cm. for 75 min. The peptide was obtained as a well-separated band and eluted. The haemoglobin *S* No. 4 peptide could be produced in a fairly pure state by eluting the slowest positively charged band from an extended one-dimensional paper electrophoresis of the peptide mixture in the pH 6.4 buffer.[1] In both cases qualitative amino-acid analysis by paper chromatography showed the presence of histidine, valine, leucine, threonine, proline, glutamic acid and lysine. There was more glutamic acid in the haemoglobin *A* peptide, but more valine in the haemoglobin *S* peptide. In view of the known specificity of trypsin,[3] it was to be expected that these peptides, obtained by tryptic hydrolysis, had lysine at the C-terminal end. This agreed with all the results from the partial acid hydrolysis studies, as reported below.

Partial hydrolysis in 12 *N* hydrochloric acid at 37° C. for two or three days, followed by 'finger-printing,'[1] gave the peptides indicated in Fig. 1, and also free amino-acids, which are omitted from the figure. The N-terminal amino-acids of most of these peptides were determined by the fluoro-2,

[1] V. M. Ingram. 1956. Nature. **178:** 792.

[2] H. Michl. 1951. Monatsh. Chem. **82:** 489.

[3] F. Sanger and H. Tuppy. 1951. Biochem. J. **49:** 463, 481. F. Sanger and E. O. P. Thompson. 1953. Biochem. J. **53:** 353, 356.

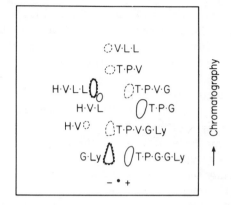

Fig. 1. Acid degradation and structure of the No. 4 peptides from haemoglobins *A* and *S*. Haemoglobin *A* (full lines): His⁺— Val—Leu—Leu—Thr—Pro—*Glu*—Lys. Haemoglobin *S* (broken lines): His⁺—Val—Leu—Leu—Thr—Pro—*Val*—Glu—Lys⁺.

4-dinitrobenzene method.[4] Together with the amino-acid compositions, these fragments indicated the sequences of the No. 4 peptides of haemoglobins *A* and *S* shown in Fig. 1. The only ambiguity was the amino-acid following threonine. Here the relevant products from the hydrochloric acid splitting—threonyl-prolyl-glutamyl-glutamyl-lysine and threonyl-prolyl-valyl-glutamyl-lysine—were subjected, on paper strips, to a stepwise Edman degradation for two cycles.[4,5] The results indicated the sequence threonyl-prolyl- in both cases. The charge distribution of the two No. 4 peptides shown in Fig. 1 was deduced from the electrophoretic behaviour of the two peptides, especially in relation to the behaviour of the smaller split peptides. The only difference found between the two No. 4 peptides is that the first glutamic acid residue of the haemoglobin *A* peptide is replaced by valine in the haemoglobin *S* peptide.

It is known from X-ray crystallographic[6] and from chemical[7] studies that the human haemoglobin molecule of molecular weight 66,700 is composed of two identical half-molecules, each approximately 33,000. It is believed that this substitution, which occurs in each of the two identical half-molecules, constitutes the only chemical difference between normal and sickle cell anaemia haemoglobins. Certainly the haem groups of the two proteins are the same.[8] The fact that in each half-molecule a glutamic acid is replaced by

[4] H. Fraenkel-Conrat, J. I. Harris and A. L. Levy. 1955. Methods of biochemical analysis. 2: 359.

[5] P. Edman. 1950. Acta Chem. Scand. 4: 277, 283.

[6] M. F. Perutz, A. M. Liquori and F. Eirich. 1951. Nature. 167: 929.

[7] W. A. Schroeder, H. S. Rhinesmith and L. Pauling.

[8] E. Havinga and H. A. Itano. 1953. Proc. U. S. Nat. Acad. Sci. 39: 65.

the neutral amino-acid valine agrees with previous findings that the whole haemoglobin S molecule has two to three carboxyl groups fewer than the normal protein.[9,10] All the other peptides of the tryptic digest occupy identical, and characteristic, positions in the two 'finger-prints.' Qualitative amino-acid analyses of these peptides have now been carried out, but have failed to reveal any differences between them. It would seem probable, therefore, that they have identical structures, leaving the two No. 4 peptides as the only ones that differ.

About 30 per cent of the haemoglobin molecule is not susceptible to attack by trypsin and does not appear on the 'finger-print.' To eliminate the possibility that an additional difference resides in these large haemoglobin A and S fragments, they were digested with chymotrypsin, which attacks them readily. Again two peptide mixtures were obtained, which were examined both by 'finger-printing' and by careful paper chromatography of the neutral peptides. No differences between them could be detected.

We owe to Pauling and his collaborators[9] the realization that sickle cell anaemia is an example of an inherited 'molecular disease' and that it is due to an alteration in the structure of a large protein molecule, an alteration leading to a protein which is by all criteria still a haemoglobin. It is now clear that, per half-molecule of haemoglobin, this change consists in a replacement of only one of nearly 300 amino-acids, namely, glutamic acid, by another, valine—a very small change indeed.

Differences between closely related proteins, involving only a very small number of amino-acids, are known; the clearest examples are the differences between horse, whale, sheep, pig and cattle insulins, which show changes in only one sequence of three amino-acids.[11] However, since these are interspecies differences, the genetic mechanism underlying them is by no means clear and cytoplasmic inheritance has not yet been ruled out. The abnormal human haemoglobins, on the other hand, are a group of very closely related proteins within the same species. It is certain that the inheritance of these proteins is Mendelian in character and occurs through the chromosomal genes. Neel[12] has shown that a single mutational step of such a gene, the one responsible for making haemoglobin, produces the new abnormal sickle cell anaemia haemoglobin. Previous investigations on the normal and the sickle cell anaemia protein could not decide whether the difference between them is due to a difference in folding of identical polypeptide chains or to a difference in the amino-acid sequences of the two chains. While there may also be changes in folding, it has now been definitely established that the amino-acid sequences of the two proteins differ, and differ at only one point.

[9] L. Pauling, H. A. Itano, S. J. Singer and I. C. Wells. 1949. Science. **110**: 543.

[10] I. H. Scheinberg, R. S. Harris and J. L. Spitzer. 1954. Proc. U. S. Nat. Acad. Sci. **40**: 777.

[11] J. I. Harris, F. Sanger and M. A. Naughton. 1956. Arch. Biochem. Biophys. **65**: 427.

[12] J. V. Neel. 1949. Science. **110**: 64.

Thus it can be seen that an alteration in a Mendelian gene causes an alteration in the amino-acid sequence of the corresponding polypeptide chain. In the case of sickle cell anaemia haemoglobin, this is the smallest alteration possible—only one amino-acid is affected—reflecting, presumably, a change in a very small portion of the haemoglobin gene. It is not known, but it may well be that this involves a replacement of no more than a single base-pair in the chain of the deoxyribonucleic acid of the gene.

It is well known that mutations lead to very small chemical differences between, for example, flower pigments.[13] It seems likely that these mutations produce first a change in a protein, in this case probably an enzyme, which in turn causes the production of a changed flower pigment. These enzymes, which have not yet been investigated for differences, stand in closer relationship to the gene than do the flower pigments themselves. The protein haemoglobin is just as close. It has therefore been called the first gene product, and is probably the first protein to be made by the gene.

The divisibility of genes in a virus was shown previously in bacteriophage by Benzer[14] and Streisinger,[15] who studied the effects of many different mutations of a gene on the behaviour of the virus. Such sub-units in genes have also been shown in *Aspergillus*[16] and *Neurospora*.[17] The results presented in this communication are certainly what one would expect on the basis of the widely accepted hypothesis of gene action; the sequence of base-pairs along the chain of nucleic acid provides the information which determines the sequence of amino-acids in the polypeptide chain for which the particular gene, or length of nucleic acid, is responsible. A substitution in the nucleic acid leads to a substitution in the polypeptide.

The abnormally low solubility of reduced haemoglobin *S*, which causes the sickling of the erythrocytes in the anaemia, is presumably a function of the charge distribution on the surface of the molecule. The replacement of two charged glutamic acid residues for two uncharged valines is presumably enough to alter this distribution towards one favouring abnormally easy crystallization.

It is hoped that similar studies of other abnormal human haemoglobins[18] will provide further insight into the effects of gene mutations.

Full details of this work will be published shortly elsewhere. I am indebted to Drs. S. Brenner and G. Seaman, Cambridge, for supplying blood from patients with homozygous sickle cell anaemia. It is a pleasure to acknowledge

[13] J. B. S. Haldane. 1954. Biochemistry of genetics. Allen and Unwin, London.

[14] S. Benzer. 1957. *In* W. D. McElroy and B. Glass (editors). The chemical basis of heredity. The Johns Hopkins University Press, Baltimore: 70.

[15] G. Streisinger and N. C. Franklin. 1956. Cold Spring Harbor Symp. Quant. Biol. **21**: 103.

[16] R. H. Pritchard. 1955. Heredity. **9**: 343.

[17] N. H. Giles, C. W. H. Partridge and N. J. Nelson. 1957. Proc. U. S. Nat. Acad: Sci. **43**: 305.

[18] H. A. Itano. 1956. Ann. Rev. Biochem. **25**: 331.

the constant interest and encouragement shown by Drs. M. F. Perutz and F. H. C. Crick. Some of the enzymatic digestion and 'finger-prints' were done by Mr. J. A. Hunt; Miss Rita Prior rendered invaluable assistance.

Allelomorphism and the Chemical Differences of the Human Haemoglobins A, S and C*

J. A. HUNT

V. M. INGRAM

Medical Research Council Unit for Research on the Molecular Structure of Biological Systems, Cavendish Laboratory, Cambridge.

In previous communications on this subject, one of us[1,2] reported that normal human haemoglobin (A) and sickle-cell haemoglobin (S) differ in only one out of nearly 300 amino-acids in the half-molecule, and that this is the only demonstrable difference in primary chemical structure. We now wish to report on a similar investigation into the structure of another abnormal human haemoglobin—that of haemoglobin C disease.

The protein was obtained from individuals known to be homozygous for the haemoglobin C gene. It was first denatured by heat and then digested with trypsin, and the resulting mixture of peptides was analysed by the two-dimensional combination of paper electrophoresis and paper chromatography called 'fingerprinting.'[1,2] The trypsin-resistant 'core' of haemoglobin C was treated with hydrochloric acid-acetone to remove the haem group. It was then made completely soluble by digestion with chymotrypsin, resulting in a second mixture of peptides. Further examination followed, both by fingerprinting and by more detailed paper chromatography and electrophoresis of groups of peptides from those parts of the fingerprints where the resolution had not been good enough.

When fingerprints of both the chymotryptic and tryptic digests were compared with those of haemoglobins A or S, all the peptides of the normal protein were found in their correct positions with the exception of one, which

* Reprinted by authors' and publisher's permission from Nature. 1958. **181**: 1062-1063.

[1] V. M. Ingram. 1956. Nature. **178**: 792.

[2] V. M. Ingram. 1957. Nature. **180**: 326.

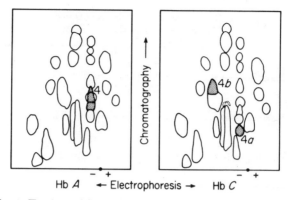

Fig. 1. Tracings of fingerprint of the trypsin digests from haemoglobin *A* and *C*.

had disappeared. Its place was taken by two peptides in new positions (Fig. 1). The missing peptide is No. 4, the same one which carries the difference between haemoglobins *A* and *S*. Therefore it is clear that the identical portion of the haemoglobin *A* molecule is involved in the change to haemoglobin *C*. Moreover this appears to be the only change, since all the other peptides in the tryptic fingerprint had amino-acid compositions indistinguishable from those of their haemoglobin *A*, or *S*, counterparts. The peptides of the 'core' still remain to be analysed.

The two new haemoglobin *C* peptides, called 4*a* and 4*b*, were isolated from tryptic digests by eluting appropriate peptide bands obtained by paper electrophoresis,[3] at *p*H 6.4 at 20 V./cm.; this was followed by a second purification using cooled paper electrophoresis at *p*H 3.6[3] and 35 V./cm. The amino-acid composition and the N-terminal amino-acid of each peptide were determined qualitatively using the methods previously described.[2] The sequence of amino-acids was found by partial acid hydrolysis and end-group analysis[4] of the products.

The amino-acid sequences of the No. 4*a* and 4*b* peptides from haemoglobin *C* are given in the last line of Table 1. Together they add up to the sequence of amino-acids found in the normal No. 4 peptide with the exception of the first glutamic acid residue, which is replaced by lysine. The splitting of the No. 4 peptide into two components during trypsin digestion is now explained, since the new lysine residue constitutes an additional trypsin-sensitive bond. On the basis of these findings we conclude that haemoglobin *C* differs from haemoglobin *A* and *S* by only a single amino-acid residue out of nearly 300 in the half-molecule. Moreover, the same glutamic acid residue of haemoglobin *A* which was changed to valine

[3] H. Michl. 1951. Monatsh. Chem. **82**: 489.

[4] H. Fraenkel-Conrat, J. I. Harris and A. L. Levy. 1955. Methods of biochemical analysis. **2**: 359.

Table 1. STRUCTURE OF THE HAEMOGLOBIN *A* AND *S* NO. 4 PEPTIDES
AND THE HAEMOGLOBIN *C* NOS. 4*a* AND 4*b* PEPTIDES

$$
\begin{array}{ll}
& \quad\quad ++ \qquad\qquad\qquad\qquad\quad - \quad - \ +- \\
\text{Haemoglobin } A \ldots & \text{His–Val–Leu–Leu–Thr–Pro–}\textit{Glu}\text{–Glu–Lys} \ldots \\
& \qquad \uparrow \qquad\qquad\qquad\qquad\qquad\qquad\qquad \uparrow \\[4pt]
& \quad\quad ++ \qquad\qquad\qquad\qquad\qquad - \quad +- \\
\text{Haemoglobin } S \ldots & \text{His—Val—Leu—Leu—Thr—Pro—}\textit{Val}\text{—Glu—Lys} \ldots \\
& \qquad \uparrow \qquad\qquad\qquad\qquad\qquad\qquad\qquad\quad \uparrow \\[4pt]
& \quad\quad ++ \qquad\qquad\qquad\quad +- \quad +- \ +- \\
\text{Haemoglobin } C \ldots & \text{His–Val–Leu–Leu–Thr–Pro–}\textit{Lys}\ \ \text{Glu–Lys} \ldots \\
& \qquad \uparrow \qquad\qquad\qquad\qquad \uparrow \qquad\quad \uparrow
\end{array}
$$

His = histidyl-, Val = valyl-, Leu = leucyl-, Thr = threonyl-, Pro = prolyl-, Glu = glutamyl-, Lys = lysine.

in haemoglobin *S* is now replaced by lysine in haemoglobin *C*. This change from an acidic to a basic amino-acid, involving the loss of two net negative charges per half-molecule, is in agreement with the observed electrophoretic behaviour of haemoglobin *C*.[5]

These results have interesting genetic implications. They are the first steps in a search for a correlation between the linear fine structure of a gene such as that determined recently by Benzer[6] and Pontecorvo,[7] and the linear structure of the polypeptide chain of the protein the synthesis of which that gene controls.

The gene mutations which cause the production of the abnormal haemoglobins *S* and *C* are inherited in a Mendelian manner through nuclear genes.[8-10] Haemoglobin *C* provides a second example, after haemoglobin *S*, of the effect exerted by a mutation of this kind on the protein which the gene produces. In both cases the effect is small, since only one out of nearly 300 amino-acids has been altered. We would assume that there have been small alterations in corresponding places on the gene. Haemoglobin *C* and *S* are most probably independent examples of the same phenomenon, since there is no reason for believing that the two mutations did not arise independently. The fact that both abnormalities occur with high frequency and alter the same amino-acid might well be an accident of natural selection and not an indication of a high mutation-rate at this one particular locus.

[5] I. H. Scheinberg, R. S. Harris and J. L. Spitzer. 1954. Proc. U. S. Nat. Acad. Sci. **40**: 777.

[6] S. Benzer. 1957. W. D. McElroy and B. Glass (editors). The chemical basis of heredity. The Johns Hopkins University Press, Baltimore: 70.

[7] G. Pontecorvo. 1956. Cold Spring Harbor Symp. Quant. Biol. **21**: 171.

[8] J. V. Neel. 1956. Ann. Human Genet. **21**: 1.

[9] W. W. Zuelzer, J. V. Neel and A. R. Robinson. 1956. Progress in hematology. Grune and Stratton, New York: 1.

[10] H. A. Itano. 1956. Ann. Rev. Biochem. **25**: 331.

Our results also shed light on the position of these two mutations on the haemoglobin gene or genes. Genetic evidence [9-11] shows that the haemoglobin S and C mutations are allelic or occur at linked sites; but the statistical evidence is not sufficiently strong to distinguish between these two possibilities. If we assume a direct relationship between the internal (linear) structure of the gene, and the linear arrangement of the amino-acid residues in the haemoglobin molecule, then the finding that the same amino-acid residue, glutamic acid, is altered in both mutations implies that they are indeed allelic mutations and occupy the same site on the gene. Thus if these ideas are correct the chemical investigation of proteins such as the human haemoglobins can provide a powerful, though indirect, tool to help the geneticist in mapping the positions on the gene where certain mutations occur.

In order to obtain sufficient statistical data and a sufficient number of mutants, such a programme must eventually turn to proteins from microorganisms. However, it is hoped that the abnormal human haemoglobins will provide a few more useful examples of the effects of gene mutations on protein structure.

We are very grateful to Dr. H. Lehmann, London, Dr. H. A. Itano, Bethesda, and Dr. I. H. Scheinberg, New York, for generous samples of haemoglobin C. We would also like to thank them and Drs. M. F. Perutz and F. H. C. Crick, Cambridge, and Prof. J. V. Neel, Ann Arbor, for many stimulating discussions.

One of us (J.A.H.) is grateful to the Medical Research Council for a scholarship.

A Terminal Peptide Sequence of Human Haemoglobin?*

J. A. HUNT

Medical Research Council Unit for Molecular Biology, Cavendish Laboratory, Cambridge, England.

V. M. INGRAM

Division of Biochemistry, Department of Biology, Massachusetts Institute of Technology, Cambridge, Mass.

* Reprinted by authors' and publisher's permission from Nature. 1959. **184**: 640-641.

It was reported recently[1,2,3] that the chemical difference between the normal human haemoglobin *A* and the abnormal haemoglobins *S* and *C* resides in a tryptic peptide, called peptide 4, to which the following structure was assigned: histidyl-valyl-leucyl-leucyl-threonyl-prolyl-*glutamyl*-glutamyl-lysine. In haemoglobins *S* and *C* the glutamic acid residue which is in italics is replaced by a valine and a lysine residue, respectively. Although the evidence available at the time of publication made the above structure appear likely, repeated attempts to confirm it by the Edman stepwise degradation method[4] have not agreed with this formulation. We now wish to report that the sequence of peptide 4 in the haemoglobins *A* and *C* is as indicated in Table 1, with histidine in position 2 and valine as the N-terminal

Table 1. STRUCTURE OF HAEMOGLOBIN PEPTIDES 4.

Haemoglobin *A*	Val.His.Leu.Thr.Pro.*Glu*.Glu.Lys.
Haemoglobin *S*	Val.His.Leu.Thr.Pro.*Val*.Glu.Lys.
Haemoglobin *C*	Val.His.Leu.Thr.Pro.*Lys*.Glu.Lys.

Val = valyl-, His = histidyl-, Leu = leucyl-, Thr = threonyl-, Pro = prolyl-, Glu = glutamyl-, Lys = lysine.

amino-acid. Furthermore, this peptide is likely to be N-terminal in one of the haemoglobin chains. The structure of peptide 4 from haemoglobin *S* is still under investigation, but it seems likely—especially in the light of the work of Hill and Schwartz (following communication) that its structure is as shown. It should be noted that the sequence around the amino-acid which changes and the changes themselves in these mutational alterations are not affected by the new structure.

The first suspicion arose when one of us (J.A.H.) found that application of Sjöquist's modification[4] of the Edman stepwise degradation yielded valine as the N-terminal amino-acid for peptide 4 from haemoglobin *A*[1,2] and peptide 4*b* from haemoglobin *C*.[3] Only traces of histidine could be obtained at this step. Histidine, or rather its phenylthiohydantoin, was tested for by removing *in vacuo* the acid used in the method and extracting a slightly alkaline solution with ethyl acetate. On the other hand the second step did give histidine, but in poor yield, and the third step yielded mainly leucine in reasonable yield. These amino-acids were identified by two-dimensional paper chromatography after hydrolysis of their phenylthio-hydantoins with hydriodic acid.[5] Qualitative analysis[6] of the two peptides

[1] V. M. Ingram. 1956. Nature. **178**: 792.
[2] V. M. Ingram. 1957. Nature. **180**: 326.
[3] J. A. Hunt and V. M. Ingram. 1958. Nature. **181**: 1062.
[4] J. Sjöquist. 1958. Arkiv. Kemi. **11**: 129.
[5] G. Schramm, G. Braunitzer and J. W. Schneider. 1955. **176**: 456.
[6] J. A. Hunt. (Unpublished.)

after one and two steps of the Edman degradation showed that valine was much reduced after one step and that after two steps both valine and histidine were absent from the residue. It appears that the peptide 4 begins with the sequence valyl-histidyl-leucyl-. However, repeated attempts to obtain dinitrophenyl-valine after reaction with fluoro-2:4-dinitrobenzene[7] were unsuccessful. Quantitative amino-acid analyses[6] after paper chromatography indicated that there is only a single leucine residue in the peptides 4.

At this point a Spinco automatic amino-acid analyser, modelled on Moore and Stein's equipment,[8] became available. Analysis of haemoglobin A peptide 4 showed at once and unequivocally that only one instead of two leucines is present together with the other amino-acids in their expected quantities.

Haemoglobin A peptide 4 was submitted (V.M.I.) once again to one step of the Sjöquist degradation,[4] but both the N-terminal amino-acid derivative and the remaining peptide were analysed quantitatively,[9] the latter on the automatic amino-acid analyser. The results were clear. After cyclization of the phenylthiocarbamyl peptide under Sjöquist's conditions, an extract of the diluted acid solution showed the spectrum typical of a phenylthiohydantoin.[4] After removal of the acid, the slightly alkaline solution did not yield any more phenylthiohydantoin, as would have been expected had histidine been present as the N-terminal amino-acid. After hydrolysis with hydriodic acid the acid extract showed that valine was practically the only amino-acid present. The rest of the peptide was hydrolysed and analysed quantitatively. All the amino-acids were present, except for the valine which was reduced to 10 per cent of its usual value. Clearly the peptide had N-terminal valine. Histidine was still present although reduced slightly in amount. The recovery of lysine was only about 50 per cent, due perhaps to incomplete hydrolysis of its ε-phenylthio-carbamyl-derivative. On the basis of these results we feel that the structures shown in Table 1 are now correct. Hill and Schwartz (following communication) have independently arrived at the same structure for haemoglobin A peptide 4 in connection with their work on haemoglobin G.

These results are interesting, because Rhinesmith, Schroeder and Martin[10] found that the β-chain of haemoglobin, which is known[11] to contain peptide 4, begins with the sequence valyl-histidyl-leucyl- followed by a bond which is relatively easily cleaved by mild acid hydrolysis. Such a bond is the -leucyl-threonyl- sequence shown in Table 1. It seems likely, therefore,

[7] H. Fraenkel-Conrat, J. I. Harris and A. L. Levy. 1955. Methods of biochemical analysis. **2**: 359.

[8] D. H. Spackman, S. Moore and W. H. Stein. 1958. Anal. Chem. **30**: 1185.

[9] C. W. H. Hirs, S. Moore and W. H. Stein. Methuen, 1958. Neuberge (editor). Symp. Protein Structure: 211.

[10] H. S. Rhinesmith, W. A. Schroeder and N. Martin. 1958. J. Am. Chem. Soc. **80**: 3368.

[11] V. M. Ingram. 1959. Nature. **183**: 1795.

that peptide 4 stands at the N-terminus of the β-chain of haemoglobin and that the glutamic acid residue which changes in haemoglobins *S* and *C* is in position number six along this chain. If this is true, then in some manner as yet not understood these alterations at the N-terminus of the β-chain appear to exert a profound effect on the physical behaviour of the whole molecule as shown for example by the drastically low solubility[12] of reduced haemoglobin *S*.

It is still not clear why the dinitrophenyl method does not yield dinitrophenyl-valine from these peptides, yet destroys histidine. Rhinesmith, Schroeder and Pauling[13] also noted this strange behaviour which in part led to the original formula for peptide 4. Furthermore, our experience reinforces that of other workers on the importance of reliable quantitative amino-acid analyses[9] on these peptides and their fragments. It seems that estimation by inspection of chromatograms cannot always decide reliably between the presence of one or two equivalents of a particular amino-acid.

We wish to acknowledge the courtesy of Drs. Hill and Schwartz in allowing us to see their manuscript prior to publication.

One of us (J.A.H.) is grateful to the Medical Research Council for a scholarship. This work was supported in part by a grant from the Medical Foundation, Inc., Boston.

[12] M. F. Perutz and J. M. Mitchison. 1950. Nature. **166**: 677.

[13] H. S. Rhinesmith, W. A. Schroeder and L. Pauling. 1957. J. Am. Chem. Soc. **79**: 4682.

Protection Afforded by Sickle-Cell Trait Against Subtertian Malarial Infection*

A. C. ALLISON

From the Clinical Pathology Laboratory, the Radcliffe Infirmary, Oxford

The concept of natural selection is inextricably bound up in the development of genetics. Mutation, unknown to Darwin, provides the raw stuff upon which natural selection can operate. Selection provides one of the ways by which genes can "spread" in a population. The means by which selection operates include all environmental factors by which a particular individual is favored over another. The key to understanding selection is the word "environment." Allison provides evidence, since substantiated, of the advantage which accrues to the individual with sickle cell trait in a malarial environment. Such an observation is of compelling importance to medicine since it describes one of the ways in which genes and their products influence resistance to disease.

The aetiology of sickle-cell anaemia presents an outstanding problem common to both genetics and medicine. It is now universally accepted that the sickle-cell anomaly is caused by a single mutant gene which is responsible for the production of a type of haemoglobin differing in several important respects from normal adult haemoglobin (Pauling *et al.*, 1949; Perutz and Mitchison, 1950). Carriers of the sickle-cell trait who are heterozygous for the sickle-cell gene have a mixture of this relatively insoluble haemoglobin and normal haemoglobin; hence their erythrocytes do not sickle *in vivo*, whereas some at least of the homozygotes, who have a much greater proportion of sickle-cell haemoglobin, have sickle cells in the circulating blood, with inevitable haemolysis and a severe, often fatal, haemolytic anaemia. There is also a much smaller group of sickle-cell anaemia patients who are heterozygous for the sickle-cell gene as well as for some other hereditary abnormality of haemoglobin synthesis (Neel, 1952).

* Reprinted by author's and publisher's permission from Brit. Med. J. 1954. 1: 290–294.

It is thus possible to approach the problem from the clinical or the genetical side. From the clinical point of view it is important to distinguish between carriers of the sickle-cell trait who show no other haematological abnormalities and patients with sickle-cell anaemia, who have a haemolytic disease which can reasonably be attributed to sickling of the erythrocytes. From the genetical point of view the main distinction is to be drawn between those who are homozygous and those who are heterozygous for the sickle-cell gene. In the great majority of instances two classifications coincide—that is, most individuals with the sickle-cell trait are heterozygous and most cases of sickle-cell anaemia, in Africa at least, are homozygous for the sickle-cell gene.

The sickle-cell trait is remarkably common in some parts of the world. Among many African Negro tribes 20% or more of the total population have the trait, and frequencies of 40% have been found in several African tribes (Lehmann and Raper, 1949; Allison, 1954). In parts of Greece frequencies of 17% have been described (Choremis *et al.*, 1953), and as many as 30% of the population in Indian aboriginal groups are affected (Lehmann and Cutbush, 1952).

Wherever the sickle-cell trait is known to occur sickle-cell anaemia will also be found. For a time it was thought by some workers that sickle-cell anaemia was rare among African Negroes, but so many cases have been described during the past few years that this view is no longer tenable (Lambotte-Legrand and Lambotte-Legrand, 1951; Foy *et al.*, 1951; Edington, 1953; Vandepitte and Louis, 1953).

The main problem can be stated briefly: how can the sickle-cell gene be maintained at such a high frequency among so many peoples in spite of the constant elimination of these genes through deaths from the anaemia? Since most sickle-cell anaemia subjects are homozygotes, the failure of each one to reproduce usually means the loss of two sickle-cell genes in every generation. It can be estimated that for the lost genes to be replaced by recurrent mutation so as to leave a balanced state, assuming that the sickle-cell trait—that is, the heterozygous condition—is neutral from the point of view of natural selection, it would be necessary to have a mutation rate of the order of 10^{-1}. This is about 3,000 times greater than naturally occurring mutation rates calculated for man and, with rare exceptions, in many other animals—3.2×10^{-5} in the case of haemophilia (Haldane, 1947). A mutation rate of this order of magnitude can reasonably be excluded as an explanation of the remarkably high frequencies of the sickle-cell trait observed in Africa and elsewhere.

POSSIBILITY OF SELECTIVE ADVANTAGE

Of the other explanations which can be advanced to meet the situation, one has received little attention: the possibility that individuals with the sickle-cell trait might under certain conditions have a selective advantage over those without the trait. It was stated for many years that the sickle-cell trait was in itself a cause of morbidity, but this belief seems to have been based upon unsatisfactory criteria for distinguishing the trait from sickle-cell anaemia. The current view is that the sickle-cell trait is devoid of selective value. Henderson and Thornell (1946) found that in American Negro air cadets who had passed a searching physical examination the incidence of the sickle-cell trait was the same as in the general Negro population of the United States. Lehmann and Milne (1949) were unable to discover any correlation between haemoglobin levels and the presence or absence of the sickle-cell trait in Uganda Africans. And Humphreys (1952) could find no evidence that the sickle-cell trait was responsible for any morbidity in Nigerian soldiers.

However, during the course of field work undertaken in Africa in 1949 I was led to question the view that the sickle-cell trait is neutral from the point of view of natural selection and to reconsider the possibility that it is associated with a selective advantage. I noted then that the incidence of the sickle-cell trait was higher in regions where malaria was prevalent than elsewhere. The figures presented by Lehmann and Raper (1949) for the frequency of the sickle-cell trait in different parts of Uganda lent some support to this view, as did the published reports from elsewhere. Thus the trait is fairly common in parts of Italy and Greece, but rare in other European countries; in Greece the trait attains its highest frequencies in areas which are conspicuously malarious (Choremis et al., 1951).

RELATION BETWEEN MALARIA AND SICKLE-CELL TRAIT

Other reports appeared suggesting more directly that there might be a relationship between malaria and the sickle-cell trait. Beet (1946) had observed that in a group of 102 sicklers from the Balovale district of Northern Rhodesia only 10 (9.8%) had blood slides showing malaria parasites, whereas in a comparable group of 491 non-sicklers 75 (15.3%) had malaria parasites. The difference in incidence of malaria in the two groups is statistically highly significant ($x^2 = 19.349$ for 1 d.f.);[1] hence Beet's figures imply strongly that malaria is less frequent among individuals with the sickle-cell trait than among those without the trait. The difference in malarial susceptibility between sicklers and others seemed to be most pronounced at the time of the year when malaria transmission was lowest.

Later in the Fort Jameson district of Northern Rhodesia, Beet (1947) found that the same difference was present, although it was much less pronounced. Of 1,019 non-sicklers, 312 (30.6%) had blood slides with malaria parasites, whereas of 149 sicklers 42 (28.2%) showed malaria

[1] These and other statistics in this paper are my own, using available figures.

parasites. This difference is not statistically significant. However, among the sicklers from Fort Jameson enlarged spleens were less common than among non-sicklers. In a series of 569 individuals there were 87 with the sickle-cell trait; 24 (27.9%) of these had palpable spleens, as compared with 188 (39.0%) with splenomegaly out of 482 non-sicklers. This difference is again statistically significant ($x^2 = 4.11$ for 1 d.f.). Beet concluded that Africans with the sickle-cell trait were probably liable to recurrent attacks of thrombosis, with resultant shrinkage of the spleen.

Brain (1952a), also working in Rhodesia, confirmed Beet's observation that the spleen is palpable in a much lower proportion of sicklers than of non-sicklers; he went on to suggest that the finding might be explained by diminished susceptibility to malaria on the part of the sicklers. Moreover, Brain (1952b) compared the proportion of hospitalized cases in groups of African mine-workers with and without the sickle-cell trait. He found that the sicklers actually spent less time in hospital, on an average, than did the control group of non-sicklers. The incidence of malaria and pyrexias of unknown origin was much lower in the group with sickle cells.

It became imperative, then, to ascertain by more direct methods of investigation whether sickle cells can afford some degree of protection against malarial infection, thereby conferring a selective advantage on possessors of the sickle-cell trait in regions where malaria is hyperendemic. An opportunity to do this came during the course of a visit to East Africa in 1953.

INCIDENCE OF MALARIAL PARASITAEMIA IN AFRICAN CHILDREN WITH AND WITHOUT THE SICKLE-CELL TRAIT

The observations of Beet and of Brain on differences in parasite rates and spleen rates are open to criticism because the populations were heterogeneous and were drawn from relatively wide areas. It was decided, therefore, to carry out similar tests on a relatively small circumscribed community, where all those under observation belong to a single tribe. Children were chosen rather than adults as subjects for the observations so as to minimize the effect of acquired immunity to malaria. The recorded incidence of parasitaemia in a group of 290 Ganda children, aged 5 months to 5 years, from the area surrounding Kampala (excluding the non-malarious township) is presented in Table I. The presence of sickling was demonstrated by

Table I.

	With parasitaemia	Without parasitaemia	Total
Sicklers......	12 (27.9%)	31 (72.1%)	43
Non-sicklers...	113 (45.7%)	134 (53.3%)	247

chemical reduction of blood with isotonic sodium metabisulphite (Daland and Castle, 1948). Fresh reducing solutions were made up daily.

It is apparent that the incidence of parasitaemia is lower in the sickle-cell group than in the group without sickle cells. The difference is statistically significant ($x^2 = 5.1$ for 1 d.f.). In order to test as many families as possible only one child was taken from each family. There is no reason to suppose that these groups are not comparable, apart from the presence or absence of the sickle-cell trait.

The parasite density in the two groups also differed: of 12 sicklers with malaria, 8 (66.7%) had only slight parasitaemia (group 1 on an arbitrary rating), while 4 (33.3%) had a moderate parasitaemia (group 2). Of the 113 non-sicklers with malaria, 34% had slight parasitaemia (group 1), the parasite density in the remainder being moderate or severe (group 2 or 3).

It may be noted, incidentally, that of the four cases in the sickle-cell group with moderate parasitaemia three had *P. malariae*, even though this species is much less common than *P. falciparum* around Kampala. It seems possible from these and other observations that the protection afforded by the sickle-cell trait is more effective against *P. falciparum* than against other species of plasmodia, but much further work is necessary to decide the point.

These results suggest that African children with the sickle-cell trait have malaria less frequently or for shorter periods, and perhaps also less severely, than children without the trait. Further evidence regarding the protective action of the sickle-cell trait could be obtained only by direct observation on the course of artificially induced malarial infection in volunteers.

PROGRESS OF MALARIAL INFECTION IN ADULT AFRICANS WITH AND WITHOUT THE SICKLE-CELL TRAIT

Fifteen Luo with the trait and 15 Luo without the trait were accepted for this investigation. All the volunteers were adult males who had been away from a malarious environment for at least 18 months. The two groups were of a similar age and appeared to be strictly comparable apart from the presence or absence of the sickle-cell trait. Two strains of *P. falciparum* were used—one originally isolated in Malaya and one from near Mombasa, Kenya; in Table II these are marked with the subscripts 1 and 2 respectively. The infection was introduced by subinoculation with 15 ml. of blood containing a large number of trophozoites (B in the table) or by biting with heavily infected *Anopheles gambiae* (M in the table). At least 3 out of the 10 mosquitoes applied had bitten each individual, and the presence of sporozoites was confirmed by dissection of the mosquitoes.

The cases were followed for 40 days. Parasite counts for each case were made by comparison with the number of leucocytes in 200 oil-immersion fields of thick films, the absolute leucocyte counts being checked at intervals.

Table II.

No.	Mode of infection and strain	8	10	12	14	16	18	20	22	24	26	28	30	32	34	36	38	40
									Day after infection									
								Luo with no sickle-cells										
1	$M_2\,B_1$	0.03	—	0.07	2.5	5.0	2.5	5.0	1.2	0.4	0.02	0.01	—	—	0.1	0.01	0.01	ST
2	$M_2\,B_1$	—	—	—	—	—	—	—	0.03	0.13	0.41	5.0	2.5	1.25	1.67	0.03	—	ST
3	$M_2\,B_1$	—	—	—	—	0.02	0.02	0.5	0.1	0.02	0.20	1.0	1.0	0.83	0.25	0.2	5.0	2.0 S
4	$M_2\,B_1$	—	5.0	10.0	10.0	1.0	1.0	1.67	0.83	0.12	0.2	1.0	1.2	1.0	0.25	0.17	—	ST
5	$M_2\,B_2$	0.02	—	—	—	0.05	0.1	0.01	0.25	0.05	0.07	0.25	—	—	0.03	—	—	ST
6	B_1	—	—	—	—	15.0	50.0	ST	—	—	—	—	—	—	—	—	—	—
7	B_2	—	—	—	—	1.67	0.33	—	ST	—	—	—	—	—	—	—	—	—
8	B_2	—	—	—	—	5.0	—	—	—	ST	—	—	—	—	—	—	—	—
9	B_1	—	—	0.13	5.0	—	—	0.1	0.5	—	—	1.0	0.1	2.5	10.0	5.0	0.5	ST
10	B_2	—	0.05	—	—	—	—	0.05	0.05	2.5	—	0.67	—	0.1	0.05	5.0	5.0	ST
11	B_2	—	—	0.3	0.3	—	—	0.2	ST	—	—	—	—	—	—	—	—	—
12	B_2	—	—	0.3	—	0.3	0.1	0.3	ST	—	—	—	—	—	—	—	—	—
13	B_2	—	—	—	—	—	—	—	—	—	—	—	—	—	—	—	ST	—
14	B_2	2.0	1.7	2.0	60.0	5.0	0.6	ST	—	—	—	—	—	—	—	—	—	—
15	B_2	0.05	0.3	—	0.4	0.1	0.3	ST	—	—	—	—	—	—	—	—	—	—
								Luo with sickle-cell trait										
1	$M_1\,B_2$	—	—	—	—	—	—	—	—	—	—	—	—	—	—	—	—	ST
2	$M_1\,B_2$	—	—	—	—	—	—	—	—	—	—	—	—	—	—	—	—	ST
3	$M_1\,B_1$	—	—	—	—	—	—	—	—	—	—	—	—	—	—	—	—	ST
4	$M_1\,B_1$	—	—	—	—	—	—	—	—	—	—	—	—	—	—	—	—	ST
5	$M_1\,B_1$	—	—	—	—	—	—	—	—	—	—	—	—	—	—	—	—	ST
6	$M_1\,B_1$	—	—	—	—	—	—	—	—	—	—	—	—	—	—	—	—	ST
7	$M_1\,B_1$	—	—	—	—	—	—	—	—	—	—	—	—	—	—	5.0	0.5	ST
8	$M_1\,B_1$	0.7	—	—	—	—	—	—	—	—	—	—	—	—	—	—	—	ST
9	$M_1\,B_1$	—	—	—	—	—	—	—	—	—	—	—	—	—	0.03	—	—	ST
10	$M_1\,B_1$	—	—	—	—	—	—	—	—	—	—	0.03	0.1	0.03	—	—	—	ST
11	$B_2\,M_2$	—	—	—	—	—	—	—	—	—	—	—	—	—	—	—	—	ST
12	$B_2\,M_2$	—	—	—	—	—	—	—	—	—	—	—	—	—	—	—	—	ST
13	$B_2\,M_2$	—	—	—	—	—	—	—	—	—	—	—	—	—	—	—	—	ST
14	$B_2\,M_2$	—	—	—	—	—	—	—	—	—	—	—	—	—	—	—	—	ST
15	$B_2\,M_2$	—	—	—	—	—	—	—	—	—	—	—	—	—	—	—	—	ST

Figures represent parasite counts in hundreds per mm.^{3} of blood.
ST = Stopped by chemotherapy.

The abbreviated results of these counts are shown in Table II. In the few cases in which parasitaemia was pronounced and the symptoms were relatively severe the progress of the disease was arrested. At the end of the period of observation in every case a prolonged course of antimalarial chemotherapy was given.

DISCUSSION

It is apparent that the infection has become established in 14 cases without the sickle-cell trait. The parasitaemia is relatively light, however, when compared with that observed in non-immune populations—for example, the Africans described by Thomas *et al.* (1953). This is to be expected: the Luo come from a part of the country where malaria is hyperendemic, and they have acquired a considerable immunity to malarial infection in childhood. This factor makes the interpretation of the observations rather more difficult; however, it could not be avoided, since all the East African tribes who have high sickling rates come from malarious areas, and the acquired immunity should operate with equal force in the groups with and without sickle-cells. The acquired immunity was actually an advantage, since the symptoms were mild and the chances of complication very slight.

In the group with sickle cells, on the other hand, the malaria parasites have obviously had great difficulty in establishing themselves, in spite of repeated artificial infection. Only two of the cases show parasites, and the parasite counts in these cases are comparatively low. The striking difference in the progress of malarial infection in the two groups is taken as evidence that the abnormal erythrocytes in individuals with the sickle-cell trait are less easily parasitized than are normal erythrocytes.

It can therefore be concluded that individuals with the sickle-cell trait will, in all probability suffer from malaria less often and less severely than those without the trait. Hence in areas where malaria is hyperendemic children having the trait will tend to survive, while some children without the trait are eliminated before they acquire a solid immunity to malarial infection. The protection against malaria might also increase the fertility of possessors of the trait. The proportion of individuals with sickle cells in any population, then, will be the result of a balance between two factors; the severity of malaria, which will tend to increase the frequency of the gene, and the rate of elimination of the sickle-cell genes in individuals dying of sickle-cell anaemia. Or, genetically speaking, this is a balanced polymorphism where the heterozygote has an advantage over either homozygote.

The incidence of the trait in East Africa has recently been investigated in detail (Allison, 1954), and found to vary in accordance with the above hypothesis. High frequencies are observed among the tribes living in regions where malaria is hyperendemic (for example, around Lake Victoria and in the Eastern Coastal Belt), whereas low frequencies occur consistently in the malaria-free or epidemic zones (for example, the Kigezi district of Uganda; the Kenya Highlands; and the Kilimanjaro, Mount Meru, and Usumbara regions of Tanganyika). This difference is often independent of ethnic and linguistic grouping: thus, the incidence of the sickle-cell trait among Bantu-speaking tribes ranges from 0 (among the Kamba, Chagga, etc.) to 40% (among the Amba, Simbiti, etc.). The world distribution of the sickle-cell trait is also in accordance with the view presented here that malarial endemicity is a very important factor in determining the frequency of the sickle-cell trait. The genetical and anthropological implications of this view are evident.

The fact that sickle cells should be less easily parasitized by plasmodia than are normal erythrocytes is presumably attributable to their haemoglobin component, although there may be other differences, not yet observed, between the two cell-types. Sickle-cell haemoglobin is unlike normal adult haemoglobin in important physico-chemical properties, notably in the relative insolubility of the sickle-cell haemoglobin when reduced (Perutz and Mitchison, 1950). The malaria parasite is able to metabolize haemoglobin very completely in the intact red cell, the haematin pigment remaining as a by-product of haemoglobin breakdown (Fairley and Bromfield, 1934; Moulder and Evans, 1946). That plasmodia are greatly affected by relatively small differences in their environment is suggested by their remarkable species specificity. Thus the difficulty of establishing an infection in monkeys with human malaria parasites, and vice versa, is generally recognized.

How far species differences in the haemoglobins themselves, known from immunological and other studies, are responsible for the species specificity of plasmodia it is impossible to say. However, the physico-chemical differences between human adult haemoglobin and monkey haemoglobin appear to be less pronounced than the differences between either type and sickle-cell haemoglobin. It is clear that the natural resistance to malaria among individuals with the sickle-cell trait is relative, not absolute. This is perhaps attributable to differences in the expressivity of the sickle-cell gene, which may be responsible for the production of from nearly 50% to only a very small amount of sickle-cell haemoglobin (Wells and Itano, 1951; Singer and Fisher, 1953). Moreover, the sickle-cell haemoglobin may not be evenly distributed in the cell population: most observers recognize that there are cases in which only some of the red cells are sickled even after prolonged reduction. However, even a relative resistance to malaria may be enough to help those with the sickle-cell trait through the dangerous years of early childhood, during which an active immunity to the disease is developed.

The above observations focus attention upon the importance of haemoglobin to plasmodia in the erythrocytic phase. Hence, it is worth considering

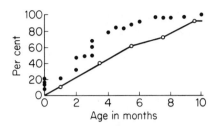

The apparent relationship between the appearance of adult-type haemoglobin (dots) and malarial infection (circles) in the newborn. Each dot represents a test on a single individual, using an alkali denaturation technique (Allison, unpublished observations); the circles represent the percentage of Luo children showing malaria parasites (Garnham, 1949).

whether erythrocytes containing other specialized or abnormal types of haemoglobin might be resistant to malaria also. Thus, human foetal haemoglobin differs from human adult haemoglobin in many properties. Red cells containing foetal haemoglobin continue to circulate in the newborn for the first three months of life, after which they are quite rapidly replaced by cells containing normal adult haemoglobin. It has long been known that the newborn has a considerable degree of resistance to malarial infection: Garnham (1949), for instance, found that in the Kavirondo district of Kenya at the end of the second month of life only 10% of babies were infected; after this age the percentage affected rises rapidly, until by the ninth month practically all children have the disease. The correspondence between the appearance of cells containing normal adult-type haemoglobin and malarial susceptibility is illustrated in the Chart. The correspondence may of course be fortuitous, but it is striking enough to merit further investigation, even though other factors, such as a milk diet deficient in p-aminobenzoic acid (Maegraith et al., 1952; Hawking, 1953) and immunity acquired from the mother (Hackett, 1941) may play a part in the natural resistance of the newborn to malaria.

Finally, it is possible that the explanation offered above for the maintenance of the sickle-cell trait may also apply to thalassaemia. The problems presented by the two diseases are very similar; many homozygotes, and possibly some heterozygotes, are known to die of thalassaemia, and yet the condition remains remarkably common in Italy and Greece, where as many as 10% of the individuals in certain areas are affected (Bianco et al., 1952). Greek and Italian authors have commented that cases of thalassaemia usually come from districts severely afflicted with malaria (Choremis et al., 1951). Perhaps those who are heterozygous for the thalassaemia gene suffer less from malaria than their compatriots: the fertility of the heterozygotes appears to be greater (Bianco et al., 1952). Selective advantage of the heterozygote with the sickle-cell gene, and possibly the heterozygote with the thalassaemia gene also, would explain why such high gene frequencies can be attained in the case of these conditions while other genetically transmitted abnormalities of the blood cells remain uncommon, not very much above the estimated mutation rate—for example, hereditary spherocytosis (Race, 1942).

SUMMARY

A study has been made of the relationship between the sickle-cell trait and subtertian malarial infection. It has been found that in indigenous East Africans the sickle-cell trait affords a considerable degree of protection against subtertian malaria. The incidence of parasitaemia in 43 Ganda children with the sickle-cell trait was significantly lower than in a comparable group of 247 children without the trait. An infection with *P. falciparum* was established in 14 out of 15 Africans without the sickle-cell trait, whereas in a comparable group of 15 Africans with the trait only 2 developed parasites.

It is concluded that the abnormal erythrocytes of individuals with the sickle-cell trait are less easily parasitized by *P. falciparum* than are normal erythrocytes. Hence those who are heterozygous for the sickle-cell gene will have a selective advantage in regions where malaria is hyperendemic. This fact may explain why the sickle-cell gene remains common in these areas in spite of the elimination of genes in patients dying of sickle-cell anaemia. The implications of these observations in other branches of haematology are discussed.

This investigation was made possible by a grant received from the Colonial Office at the recommendation of the Colonial Medical Research Committee. Acknowledgment is made to the Directors of Medical Services, Kenya and Uganda, to Dr. E. J. Foley, Nairobi, to the staff of the Mulago Hospital, Kampala, and to the volunteers for their kind cooperation. To Dr. G. I. Robertson, Nairobi, a special debt of gratitude is due for constant help and advice. Drs. A. E. Mourant, R. G. Macfarlane, and A. H. T. Robb-Smith read the manuscript and made valuable comments and suggestions.

REFERENCES

(1) A. C. Allison. July 1954. Transactions of the Royal Society of Tropical Medical Hygiene. **48**: 312-318.

(2) E. A. Beet. 1946. E. Afr. Med. J. **23**: 75.

(3) E. A. Beet. 1947. E. Afr. Med. J. **24**: 212.

(4) I. Bianco, G. Montalenti, E. Silvestroni and M. Siniscalco. 1952. Ann. Eugen., Lond. **16**: 299.

(5) P. Brain. 1952a. Brit. Med. J. **2**: 880.

(6) P. Brain. 1952b. E. Afr. Med. J. **26**: 925.

(7) C. Choremis, N. Zervos, V. Constantinides and Leda Zannos. 1951. Lancet. **1**: 1147.

(8) C. Choremis, Elizabeth W. Ikin, H. Lehmann, A. E. Mourant and Leda Zannos. 1953. Lancet. **2**: 909.

(9) G. A. Daland and W. B. Castle. 1948. J. Lab. Clin. Med. **33**: 1082.

(10) G. M. Edington. 1953. Brit. Med. J. **2**: 957.

(11) Sir N. H. Fairley and R. J. Bromfield. 1934. Trans. Roy. Soc. Trop. Med. Hyg. **28**: 141.

(12) H. Foy, A. Kondi and W. Brass. 1951. E. Afr. Med. J. **28**: 1.

(13) P. C. C. Garnham. 1949. Ann. Trop. Med. Parasit. **43**: 47.

(14) L. W. Hackett. 1941. Publ. Amer. Ass. Advanc. Sci. **15**: 148.

(15) J. B. S. Haldane. 1947. Ann. Eugen., Lond. **13**: 262.

(16) F. Hawking. 1953. Brit. Med. J. **1**: 1201.

(17) A. B. Henderson and H. E. Thornell. 1946. J. Lab. Clin. Med. **31**: 769.

(18) J. Humphreys. 1952. J. Trop. Med. Hyg. **55**: 166.

(19) J. Lambotte-Legrand and C. Lambotte-Legrand. 1951. Institut Royal Colonial Belge. Sect. d. Sci. Nat. et Med. Memoires. **XIX**(7): 98.

(20) H. Lehmann and Marie Cutbush. 1952. Brit. Med. J. **1**: 404.

(21) H. Lehmann and A. H. Milne. 1949. E. Afr. Med. J. **26**: 247.

(22) H. Lehmann and A. B. Raper. 1949. Nature, Lond. **164**: 494.

(23) B. G. Maegraith, T. Deegan and E. S. Jones. 1952. Brit. Med. J. **2**: 1382.

(24) J. W. Moulder and E. A. Evans. 1946. J. Biol. Chem. **164**: 145.

(25) J. V. Neel. 1950. Cold Springs Harbor Symp. Quant. Biol. **15**: 141.

(26) J. V. Neel. 1952. Blood. **7**: 467.

(27) L. Pauling, H. A. Itano, S. J. Singer and I. C. Wells. 1949. Science. **110**: 543.

(28) M. F. Perutz and J. M. Mitchison. 1950. Nature, Lond. **166**: 677.

(29) R. R. Race. 1942. Ann. Eugen., Lond. **11**: 365.

(30) K. Singer and B. Fisher. 1953. Blood. **8**: 270.

(31) A. T. G. Thomas, G. I. Robertson and D. G. Davey. Trans. Roy. Soc. Trop. Med. Hyg. **47**: 388.

(32) J. M. Vandepitte and L. A. Louis. 1953. Lancet. **2**: 806.

(33) I. C. Wells and H. A. Itano. 1951. J. Biol. Chem. **188**: 65.

Gene Evolution and the Haemoglobins*

VERNON M. INGRAM
Division of Biochemistry, Department of Biology, Massachusetts Institute of Technology,
Cambridge, Mass.

*Until very recently the methods for studying evolution have been limited
in great part to the fossil record. Such limitation is vanishing because
of detailed analyses of gene products which are now practicable. The
view of evolution taken in this paper by Ingram provides further strength
to the argument that man can be an admirable organism for the understanding of other living things. In this view of evolution an alliance
between the processes of gene duplication and mutation provides flexi-
bility and potentially permits adaptation for a future world while
retaining adaptation in the present one.*

The four types of polypeptide chain which go to make up the molecules of
the three normal human haemoglobins are believed to be controlled by
four independent genes.[1] The following article is an attempt to discuss the
chemical and genetic relationship between these chains from an evolutionary
point of view; to a lesser extent, because much less is known, the haemoglobins of other vertebrates will also be mentioned. It should be emphasized
that the main purpose of this discussion, and of the evolutionary scheme
to be proposed, is to provide a basis for the discussion of the evolution of
genes in general and haemoglobin genes in particular. Questions are raised
which will, in part, be answered soon by the chemical work on vertebrate
haemoglobins which is now proceeding in various laboratories (see, for
example, ref. 2).

The study of the chemistry of the human haemoglobins has already

---

* Reprinted by author's and publisher's permission from Nature. 1961. **189:** 704-708.
[1] V. M. Ingram. 1959. In, Genetics. Macy Found. Symp. **141:** 147; 1961 Haemoglobin
and its abnormalities. C. C. Thomas.

provided evidence of the kind of phenotypic effects to be expected from gene mutations as, for example, in the known single amino-acid substitutions in the peptide chains of abnormal haemoglobins.[1] It is on such changes in protein structure that the forces of natural selection are assumed to act. From the evolutionary and the practical point of view it is convenient to study a commonly occurring protein, such as haemoglobin, which is found in all vertebrates. Haemoglobin is not only accessible for chemical study but is also sure to have played an important part in vertebrate evolution, because of its vital physiological function as the carrier of oxygen.

Most of the discussion which follows will centre around the chemical findings in the human haemoglobins, since they are by far the best studied of vertebrate haemoglobins. However, the basic similarities in chemical structure between man's haemoglobins and those of other mammals and lower vertebrates are very striking.[2] All known vertebrate haemoglobins— except those of the lamprey and the hagfish—are built on the same molecular pattern: they consist of four polypeptide chains of roughly 17,000 molecular weight, with one haem group each. The haemoglobin of the lamprey is peculiar in consisting of a single polypeptide chain of molecular weight 17,000. The hagfish haemoglobin appears to be similar, or possibly a dimer of 34,000 molecular weight.[3]

The peptide chains in the other vertebrates are of two different types; for example, human adult haemoglobin consists of two so-called α-chains and two β-chains. There is usually interaction between the four haem groups in their reaction with molecular oxygen; in other words, a plot of the degree of oxygenation of the haemoglobin molecules against the partial pressure of oxygen is sigmoid in shape.[4] This fact enhances enormously the physiological efficiency of the haemoglobin molecule as our oxygen carrier,[5] since it favours complete saturation with oxygen in the lungs and complete discharge in the tissues. This great similarity which characterizes most vertebrate haemoglobins suggests that we are studying that aspect of the evolution of a particular protein molecule which is concerned with detailed development of an already well-defined molecule. It is true that the haemoglobin quadruples its size during this evolution (if we include the lamprey haemoglobin), but the change is due to the aggregation of four fairly similar protein sub-units (peptide chains), rather than to an actual lengthening of a molecule. In the evolutionary scheme to be discussed it is suggested that the increase in complexity, and in diversity, of the haemoglobins is an illustration of a more general process of gene evolution which results in an increase of the number of genes.

[2] E. Zuckerkandl, R. T. Jones and L. Pauling. 1960. Proc. U. S. Nat. Acad. Sci. **46**: 1349.

[3] W. B. Gratzer and A. C. Allison. 1960. Biol. Rev. **35**: 459.

[4] J. T. Edsall. 1958. In, Hemoglobin. National Research Council, Washington.

[5] A. Riggs. 1959. Nature. **183**: 1037.

HUMAN HAEMOGLOBINS

The following striking situation is found in the human haemoglobins:

(1) The three normal human haemoglobins all possess a common half-molecule which may be written $-\alpha_2^A$. This formulation indicates that this half-molecule unit is composed of two normal α-peptide chains as first described for normal adult haemoglobin A. However, the other half of each of the three haemoglobins consists of different types of peptide chain, β, γ or δ, one type for each haemoglobin. All four chains are of roughly equal size with a chain molecular weight of about 17,000. These three haemoglobins may be formulated as follows:

Adult	= haemoglobin A	$= a_2^A \beta_2^A$
Foetal	= haemoglobin F	$= a_2^A \gamma_2^F$
Kunkel's minor component[6]	= haemoglobin A_2	$= a_2^A \delta_2^{A2}$

This list may have to be extended as the study of other minor haemoglobins continues.[7]

I postulate[1] that four genes are involved in the manufacture of these peptide chains, so that the *genotype* of a normal individual may be written as:

$$\alpha^A/\alpha^A,\ \beta^A/\beta^A,\ \gamma^F/\gamma^F,\ \delta^A{}_2/\delta^A{}_2$$

In this view the products of the α-genes are common to all the human haemoglobins.

(2) In total amino-acid composition[8] the four types of chains compare as follows:

α^A and β^A — differ in perhaps 21 out of nearly 140 amino-acids
γ^F and β^A — differ in perhaps 23 out of nearly 140 amino-acids
$\delta^A{}_2$ and β^A — differ in less than 10 amino-acids.

In addition, γ^F is the only one of these chains to contain the amino-acid *iso*leucine—four residues per chain.

(3) The α^A-chain begins with the amino-acid sequence[7] Val-Leu- . . . ; the β^A-chain and the $\delta^A{}_2$-chain begin with Val-His-Leu . . . . The γ^F-chain begins with the sequence Gly-His-Phe-, which although different from the β-chain shows a clear affinity in the type of amino-acid with the beginning of the β^A-chain. In both cases, the first amino-acid is neutral and aliphatic, the second is the basic amino-acid histidine, and the third has a non-polar side-chain.

The peptide chain beginning with the Val-Leu-sequence (α-chain) has a counterpart[3] not only in all known mammalian haemoglobins but also in

[6] H. G. Kunkel and G. Wallenius. 1955. Science. **122**: 288.

[7] W. A. Schroeder. 1959. Prog. Chem. Org. Nat. Prod. **17**: 322.

[8] W. H. Stein, H. G. Kunkel, R. D. Cole, D. H. Spackman and S. Moore. 1957. Biochim. Biophys. Acta. **24**: 640; R. J. Hill and L. C. Craig. 1959. J. Amer. Chem. Soc. **81**: 2272.

the haemoglobins of all the lower vertebrates so far examined, except for the haemoglobin of the lamprey. This is not to say that the Val-Leu-chains of other animals resemble the human chain precisely, but rather that there might be a strong 'family resemblance.' It is of interest to attempt to explain the repeated occurrence and strange similarity of the Val-Leu- (the α) chain in the vertebrates.

The following postulates are used in developing a scheme for the evolution of the haemoglobin genes.

POSTULATE 1.

Mutations of a gene result in either single or multiple amino-acid substitutions in the peptide chain which that gene controls, or inversions of part of the amino-acid sequence, or a combination of these possibilities. The new haemoglobin peptide chains produced by such mutations are then either favoured or discarded in the course of natural selection.

POSTULATE 2.

At several points in the course of evolution a gene for a particular haemoglobin peptide chain has undergone *duplication*, followed by, or simultaneous with, translocation. The two initially equivalent genes have then evolved independently, governed by the selective pressure of their environment on their protein products. Such mechanisms have been previously postulated; for example, ref. 9. The role of gene duplication[9,10] in evolution has been discussed by Stephens.[11] His conclusion was that the case for duplication as an important factor in evolution was so far neither proved nor disproved.

It is of course equally possible to postulate the occurrence of chromosome duplication, with subsequent independent evolution of the initially identical chromosomes. Such a scheme would fit into the proposed hypothesis equally well.

It seems likely that α-, β- and γ-genes are located on different chromosomes, since they segregate independently, whereas β- and δ-genes appear to be linked.[12]

POSTULATE 3.

Once the α-chain, or rather the α_2-dimer, is required to fit precisely with at least two other dimers—β_2 and γ_2—the α-chain is no longer as free to be varied by mutation. It has become 'conservative' and its rate of evolution will be less than that of the other chains, as is perhaps seen in the persistence of the Val-Leu- beginning of the α-chain of the vertebrates.

[9] E. B. Lewis. 1951. Cold Spring Harbor Symp. Quant. Biol. **16:** 159.

[10] C. B. Bridges. 1936. Science. **83:** 210.

[11] S. G. Stephens. 1951. Adv. Genetics. **4:** 247.

[12] R. Ceppellini. 1959. Ciba Foundation Symposium, Biochemistry in Human Genetics. London, W. and A. Churchill, Ltd.

In addition, one can postulate that mutations of the α-gene produce mutant α-chains which are more severely selected against in the later stages of evolution than are mutants of other chains. This is likely to be so, because in the later stages of evolution the α-chains participate in the formation of foetal haemoglobin, a vulnerable point in the life-cycle of the animal. It is a fact that mutants of the human α-chain never reach a high frequency of distribution, in contrast to some β-chain mutants, although we know of as many different kinds of α-chain mutants as of β-chain mutants.

SCHEME FOR THE EVOLUTION OF THE HAEMOGLOBIN GENES

We might suppose that originally the haemoglobin molecule was rather like the present-day myoglobin molecule, that is, that it had a single peptide chain with a single haem group, and that therefore it could now show haem-haem interaction. The size of this molecule might vary, but eventually it might be stabilized at a value of around 17,000 molecular weight.

At this stage of evolution, presumably earlier than the teleost fishes, the haem protein inside the muscle cells is assumed to be the same as that in the circulation. The muscle haem protein became myoglobin in the course of evolution; it retained a molecular weight of 17,000 and a complexity of only one haem group and one peptide chain per molecule. It was, of course, still subject to mutational changes, as can be seen from the fact that its present-day amino-acid composition and sequence in a given animal often differs considerably from that of any of the analogous haemoglobin chains.[13] For example, human myoglobin contains *iso*leucine, but no cysteine, whereas the reverse is true of human adult haemoglobin.

On the other hand, one can foresee limits to the kind of mutations which would be tolerated. The X-ray studies of Kendrew[14] and of Perutz[15] show that the three-dimensional arrangement of chains in myoglobin and the haemoglobin sub-units (also of 17,000 molecular weight) are remarkably similar, though not identical. This statement applies also to the two kinds of sub-units found in haemoglobin itself. Presumably, mutational alterations in the course of evolution which would drastically affect the three-dimensional structure were not tolerated. Such considerations imply that the configuration of the peptide chains in myoglobin and haemoglobin became stabilized early in evolutionary history, at least in its most important features.

During the evolution of the primitive haemoglobin chain—provisionally

[13] A. Rossi-Fanelli, D. Cavallini and C. de Marco. 1955. Biochim. Biophys. Acta. **17**: 377.

[14] J. C. Kendrew, R. E. Dickerson, B. E. Strandberg, R. G. Hart, D. R. Davies, D. C. Phillips and V. C. Shore. 1960. Nature. **185**: 422.

[15] M. F. Perutz, M. G. Rossman, A. F. Cullis, H. Muirhead, G. Will and A. C. T. North. 1960. Nature. **185**: 416.

called the 'α'-chain—there occurred a gene duplication followed or accompanied by translocation. From now on the two duplicate 'α'-chain genes could evolve independently—one to become the modern myoglobin gene, the other to become the α-chain gene of present-day haemoglobin. Eventually, according to the scheme, the α-chain gene would evolve in such a way that its product, the α-chain, had the property of dimerization in solution to form α_2 molecules. Such a property would be favoured strongly, if it entailed, in addition, the possibility of haem-haem interaction between the two haem groups of the new dimer molecule and therefore the possibility of more efficient oxygenation and deoxygenation. Once produced, such a mutation is unlikely to be lost in the further evolution of haemoglobin.

At this stage, the sequence of the 'α'-chains is still variable within the dictates of structural requirements, since there is nothing yet to put additional restrictions on it.

We might next postulate that the genes of the α_2-chains duplicated again. After this gene duplication two types of dimer—α_2 and γ_2—would evolve side by side. Sooner or later, these chains would have evolved sufficiently to be able to form tetramers with even greater selective advantage because of the increased haem-haem interaction likely to be found in such tetramers. The characteristics of the genes responsible for the ability of the chains to form tetramers would certainly be fixed. This stage of haemoglobin evolution seems to have been reached already in some teleost fishes, because they already possess a four-chain haemoglobin.[3]

The third gene duplication and translocation is pictured as occurring with the γ-chain gene, giving rise to a new γ-gene destined to evolve into the β-chain gene. At this gene duplication the property of forming tetramers is already firmly established. The new gene can develop along its own line to provide a haemoglobin tetramer—$\alpha_2\beta_2$—particularly adapted for the adult body. On the other hand, the old γ-chain continues to develop and to provide half the molecule of the foetal haemoglobin ($\alpha_2\gamma_2$). It is the γ-chain gene, rather than the α-chain gene, which is said to duplicate here, because the γ-chain dimers, γ_2, have already the necessary complementariness for forming tetramers with α_2. This complementariness will be automatically a property of the product of the new gene. In addition, we shall see later that β- and γ-chains are more closely related to one another than either is to the α-chain. Therefore we might consider them to have diverged at a later stage.

At this point of evolution, three independent genes—α, β, γ—are assumed to be present, each one capable of forming chains which dimerize and which aggregate to the tetramers $\alpha_2\beta_2$ or $\alpha_2\gamma_2$. Haem-haem interaction is strongly present in the tetramers. Such a situation has an important effect on the further evolution of the α-chain. This chain, or rather its dimer α_2, is required to fit with two different partners, β_2 and γ_2. As a result, less variation is allowed to the α-chain; it has become 'conservative.' Perhaps such conservation is in part responsible for the apparently universal presence of α-chains beginning with Val-Leu- in the haemoglobins of the higher vertebrates. There is an alternative explanation for the apparently greater stability of the α-genes; this gene controls also the foetal haemoglobin and therefore may not undergo extensive mutational alterations, since the foetus is a much more delicate organism. The very fact that any alteration in the α-chain gene, and therefore in the α-chain, seems to affect all types of haemoglobin may be sufficient to explain the apparent 'conservatism.'

On the other hand, there is no *a priori* reason why different parts of a molecule as complex as a protein should develop at the same rate. The difference in apparent stability between the α-chain and the others could be no more than what would be expected as normal variation. It will be interesting to see just how similar the Val-Leu- chains of different vertebrates are.

At the fourth and last gene duplication in the scheme we suppose that it is the β-gene which becomes duplicate, leading to the δ-chain genes controlling the δ-chains of haemoglobin A_2. The origin of this δ-chain is placed near the end of the evolutionary scheme, because of its great chemical similarity to the β-chain.[16] Furthermore, the presence of a haemoglobin A_2-like component seems to be confined to the higher primates.[17] In this view, haemoglobin A_2 is a new haemoglobin rather than an archaic one, as has often been supposed. It has been reported to have a higher affinity for oxygen[18] and perhaps it is a more efficient haemoglobin, destined to replace eventually $\alpha_2\beta_2$ (ref. 19). Its proportion is certainly doubled in some thalassaemias,[17] perhaps as a compensating mechanism. There is genetic evidence that the genes for δ- and for β-chains are linked,[12] indicating perhaps that the process of translocation of the new δ-gene has not yet occurred.

Where does the lamprey fit into this scheme? One form, *Petromyzon planeri*, has two foetal and two (different) adult haemoglobins.[20] The molecular weight of the adult mixture is given as 17,000 (ref. 3). Perhaps these lamprey haemoglobins are the result of an independent evolution scheme similar to the one discussed in the present article, but which has never included the mutations which led to the formation of dimers and tetramers. We might regard the lampreys as having branched off before or just after the first gene duplication in the scheme of Fig. 1. Unfortunately, nothing seems to be known about the presence or absence of a separate myoglobin in the lampreys.

[16] V. M. Ingram and A. O. W. Stretton. 1961. Nature. **190:** 1079.

[17] H. G. Kunkel, R. Ceppellini, U. Muller-Eberhard and J. Wolf. 1957. J. Clin. Invest. **36:** 1615.

[18] C. A. Meyering, A. L. M. Israels, T. Sebens and T. H. J. Huisman. 1960. Clin. Chim. Acta. **5:** 208.

[19] A. O. W. Stretton. 1960. Ph.D. Thesis. Cambridge.

[20] N. Adinolfi, G. Chieffi and M. Siniscalco. 1959. Nature. **184:** 1325.

Table 1. COMPARISON OF THE N-TERMINAL SEQUENCES OF THE α- AND β-PEPTIDE
CHAINS OF HUMAN HAEMOGLOBIN A[21]

α-chain	Val-Leu-Ser-Pro-Ala-Asp-Lys-Thr-Asp-Val-Lys-Ala-Ala-Try-Gly-Lys-Val-
	1 2 3 4 5 6 7 8 9 10 11 12 13 14 15 16 17
	Gly-Ala-His-Ala-Gly-Glu-Tyr-Gly-(Ala,Glu)-Ala-
	18 19 20 21 22 23 24 25 (26 27 28
	Leu-Glu-Arg-Met-Phe-Leu-Ser-Phe-Thr-Pro-Thr-Lys-
	29 30 31 32 33 34 35 36 37 38 39 40
β-chain	Val-His-Leu-Thr-Pro-Glu-Glu-Lys-Ser-Ala-Val-Thr-Ala-Leu-Try-Gly-Lys-
	1 2 3 4 5 6 7 8 9 10 11 12 13 14 15 16 17
	Val-Asp-Val-Asp-Glu-Val-Gly-Gly-Glu-Ala-Leu-Gly-Arg-Leu-
	18 19 20 21 22 23 24 25 26 27 28 29 30 31

DISCUSSION

The proposed scheme expresses a desire to explain the striking chemical similarity between α, β, γ and δ human haemoglobin chains in terms of their evolution from a common precursor.

Braunitzer *et al.*[21] have published some preliminary findings of the amino-acid sequences in the first 30-40 positions of the human α- and β-chains (Table 1). Between the two sequences there is a strong 'family resemblance' of the degree expected for the two gene products which have evolved independently, but from a common ancestor. Also Gratzer and Allison[3] have very recently discussed the possibility that the haemoglobin chains might have evolved from a common ancestor.

It has been suggested to me that the four genes controlling the four chains might have evolved from four unrelated genes which originally

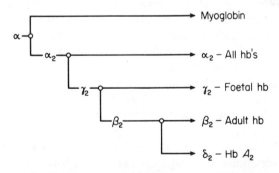

Fig. 1. Evolution of the haemoglobin chains. The α-chain is the ancestral peptide chain. —◯— indicates a point of gene duplication followed by translocation of the new gene.

[21] G. Braunitzer, B. Liebold, R. Muller and V. Rudloff. 1960. Z. Physiol. Chem. **320**: 170.

controlled the synthesis of quite unrelated proteins; thus there would have been no increase in the total number of genes. By a process of parallel evolution—successive and independent mutations—each of these four genes eventually changed so that it made one of the haemoglobin peptide chains. The last stages of evolution, when pairs of genes were involved in producing parts of a complex molecule, must then be called on to produce similarity in chemical structure and in configuration. It is easy to conceive of a selective mechanism which would favour changes in various members of a molecular aggregate, so that the members might fit together better. However, it is hard to think of such a mechanism also selecting for chemical and structural similarity of the monomers. In addition, the ability to dimerize would have to arise *de novo* four times, an unlikely situation.

Although we cannot at the moment completely reject the idea of parallel evolution of the four genes from unrelated genes, it is not a very palatable one. The similarity between the human α-, β-, γ- and δ-chains is so great: the C-terminus of the chains ends with the sequence -tyrosyl-histidine or -tyrosyl-arginine;[16,22] their common ability to incorporate an active haem group; their similar folding and chain length;[14,15] absence of *iso*leucine in α, β and δ;[8,16] and so forth. Altogether, an evolution from a common ancestor is more attractive.

CHEMICAL EVOLUTIONARY RELATIONSHIP BETWEEN THE CHAINS

How many mutational steps occurred between the original 'α'-gene and the present-day human α-gene? Or between the original 'α'-gene and the human β-gene? It is more meaningful, perhaps, to ask how many mutational events might separate the present-day human α- and β-genes. Out of 140 amino-acids, we know from the composition that approximately 20 are different. This gives a minimum of 20 mutations of the kind effecting single amino-acid substitutions.

It is believed that the evolution of the vertebrates began some 5×10^8 years ago. Let us assume a mean generation life of 5 years among the vertebrates, which implies some 10^8 generations for the evolution of vertebrate haemoglobins. A generally acceptable rate[23] per generation is 10^{-5}-10^{-6}, which leads to a figure of 100-1,000 mutations in the evolutionary history of a vertebrate haemoglobin. This figure, which is itself a minimum one, is very considerably higher than the (minimum) number of mutations which appear to distinguish α-chains from β-chains and α-chains from γ-chains.

The only conclusion which can be drawn from such a calculation is that a more than sufficient number of mutational events have passed in the

[22] G. Guidotti. 1960. Biochim. Biophys. Acta. **42**: 177.
[23] J. B. S. Haldane. 1954. Biochemistry of genetics. Allen and Unwin, London: 15.

history of the vertebrates to account for present-day differences between the various parts of the haemoglobin molecule in the human species.

COMPARISON OF THE FINGERPRINTS OF THE
HUMAN α-, β-, γ- AND δ-CHAINS

Rather than deduce the chemical relationship between the chains from their amino-acid composition, it is better to compare their 'fingerprints.'[25] The two-dimensional maps, or fingerprints, of the tryptic peptides derived from each of these four peptide chains give at least a crude idea of the similarity and dissimilarity in their amino-acid sequences and hence of the closeness of the chemical relationship between them.

HUMAN α-CHAINS AND β- OR γ-CHAINS

With the exception of peptide number 21 (ref. 24), all the peptides (some 14 for each chain) occupy different positions on the fingerprints[25] of α-chains compared with β- or γ-chains, or they can be distinguished by such methods as extended paper ionophoresis. They are therefore different in their amino-acid sequences. Peptide 22 is free lysine. It does not follow that the differing peptides of the α- and of the β- or γ-chains are totally altered. They could contain short amino-acid sequences in common.[21] In any event, the indications are that the amino-acid differences between the α- and the β- or γ-chains are distributed throughout their length.

The general comment might be made that there is a familial likeness between the distribution of peptides on the fingerprints of α-, β- and γ-chains. Surely this will reflect a structural relationship (Table 1). We would suppose that portions of their amino-acid sequences are common to all three, as is the tertiary structure of the two types of chain of horse haemoglobin, which correspond to the human α- and β-chains.

HUMAN β-CHAINS AND γ-CHAINS

Apart from peptides number 21 (a pentapeptide) and 22 (free lysine), the following peptides[25] occupy very similar positions[25] and would be closely related, if not identical: peptides 12, 14, 15β, 19, 20β, 26. The number is an impressive proportion of the whole chain. If it is correct that these peptides are indeed identical in the β- and γ-chains, it would mean that perhaps 9 peptides out of some 14 are shared by the chains. Some of these peptides are quite long. Their position along the chains is not known, except that peptide 26 is the third one from the N-terminus.[21] These conclusions underline the

[24] V. M. Ingram. 1958. Biochim. Biophys. Acta. **28**: 539.

[25] J. A. Hunt. 1959. Nature. **183**: 1373; 1959. Ph.D. Thesis. Cambridge; J. A. Hunt and H. Lehmann. 1959. Nature. **184**: 872.

chemical similarity between β- and γ-chains, which can also be deduced from their amino-acid compositions.

HUMAN β-CHAINS AND δ-CHAINS

The recent work of Stretton[16] has shown that the β-chains and the δ-chains are very closely similar in their fingerprints. In fact, out of a total of some 14 tryptic peptides, only 4 peptides are different; they are numbers 5, 12, 25 and 26. The similarity between other pairs of peptides from the β- and δ-chains has been ascertained much more carefully by amino-acid analysis than has so far been done with the γ-chains. Moreover, the differences between peptides 12, 25 and 26 from β- and from δ-chains have been shown to involve only 4 single amino-acid differences, for example, serine-threonine (in two places), threonine-asparagine, glutamic acid-alanine. These four single amino-acid differences, together with an unconfirmed fifth one, are so far the only ones definitely known between this pair of chains, each of which is some 140 residues long—a very close chemical similarity indeed.

Apart from the tryptic peptides of the α-, β-, γ- and δ-chains, there is in each case the trypsin resistant 'core' to be considered which amounts to rather more than a quarter of the chain. Here the differences between the chains are far from clear and cannot yet be usefully discussed, except to say that the 'cores' all appear to be similar.

Fingerprints of haemoglobins from other mammals (ref. 2, and Muller, C. J., unpublished) are recognizable as 'haemoglobin.' It will be interesting to compare the degree of similarity between the mammalian haemoglobins on one hand with, say, chicken or teleost haemoglobin.

Recently, Zuckerkandl[2] has shown that fingerprints of haemoglobin from the gorilla and chimpanzee are indistinguishable from those of human haemoglobin. A greater number of differing peptide spots are observed in the less closely related orangutan and rhesus monkey. These extraordinarily interesting findings give added proof of the validity of using a chemical study of vertebrate haemoglobins to discover evolutionary relationships.

CONCLUSION

It appears that a sufficient number of generations has passed since the beginning of vertebrate evolution to allow for the known or suspected number of mutations which separate the α-, β- and γ-chains of human haemoglobin.

The similarity in the fingerprints between β- and γ-chains of human haemoglobin supports the suggestion that these chains diverged from one another at a later stage in evolution than either from the α-chain gene.

The close similarity between β- and δ-chains gives weight to the idea that the δ-chains of haemoglobin A_2 are a recent evolutionary development from the β-chains.

The suggestion is made that a single primitive myoglobin-like haem protein is the evolutionary forerunner of all four types of peptide chain in the present-day human haemoglobins, and of the corresponding peptide chains in other vertebrate haemoglobins. Such a scheme involves an increase in the number of haemoglobin genes from one to five by repeated gene duplication and translocations; the scheme may thus illustrate a general phenomenon in gene evolution.

I acknowledge the many stimulating discussions with Drs. C. Levinth, S. F. Luria, C. Baglioni, A. O. W. Stretton, J. V. Neel and P. S. Gerald. I am also grateful to Drs. W. B. Gratzer and A. C. Allison for allowing me to read their review paper[3] before publication.

Two books have been particularly stimulating: J. B. S. Haldane, *The Biochemistry of Genetics*; and C. B. Anfinsen, *The Molecular Basis of Evolution*.

No serious attempt has been made to survey critically the literature on gene evolution or duplication. This is partly in order to present a clearer and more provocative hypothesis and partly because I do not feel qualified to evaluate the numerous contributions to that field. Recent experimental work on the animal haemoglobins has been admirably summarized in the Gratzer and Allison article.[3]

This work was supported by grants from the National Science Foundation and the National Institutes of Health, U. S. Public Health Service.

Note added in proof. Further work by G. Braunitzer and his colleagues (*Z. physiol. Chem.*, in the press) shows that the similarity of the α- and β-chains continues throughout these chains.

Biochemical Genetics: The Serum Proteins

Part Three—Section Three

The development of starch gel electrophoresis by Oliver Smithies has been of considerable importance to human genetics in providing detection of previously unknown inherited protein variation. An earlier review of the serum haptoglobins and transferrins, reprinted here, illustrates the accomplishments which can be realized by this method. Moreover, the technique itself has become, in the biochemical literature, one of the most commonly cited means of studying protein heterogeneity.

The second paper by Smithies and his colleagues admirably exemplifies contemporary approaches adopted in the pursuit of a gene. The result provides a variation on the theme of gene duplication (1) and its consequences to protein structure.

(1) See pages 164-175 of this collection. V. M. Ingram. Gene evolution and haemoglobins.

Biochemical Aspects of the Inherited Variations in Human Serum Haptoglobins and Transferrins*

O. SMITHIES

G. E. CONNELL

Connaught Medical Research Laboratories and Department of Biochemistry,
University of Toronto

HAPTOGLOBINS

Variations in the serum proteins of normal humans which are genetically controlled have recently been demonstrated by electrophoresis in starch gels. The haemoglobin-binding protein of serum (the haptoglobin of Polonovski and Jayle, 1939) was shown by Smithies (1955) to vary in different individuals. A simple genetical hypothesis involving two autosomal alleles (Hp^1 and Hp^2) was suggested by Smithies and Walker (1955, 1956) to account for the inheritance of the three haptoglobin types then known; and, in general, this hypothesis has been well substantiated by more extensive family studies (Galatius-Jensen, 1956, 1957, 1958a; Harris, Robson and Siniscalco, 1958a; Linnet-Jepson, Galatius-Jensen and Hauge, 1958). Individuals of one of the homozygous types (phenotype Hp 1–1, genotype Hp^1/Hp^1) have a single species of haptoglobin in their serum; homozygotes of the other type (phenotype Hp 2–2, genotype Hp^2/Hp^2) have a series of more than ten haptoglobins; heterozygotes (phenotype Hp 2–1, genotype Hp^2/Hp^1) have haptoglobins different from those of *either* of the homozygotes. The starch-gel electrophoresis pattern obtained with the heterozygous type of haptoglobin differs radically from that obtained with a mixture of the haptoglobins of the two homozygous types.

Three inherited forms of haptoglobin different from the three common types have recently been reported. One of these types [the Hp 2–1 (Mod.) of Connell and Smithies (1959a) and of Smithies and Hiller (1959)] is similar to the usual heterozygous type 2–1, in that the rate of migration in

* Reprinted by senior author's and publisher's permission from Ciba Foundation Symposium, Biochemistry of Human Genetics. 1959. London, J. and A. Churchill, Ltd.: 178-179.

the starch gels of the various haptoglobin components of the two types are equivalent. However, the faster migrating components are present in relatively greater amounts in the modified type. This type is relatively common in American Negroes [approximately 1 in 10, (Giblett, 1959a)] but is rare in whites (Smithies and Hiller, 1959). A second rare type of haptoglobin has recently been observed by Giblett (1959b) in the sera of an American Negro female (Mrs. B. Johnson) and her daughter. A complex series of haptoglobin zones, some of which do not migrate at the same rate as any of the previously described haptoglobins, are detectable in the gels with sera of the Johnson haptoglobin type. A third inherited rare type has recently been observed by Galatius-Jensen (1958b) in which haptoglobin zones are detectable equivalent in starch-gel mobility to those of *both* types 2–1 and 2–2.

The present writers have recently described (Connell and Smithies, 1959a) a simple adsorption and elution technique for isolating haptoglobins from serum in high purity and with good yields. The purified haptoglobins are indistinguishable in starch-gel electrophoretic behaviour from the haptoglobins in whole serum, and completely retain their haemoglobin-binding properties. Fig. 1 shows a comparison of purified haptoglobins of all types so far described (with the exception of the variant described by Galatius-Jensen).

The purified material has been examined (a) in order to establish that the various haptoglobin zones demonstrated in the starch gels represent "real" protein components and are not artifacts introduced by the electrophoretic system, and (b) to attempt to determine the differences in the genetical forms of haptoglobin at a molecular level.

The electrophoretic separations obtained in starch gels differ in many respects from those obtained in other electrophoretic systems (Poulik and Smithies, 1958), but these differences are now understood and artifacts do not appear to be introduced by the use of the gels. In the case of the haptoglobins the characteristic patterns are obtained in a variety of buffers, at widely different pH's, and at several ionic strengths. However, the experiments of Franglen and Gosselin (1958), in which metastable polymers of a dye were separated by starch-gel electrophoresis, make it necessary to demonstrate that the many haptoglobins observed in some sera (e.g. type 2–2) are not due to the formation of metastable polymers by this type of haptoglobin. This possibility has been excluded by preparing from the usual starch gels several of the separated haptoglobin zones and showing that their electrophoretic properties are unchanged after storage at 0° or 37°. No reversion to multiple zones occurs. Furthermore, the characteristic patterns of the three common types are obtained under conditions likely to dissociate ionic and hydrogen bonds, namely in gels made with dilute HCl (pH 1.7 and 2.1) and with 8 M urea (see below). Consequently, metastable polymers due to ionic or hydrogen bonds are unlikely to be

BORATE GEL

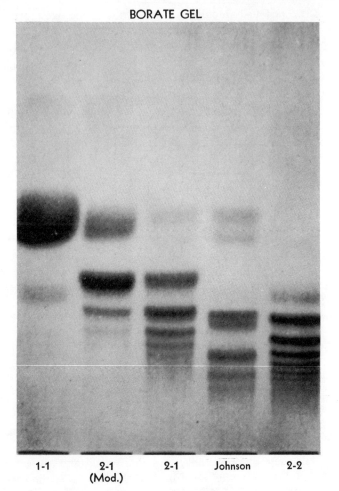

1-1   2-1   2-1   Johnson   2-2
            (Mod.)

Fig. 1. A comparison of purified haptoglobins of the types (left to right) 1–1, 2–1 (Mod.), 2–1, Johnson type, 2–2. Electrophoresis was carried out in a starch gel, pH 8.5, made with dilute borate buffer, using the procedure described by Smithies (1959). The proteins in the gel were stained with Amido-Black 10B.

involved. The presence of 0.01 M versene in the gels is also without effect on the patterns. The many haptoglobin zones observed under the usual conditions are therefore probably distinct protein components. Genetical evidence supports this conclusion. Thus, as described above, modified haptoglobin types have recently been found in which both the relative *amounts* and the relative *mobilities* of the multiple haptoglobins differ from those of the common types—a finding which strongly suggests that all the haptoglobin zones represent "real" protein components.

Studies on the physical nature of the differences in the haptoglobins, and so of the nature of gene action in the haptoglobin system, are still incomplete, but we can report several observations of our own and review some made by other workers which bear on the problem. The one- and two-dimensional starch-gel electrophoretic behaviour of haptoglobin of type 1–1 suggests that it is a single molecular species. Preliminary ultracentrifugal studies (Connell and Smithies, 1959b) on the purified protein confirm this. Bearn and Franklin (1958) reached the same conclusion from ultracentrifugal studies with purified type 1–1 haptoglobin complexed with haemoglobin C. On the other hand, the starch-gel electrophoresis results with type 2–2 haptoglobin indicate that this material contains a whole series of proteins. Two-dimensional electrophoretic experiments show that all the type 2–2 haptoglobins migrate at the same rate during filter-paper electrophoresis, although they have widely different starch-gel mobilities. This suggests that the type 2–2 haptoglobins differ from each other in molecular size (see Poulik and Smithies, 1958); the larger molecular species must also have larger net charges or the type 2–2 haptoglobins could not have identical mobilities in the filter-paper electrophoretic system. A simple hypothesis consistent with these observations is that the haptoglobins of type 2–2 include a series of polymers (n = 1, 2, 3, 4, etc.) varying in amounts inversely with the degree of polymerization. This hypothesis which could account for the relative mobilities in the gels of the components of type 2–2 haptoglobin is supported by our ultracentrifugal studies with the purified protein. During ultracentrifugal sedimentation a markedly asymmetrical boundary is formed which suggests the presence of a series of proteins of increasing molecular size in amounts which decrease in parallel with the increase in size (Fig. 2a and b). Bearn and Franklin (1958) obtained the same type of ultracentrifuge pattern with type 2–2 haptoglobin complexed with haemoglobin.

The differences in the three common haptoglobin types are unusually complex to be associated with such a simple pattern of inheritance. We observe not only a change from a single protein to a series of polymers in going from one homozygous type (1–1) to the other (2–2), but also in the heterozygotes (2–1) a pattern is obtained which is quite unlike a mixture of the two homozygous types. We have felt for some time that this complex situation might be the result of a relatively *minor* molecular difference between the haptoglobin produced under the influence of the gene Hp^2 and that produced under the influence of the gene Hp^1, such that the complex series of proteins are formed only in the presence of haptoglobins related to the gene Hp^2. A relatively small alteration in a protein, such as the introduction of a cysteine residue into the molecule, might permit the formation of a series of polymers which could not be formed by the unaltered protein. We have therefore attempted to break down the haptoglobins to simpler structures in order to detect more readily the basic similarities and differences in the various types. The results of these attempts

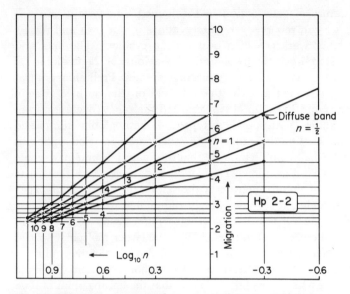

Fig. 2a. Migration versus log n (zone number) for type 2–2 hapto-globins. The distance (in arbitrary units) of migration in a starch gel of the individual protein zones of a purified preparation of type 2–2 haptoglobin (cf. Fig. 1) is plotted against the logarithm of the zone number. The zones are numbered consecutively in order of decreasing mobility and the number 1 is assigned to a different zone for each of the five curves plotted. A straight line is obtained when the number 1 is assigned to the fastest migrating heavily staining zone, and 2, 3, 4, etc. to the successive zones of decreasing mobilities. This suggests that these haptoglobins are a series of polymers ($n = 1, 2, 3, 4$, etc.). Note that the migration distance of the fastest (diffuse) haptoglobin zone corresponds to $n = \frac{1}{2}$; possibly it is a "hemimer."

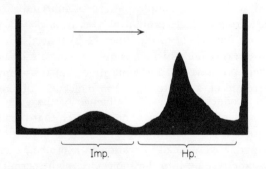

Fig. 2b. Sedimentation diagram of a 1 per cent solution in 0.1 M-NaCl of purified type 2–2 haptoglobin 80 min. after reaching 59,780 r.p.m. in a Spinco ultracentrifuge at approximately 24.5°. The boundaries corresponding to the haptoglobins and impurities are indicated.

THIOGLYCOLLATE/BORATE

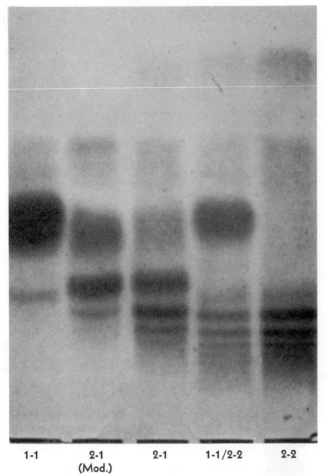

1-1	2-1 (Mod.)	2-1	1-1/2-2	2-2

Fig. 3. Starch-gel electrophoresis of haptoglobins in the presence of thioglycollate. The gel contained 0.01 M thioglycollate and dilute borate buffer. The samples are (left to right) purified haptoglobins of types 1–1, 2–1 (Mod.), 2–1, a 50/50 mixture of 1–1 and 2–2, 2–2.

are the most exciting new developments we have to report here—although they are so recent that we cannot yet draw many conclusions from them.

Since we had been considering the possibility of polymer formation through disulphide bonds, we first attempted to break down the hapto-globins by reduction with 0.01 M thioglycollate (in borate buffer at pH 8.5). We were surprised to find (Fig. 3) completely normal patterns with the purified haptoglobins under these conditions (cf. Fig. 1).

We then considered the possibility that hydrogen bonding was responsible

UREA/BORATE GEL

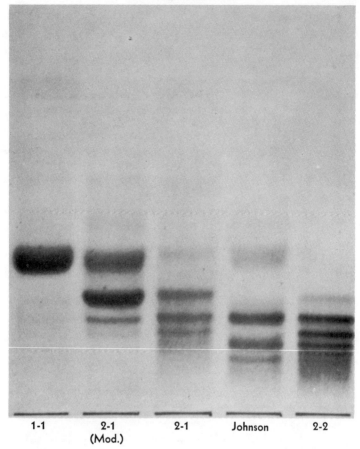

1-1   2-1   2-1   Johnson   2-2
           (Mod.)

Fig. 4. Starch-gel electrophoresis of haptoglobins in the presence of urea. The
gel contained 8 M urea and dilute borate buffer. The purified haptoglobin types
compared are (left to right) 1–1, 2–1 (Mod.), 2–1, Johnson type, 2–2.

for the stability of the postulated haptoglobin polymers and examined the
proteins in 8 M urea—a reagent known to disrupt intramolecular hydrogen
bonds. The results of an experiment with an 8 M urea/borate gel are shown
in Fig. 4. Once again the patterns are essentially indistinguishable from the
usual borate patterns. However if gels containing both thioglycollate and
8 M urea are used the haptoglobin patterns are completely changed (Fig. 5).
The haptoglobin polymers are broken down (probably as a result of the
cleavage of disulphide bonds made accessible to the thioglycollate by the
8 M urea) and the patterns become more simple. We can begin to see that

the three types differ in a somewhat less complex manner than is suggested by their usual starch-gel electrophoretic behaviour. The product of this cleavage treatment applied to type 1–1 haptoglobin migrates essentially as one component (with a greater mobility, however, than that of the untreated haptoglobin). The multiple components of the type 2–2 haptoglobin are completely broken down by the treatment with the formation of one (the major) cleavage product having the same mobility as the type 1–1 cleavage product together with at least one component of greater mobility. In con-

UREA/THIOGLY./BORATE

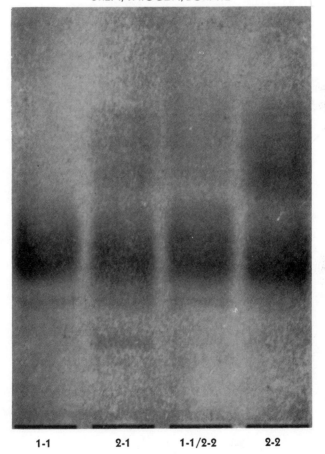

1-1   2-1   1-1/2-2   2-2

Fig. 5. The effect of thioglycollate and urea on the starch-gel electrophoretic behavior of haptoglobins. The gel contained 0.01 M thioglycollate, 8 M urea and dilute borate buffer. Samples used were (left to right) purified haptoglobins of types 1–1, 2–1, a 50/50 mixture of 1–1 and 2–2, 2–2.

trast to the results obtained with the untreated haptoglobins, the heterozygous type now appears to be intermediate between the two homozygous types, and is closely similar to a mixture of them.

We conclude from these preliminary experiments that the three common haptoglobin types (and, see below, the modified types) have in their structure disulphide bonds which are necessary for the integrity of the proteins and for polymer formation, although we cannot be certain that the monomers era actually linked together by disulphide bonds. Nevertheless, these exper-

UREA/THIOGLY./BORATE

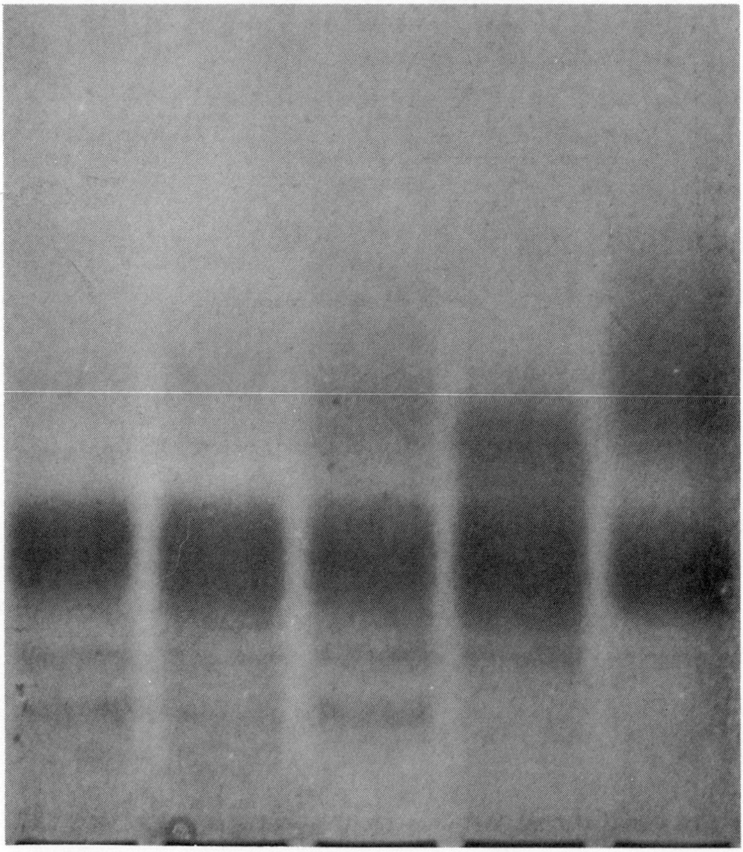

   1-1   2-1   2-1   Johnson   2-2
             (Mod.)

Fig. 6. A comparison of five purified types of haptoglobin in a thioglycollate/urea gel. Samples were of the types (left to right) 1–1, 2–1 (Mod.), 2–1, Johnson type, 2–2. The preparations used in this experiment were also used for that illustrated in Fig. 4.

iments throw considerable light on the nature of gene action in the haptoglobins. There appears to be a major part of the protein molecule common
to all the haptoglobin types. When genes other than Hp^1 are present then
additional structural elements are involved in the haptoglobin molecules.
The nature of these additional elements is as yet unknown, but they do not
appear to be the same in all the complex types. A comparison of all the
types available to us illustrates this. In Fig. 6 is shown the result of com-
paring in a urea/thioglycollate gel the same samples (5 types) as were used
for the urea experiment illustrated in Fig. 4. The faster migrating cleavage
products in the several types differ, and the differences appear to be considerably greater than could be introduced accidentally by the presence of
impurities in the preparations (see Fig. 4 for comparison of the purity of
these same preparations). The differences between the type 1–1, Johnson
type, and type 2–2 haptoglobins are particularly marked. Experiments of
this type, although at present quite crude, indicate a new approach to
solving the problem of gene action in the haptoglobins, for they will probably
enable us to separate the variable portion of the different genetical forms of
haptoglobin and hence determine the nature of the variations.

TRANSFERRINS

The presence of a β-globulin (D) not previously observed was detected
by one of us (Smithies, 1957) in the sera of 2 (out of 50) New York Negroes
and 5 (out of 23) Australian aborigines. This β-globulin was present in
approximately the same amount as, but migrated less rapidly than β-globulin
C (Poulik and Smithies, 1958) which is quantitatively the chief β-globulin
in most sera. The presence of the β-globulins C and D in the serum of an
individual was shown by Horsfall and Smithies (1958) to be under simple
genetical control by two autosomal alleles. Sera from homozygotes contain
either β-globulin C or D; sera from heterozygotes contain both β-globulins
in approximately equal amounts. A mixture of sera of the two homozygous
types is indistinguishable with respect to the β-globulins from serum taken
from a heterozygote. Smithies (1958) observed a further β-globulin variant
(B) in 4 (out of 425) Canadian whites, and suggested as a result of preliminary family studies that a third allele was possible at the β-globulin
locus. Harris, Robson and Siniscalco (1958b) observed two other variants
and quoted the pedigree of a family to illustrate the inheritance of one of
them.

The identity of the variable β-globulins was discussed by Smithies and
Hiller (1959) who concluded that they were iron-binding proteins (transferrins). Direct proof of this was obtained by Giblett, Hickman and Smithies
(1959) from experiments with radioactive iron.

At present 8 transferrins (B_0, B_1, B_2, C, D_0, D_1, D_2 and D_3) have been
recognized in man. Giblett, Hickman and Smithies (1959) note that the

transferrins (B_0, B_1 and B_2) which migrate faster than the common transferrin C are most frequently observed in whites, those (D_0, D_1, D_2 and D_3) migrating more slowly occur most often in Negroes. The limited family studies reported suggest that persons with a single transferrin are homozygotes, and those with two are heterozygotes. No individuals have been observed with more than 2 transferrins. There is no evidence as to whether or not all the inherited forms of transferrin are controlled at a single locus, since no population has been studied in which more than one transferrin variant occurs frequently.

Some evidence is available (see Smithies and Hiller, 1959) on the nature of the molecular difference between the genetical forms of transferrin. Two-dimensional starch-gel electrophoresis experiments (Fig. 7) indicate that the transferrins B_2, C and D_1 differ in their electrophoretic mobilities both in the filter-paper electrophoretic system (the horizontal direction in the figure). This suggests, but does not prove, that these transferrins, and probably the other transferrins also, differ with respect to charge rather than molecular size. If this is the case then there are at least 8 possible forms of transferrin, each carrying a different net charge. Any one amino-acid side-chain can have three charged forms: positive, zero or negative. If only one amino-acid were interchangeable in the different genetical forms of transferrin, then only three transferrins would be detectable by electrophoresis—a situation similar to that discussed by Hunt and Ingram (1959) for the haemoglobins C, S and A. So we must conclude that several amino acids are interchangeable in the transferrins if the 8 forms so far described differ only with respect to net charge.

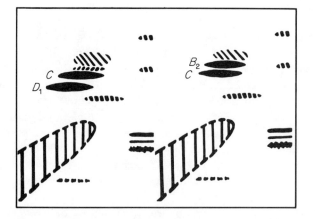

Fig. 7. A diagrammatic representation of the two-dimensional filter-paper and starch-gel electrophoretic behaviour of the transferrins B_2, C and D_1 in the sera of two heterozygous individuals. The horizontal direction in the figure corresponds to the filter-paper electrophoresis, the vertical to the starch-gel electrophoresis. The transferrins (B_2, C and D_1) are indicated in the figure.

The detection of differences in proteins by electrophoretic methods depends on either differences in charge and/or molecular dimensions in the protein molecules. The genetical forms of haptoglobin probably differ in size, and the transferrins in charge; consequently, we are able to demonstrate polymorphism in the respective proteins. Perhaps the detection of polymorphism in these systems reflects nothing unusual in the proteins concerned, but rather that they differ in a way which we can detect. Thus, although the distinguishable transferrins probably differ in charge there may well be other indistinguishable forms of transferrin which do not (e.g. no charge difference would follow the replacement of a valine residue by an isoleucine residue). Such polymorphism may be very difficult to detect if the change in biological function of the protein involved is small.

SUMMARY

The genetically controlled forms of haptoglobin (the haemoglobin-binding protein of serum) have been purified by a simple adsorption and elution technique. Electrophoretic and ultracentrifugal studies suggest that the haptoglobin of one homozygous type consists of a single molecular species. Haptoglobin of the other homozygous type probably includes a series of polymers. The heterozygous type differs from a mixture of the two homozygous types. Thioglycollate and 8 M urea alone are without effect on haptoglobins. Together these reagents cleave the haptoglobins and completely break down the polymers. Starch-gel electrophoretic studies of the products of the reductive cleavage suggest that a major part of the molecule is common to all genetical types, but that faster migrating portions of the cleaved proteins differ in the several genetical forms. The nature of gene action in the haptoglobin system may be solved by further studies of these cleavage products.

Seven serum β-globulin variants (B_0, B_1, B_2, D_0, D_1, D_2 and D_3) which are under genetical control have been described in addition to the common β-globulin C. The variable β-globulins have been identified as transferrins by their property of binding iron Fe^{59}. Family studies suggest that sera from homozygotes contain a single transferrin, and sera from heterozygotes contain two transferrins. Electrophoretic experiments indicate that the genetical forms of transferrin may differ in net charge. Several amino-acid residues must be variable in transferrin to account for the occurrence of 8 forms of transferrin if these proteins differ only with respect to net charge.

REFERENCES

(1) A. G. Bearn and E. C. Franklin. 1958. J. Exp. Med. **109**: 55.

(2) G. E. Connell and O. Smithies. 1959a. Biochem. J. **72**: 115.

(3) G. E. Connell and O. Smithies. 1959b. Unpublished observations.

(4) G. Franglen and C. Gosselin. 1958. Nature, London. **181**: 1152.

(5) F. Galatius-Jensen. 1956. Acta Med. Leg. Soc., Liège. **9**: 42.

(6) F. Galatius-Jensen. 1957. Acta Genet., Basel. **7**: 549.

(7) F. Galatius-Jensen. 1958a. Acta Genet., Basel. **8**: 232.

(8) F. Galatius-Jensen. 1958b. Acta Genet., Basel. **8**: 248.

(9) E. R. Giblett. 1959a. Nature, London. **183**: 192.

(10) E. R. Giblett. 1959b. Unpublished observations.

(11) E. R. Giblett, C. G. Hickman and O. Smithies. 1959. Nature, London. **183**: 1589.

(12) H. Harris, E. B. Robson, and M. Siniscalco. 1958a. Nature, London. **182**: 1324.

(13) H. Harris, E. B. Robson, and M. Siniscalco. 1958b. Nature, London. **182**: 452.

(14) W. R. Horsfall and O. Smithies. 1958. Science. **128**: 35.

(15) J. A. Hunt and V. M. Ingram. 1959. Biochemistry of Human Genetics. CIBA Foundation Symposium. London, J. and A. Churchill, Ltd.: 114.

(16) P. Linnet-Jepson, F. Galatius-Jensen and M. Hauge. 1958. Acta Genet., Basel. **8**: 164.

(17) M. Polonovski and M.-F. Jayle. 1939. Bull. Soc. Chim. Biol., Paris. **21**: 66.

(18) M. D. Poulik and O. Smithies. 1958. Biochem. J. **68**: 636.

(19) O. Smithies. 1955. Biochem. J. **61**: 629.

(20) O. Smithies. 1957. Nature, London. **180**: 1482.

(21) O. Smithies. 1958. Nature, London. **181**: 1203.

(22) O. Smithies. 1959. Biochem. J. **71**: 585.

(23) O. Smithies and O. Hiller. 1959. Biochem. J. **72**: 121.

(24) O. Smithies and N. F. Walker. 1955. Nature, London. **176**: 1265.

(25) O. Smithies and N. F. Walker. 1956. Nature, London. **178**: 694.

Chromosomal Rearrangements and the Evolution of Haptoglobin Genes*

O. SMITHIES

G. E. CONNELL

G. H. DIXON

Department of Medical Genetics, University of Wisconsin, and Department of
Biochemistry, University of Toronto

The three common types of haptoglobin (Hp 1–1, 2–1 and 2–2)[1-3] have
recently been divided into a total of six types (Hp 1F–1F, 1F–1S, 1S–1S,
2–1F, 2–1S and 2–2)[4] on the basis of electrophoretic differences in their
component polypeptide chains dissociated by treatment with a thiol in the
presence of urea. Family studies[5] indicate that these types are the expression
of the combinations of three alleles, Hp^{1F}, Hp^{1S} and Hp^2, each of which
gives rise to the production of a corresponding polypeptide chain (hp 1Fα,
hp 1Sα and hp 2α). All haptoglobins contain an additional polypeptide
chain, the β-chain, which appears to be unaffected by the genotype at the
Hp locus.

STRUCTURE OF HAPTOGLOBIN α-POLYPEPTIDE CHAINS

The results of our investigations[6] of the differences between the three
common haptoglobin α-polypeptide chains may be summarized in part as
follows: Amino-acid analyses of hp 1Fα and hp 1Sα suggest the replacement
of a single lysine residue in hp 1Fα by an acidic amino-acid (or its amide)

* Reprinted by senior author's and publisher's permission from Nature. 1962. **196**:
232-236.

[1] O. Smithies. 1955. Biochem. J. **61**: 629.

[2] O. Smithies and N. F. Walker. 1955. Nature. **176**: 1265.

[3] O. Smithies and N. F. Walker. 1956. Nature. **178**: 694.

[4] G. E. Connell, G. H. Dixon, and O. Smithies. 1962. Nature. **193**: 505.

[5] O. Smithies, G. E. Connell and G. H. Dixon. 1962. Amer. J. Hum. Genet. **14**: 14.

[6] O. Smithies, G. E. Connell and G. H. Dixon. Proc. Sec. Intern. Cong. Hum. Genet.
(In press.)

in hp 1Sα. In agreement with these analyses we find that the peptides obtained from hp 1Fα and hp 1Sα after chymotryptic digestion are indistinguishable by finger-printing[7] except for the replacement of one peptide (F) in hp 1Fα by another peptide (S) in hp 1Sα. The effect of pH on the mobilities of the α-chains and the native haptoglobins is also consistent with the substitution of a basic amino-acid in hp 1Fα by an amidated acidic amino-acid in hp 1Sα. On the other hand, although the amino-acid composition of hp 2α is very similar to the compositions of hp 1Fα and hp 1Sα, the peptides obtained from hp 2α differ from those obtained from hp 1Fα and hp 1Sα (Fig. 1) more extensively than can be accounted for by amino-acid substitutions. Thus, all peptides present in digests of hp 1Fα and hp 1Sα are found in digests of hp 2α together with an extra peptide (*J*); two peptides (*N* and *C*), which are common to all three α-chains, are relatively

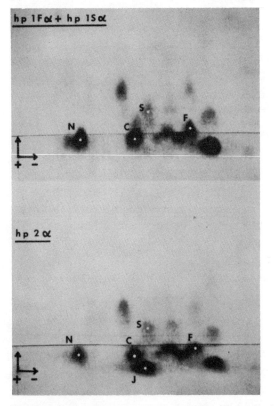

Fig. 1. Peptides from α-chymotrypsin digests of hp 1Fα + hp 1Sα, and hp 2α. The peptides labelled *F* and *S*, characteristic of hp 1Fα and hp 1Sα, both occur in hp 2α. Peptides *N* and *C* are relatively deficient in hp 2α; *J* is additional.

[7] V. M. Ingram. 1958. Biochem. Biophys. Acta. **28**: 539.

deficient in hp 2α. The amino-terminal amino-acid of peptide N and of the whole α-chains is valine, and the carboxy-terminal amino-acid of peptide C and of the whole of α-chains is glutamine, which suggests that these peptides originate from the ends of the α-chains. Amino-acid analyses of the peptides N, C and J and examination of the peptides obtained from them by further enzymatic digestion with subtilisin or trypsin, suggest that J is slightly smaller than the peptide which would be obtained by joining C and N with a pepetid bond. Peptide J has the same amino-terminal amino acid (isoleucine) as C, and the same carboxy-terminal amino-acid (tryosine) as N. Furthermore, almost all our preparations (see following) of the polypeptide hp 2α show both the peptides (F and S) characteristic of hp 1Fα and hp 1Sα. These findings are understandable if almost the whole of the amino-acid sequence of the hp 1α polypeptides occurs twice in a single molecule of hp 2α, and lead us to suggest the structures for the three haptoglobin α-polypeptides shown in outline in Fig. 2.

The general correctness of the proposed structures has now received confirmation from measurements of the molecular weights of the α-chains and of the yields from them of N-terminal amino-acid (valine) and of C-terminal amino-acid (glutamine) as shown in Table 1.

Table 1.

	Molecular weight*	N-valine† (per mg)	C-glutamine‡ (per mg)
hp 1Fα hp 1Sα	8,860 ± 400	0.034 μM 0.035 μM	0.063 μM
hp 2α	17,300 ± 1,400	0.021 μM	0.032 μM

 * By Archibald method.
 † By dinitrofluorobenzene method, uncorrected for losses during hydrolysis and chromatography.
 ‡ By carboxypeptidase method, uncorrected.

EVOLUTION OF HAPTOGLOBIN GENES

The substitution of one amino-acid residue in hp 1Fα by a different residue in hp 1Sα indicates that the genes Hp^{1F} and Hp^{1S} may differ only in a single base pair, as has been suggested for the genes controlling the haemoglobin variants A, S, C, etc.[8] On the other hand, the structure of hp 2α, in which most of the amino-acid sequence of the hp 1α polypeptides is repeated in a single molecule, indicates that the gene Hp^2 did not evolve from Hp^{1F} or Hp^{1S} by mutations involving small changes in base composition. The simplest hypothesis we can suggest (outlined in ref. 6) is that the gene

[8]V. M. Ingram. 1960. In, H. E. Sutton (editor). Genetics. Macy Foundation Symp.: 112.

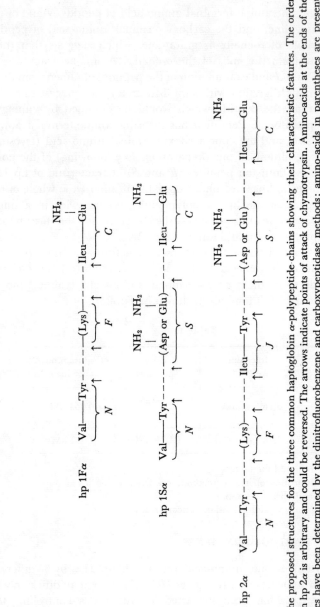

Fig. 2. Outlines of the proposed structures for the three common haptoglobin α-polypeptide chains showing their characteristic features. The order of peptides F and S in hp 2α is arbitrary and could be reversed. The arrows indicate points of attack of chymotrypsin. Amino-acids at the ends of the chymotryptic peptides have been determined by the dinitrofluorobenzene and carboxypeptidase methods; amino-acids in parentheses are present in the corresponding peptides but their positions are not known.

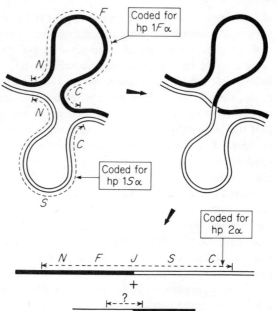

Fig. 3. Diagrammatic representation of the possible evolution of the gene Hp^2 from Hp^{1F} and Hp^{1S} by nonhomologous crossing-over in a heterozygote. The parental chromatids involved are distinguished by double and heavy lines. The regions coded for the α-polypeptides are indicated by dotted lines, and the letters locate the approximate regions corresponding to the chymotryptic peptides N, F, S, C and J referred to in the text.

Hp^2 was evolved from Hp^{1F} and Hp^{1S} by non-homologous crossing-over occurring in a heterozygous individual Hp^{1F}/Hp^{1S}. The suggested mechanism is illustrated diagrammatically in Fig. 3, and is similar to the type of process proposed by Serebrovsky[9] to account for chromosomal rearrangements in general. The net result of this non-homologous crossing-over is the production of one chromosome containing a small duplication and one with a corresponding deletion.

CHROMOSOMAL REARRANGEMENTS AND GENE EVOLUTION

Duplication of existing genes as an important factor in evolution has been discussed previously by several workers (for example, Bridges,[10] Lewis,[11] and Ingram and Stretton),[12] but the consequences at the molecular level

[9] A. S. Serebrovsky. 1929. Amer. Nat. **63**: 374.
[10] C. B. Bridges. 1935. J. Hered. **26**: 60.
[11] E. B. Lewis. 1951. Cold Spring Harbor Symp. Quant. Biol. **16**: 159.
[12] V. M. Ingram and A. O. W. Stretton. 1961. Nature. **190**: 1079.

of *partial* gene duplications do not appear to have been foreseen. Our studies with the haptoglobin system indicate that partial gene duplications can lead to the production of a continuous polypeptide which 'bridges' the beginning of the duplication. We use the term 'gene' here, and in what follows, to mean that portion of the DNA coded for a single polypeptide chain, such as an α-chain of haptoglobin. No assumptions as to the length or nature of the DNA between such genes are made, although we assume that the beginnings and/or ends of genes are specified in some way, and we recognize that the relative frequency but not the possibility of occurrence of some of the events to be discussed may be influenced by the presence and the amount of any DNA not coded for amino-acid sequences.

Partial gene duplications may or may not be completely functional so far as protein synthesis is concerned, depending on the particular point in the chromosome where the duplication begins, and on the nature of the base pair code specifying amino-acids and the ends of polypeptide chains. On theoretical grounds we would expect coding restrictions to limit the number of duplications of random length leading to the production of a polypeptide bridging the beginning of the duplication. For example, less than one in three random duplications would make 'sense' at the beginning of the duplicated region if each amino-acid is coded by one particular triplet of base pairs. On the other hand, if an amino-acid can be specified in more than one way the requirements for continuity of the corresponding polypeptide may be met more frequently at the beginning of the duplication, but may fail to be met at some other point (see Crick *et al.*[13] for further discussion of this problem). If integral numbers of amino-acid coding units are involved, the requirements for continuity may be met still more frequently and the whole of the duplication may make 'sense.' Although partly functional and non-functional duplications are thus conceivable, our experiments indicate that completely functional partial gene duplications occur.

Once it is realized that a new gene able to code for an uninterrupted sequence of amino-acids can be formed from pre-existing genes by chromosomal rearrangements, the possible importance of this process for the evolution of new proteins becomes apparent. Three of the many conceivable examples of such evolutionary events, related to duplications which could have been formed by non-homologous crossing-over, are indicated diagrammatically in Fig. 4.

A duplication, *I*, within the boundaries of a single gene, leads to a repeated sequence of amino-acids in the corresponding polypeptide (subject to the involvement of an integral number of amino-acid coding units). Unexpected properties can result from such repetitions, as, for example, the polymerization tendencies of the polypeptide hp 2α. Although the repeated sequence in hp 2α is extensive, there appears to be no *a priori* reason

[13] F. H. Crick, L. Barnett, S. Brenner and R. J. Watts-Tobin. 1961. Nature. **192**: 1227.

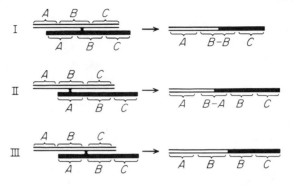

Fig. 4. Diagrammatic representation of the possible formation (by non-homologous crossing-over) and the consequences of duplications of several types. The brackets indicate DNA coded for polypeptide sequences. I. An intragenic duplication of the type suggested as involved in the evolution of Hp^2 from Hp^{1F} and Hp^{1S}; II. A duplication involving parts of two genes, leading to the formation of a new gene B–A without loss of the pre-existing genes A and B; III. A duplication of the same extent as II, but formed by crossing-over between genes. The result is a classical gene duplication, such as may have been involved in the evolution of the haemoglobin polypeptide chains.

why shorter ones could not exist. The consequences of the involvement of non-integral numbers of amino-acid coding units in a partial gene duplication will, as indicated here, depend on the nature of the code. For example, the new gene might give rise only to that part of the (pre-existing) polypeptide sequence which is coded by the DNA preceding the duplicated region, or the pre-existing sequence may be followed, as a result of the shift in reading of the DNA code (cf. Crick *et al.*[13]), by a completely new polypeptide sequence extending over part or almost all of the duplication. Any partial gene duplications which are non-functional in polypeptide synthesis, or give rise to phenotypically inactive products, may behave like amorphic mutations. However, unlike amorphic mutations due to deletions, they will revert to the normal gene occasionally, as a result of unequal but homologous crossing-over within the locus in homozygotes (see following), or as a result of unequal but homologous sister strand or intrachromatid crossing-over in heterozygotes.[14]

A duplication involving parts of two genes, *II*, can lead to the formation of a new gene coded for a polypeptide sequence combining parts of the sequences of two pre-existing proteins if integral numbers of coding units are involved. Such a polypeptide might combine in one molecule properties formerly present in separate molecules. For example, in the case of enzymes

[14] J. R. Laughnan. 1961. Proc. Symp. Mutation and Plant Breeding. NAS-NRC 891, 3.

it could have amino-acid sequences enabling it to combine with two substrate groups where its 'progenitors' could each combine with only one of them. (If non-integral numbers of coding units are involved the situation is similar to that discussed here.) Yet the evolution of such radically new proteins, by a single genetic event, need not be accompanied by loss of any genes for pre-existing proteins (Fig. 4). The alternate chromosome (not shown in the figure) formed during the non-homologous crossing-over leading to duplication *II* also has a new gene (A–B) which could code for a sequence of amino-acids with the portions corresponding to the genes *A* and *B* in the order A–B, in contrast to the order B–A for the duplication. This alternate chromosome, however, lacks the genes *A* and *B*, and so may have selective disadvantages.

Non-homologous crossing-over occurring between genes can lead to complete duplication of an existing gene (*III*).

Many types of chromosomal rearrangements, in addition to duplications, have been detected by genetic and cytological studies; for example, deletions, inversions, shifts, transpositions, etc. None of these would appear on *a priori* grounds to be confined to integral numbers of genes. We can therefore expect that protein variants will eventually be found corresponding to them, although until the base pair-amino-acid code is more completely known it is difficult to predict what proportion of these arrangements will fulfil the requirements for continuity in the corresponding polypeptides. The frequency of occurrence of cytologically detectable chromosomal rearrangements in naturally occurring populations of *Drosophila* and other species certainly indicates that rearrangements are common evolutionary events.

Other proteins, in addition to the haptoglobins, have structures which suggest that chromosomal rearrangements were involved in their evolution. Thus, the porcine pituitary hormones α-melanotropin (αMSH) and adrenocorticotrophin (ACTH) both contain the same sequence of 13 amino-acids.[15] αMSH has an acyl group on the *N*-terminal amino-group and the terminal carboxyl-group is amidated. On the other hand, ACTH has a free *N*-terminal amino-group and 26 additional amino-acid residues on the *C*-terminal end. βMSH lacks the *N*- and *C*-terminal amino-acids of αMSH and has short, completely dissimilar sequences on both ends of the common sequence. Two amino-acid residues in the common sequence are interchanged in position. These structures are strongly suggestive of evolution involving chromosomal rearrangements at some stage. Many proteolytic enzymes (for example, trypsin and chymotrypsin) have portions of their sequences in common, but in general their structures differ greatly.[16] They could also have evolved by chromosomal rearrangements.

Consequences of unequal but homologous crossing-over at the Hp locus. Several consequences of the intragenic duplication probably involved in the gene

[15] C. H. Li. 1961. Vitamins and Hormones. **19**: 313.

[16] G. H. Dixon, D. Kauffman and H. Neurath. 1958. J. Biol. Chem. **233**: 1373.

Hp^2 can be predicted by considering other systems involving duplications. The 'Bar' allele in *Drosophila* is associated with a cytologically demonstrable duplication.[17,18] Homozygotes for 'Bar' are relatively frequently involved in unequal but homologous crossing-over,[19] as a result of the displaced synapsis possible when there is a duplication in the genome. (Unequal but homologous crossing-over must be distinguished from non-homologous crossing-over, although both involve displaced synapsis. The latter, as indicated in Fig. 3, involves crossing-over between chromosomal regions which are not equivalent in their gene structure; it is consequently a rare event, and the subsequent action of the genes involved will be dependent on the requirements for continuity discussed here. Unequal but homologous crossing-over, on the other hand, involves crossing-over between chromosomal regions which are of equivalent structure but which are not in the same relative positions on the two chromosomes. Unequal but homologous crossing-over will not usually change the 'sense' of the DNA involved, and its frequency will be determined only by the frequency of displaced synapsis and by the map length of the corresponding duplicated or displaced chromosomal segment.) This unequal crossing-over in *Drosophila* gives rise to the formation of "double 'Bar,' " associated with a cytological triplication, or to reversion to 'wild-type' which lacks the original 'Bar' duplication. Homozygous individuals of the genotype Hp^2/Hp^2 are in many ways analogous to homozygotes for the 'Bar' allele. Unequal crossing-over would therefore be expected to occur occasionally in such individuals, either with the production of a triplicated haptoglobin gene (instead of the usual duplicated Hp^2 gene) or with reversion to one of the original 'wild-type' genes Hp^{1F} or Hp^{1S} (see Fig. 5 I). In the absence of information about the nature of the gene Hp^2 these events would be interpreted as mutations and the Hp locus would be described as having a high mutation rate.

A rare and unusual type of haptoglobin (the Johnson type), discovered by Dr. E. R. Giblett in a Negro woman and her daughter in Seattle, is associated with a rare gene, Hp^{2J}, in heterozygous combination with the common Hp^{1S} allele. Preliminary tests, involving comparison of the mobilities of the α-chains in starch gels at different starch concentrations,[20] indicate that the corresponding polypeptide $hp\ 2J\alpha$, is considerably larger than $hp\ 2\alpha$. This suggests that the gene Hp^{2J} could be the triplication formed by unequal but homologous crossing-over in a homozygote Hp^2/Hp^2 during displaced synapsis. This suggestion receives some confirmation from the recent discovery of the Johnson type in other widely separated racial groups (Dr. E. R. Giblett has found it in a Canadian Mennonite and two Hawaiian

[17] C. B. Bridges. 1936. Science. **83**: 210.

[18] H. J. Muller, A. A. Prokofyeva-Belgovskaya and K. V. Kossikov. 1936. C. R. Acad. Sci. U.S.S.R. **2**: 78.

[19] A. H. Sturtevant. 1925. Genetics. **10**: 117.

[20] O. Smithies. 1962. Archives Biochemistry Biophysics. Supplement **1**: 125-131.

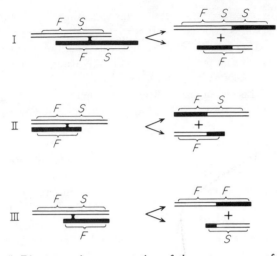

Fig. 5. Diagrammatic representation of the consequences of: **I**, unequal but homologous crossing-over occurring during displaced synapsis in a Hp^2/Hp^2 homozygote, leading to the possible evolution of a haptoglobin triplication or to reversion of Hp^2 to Hp^{1F} or Hp^{1S}; **II** and **III**, crossing-over within the locus in a heterozygous individual (Hp^2/Hp^{1F}) during the two possible synaptic configurations. This crossing-over will always be unequal and can lead to the production of four types of Hp^2 gene, and to the formation of a gamete containing the gene Hp^{1S} in an individual of genotype Hp^2/Hp^{1F}.

Chinese, Dr. K. Henningsen in a Dane, Dr. J. Hirschfeld in a Swede, Dr. R. L. Kirk in an Australian Dutch, Dr. J. Lundevall and Mrs. E. A. Fleischer in three Norwegians, Dr. B. Ramat in a Kurdish Jew). It seems highly improbable that the gene Hp^{2J} in the Seattle Negroes and these other genes have a common ancestor; yet they appear to be identical as judged by the phenotypes. The cause of their identity could be a common mechanism of formation rather than descent from a common ancestor. If the gene Hp^{2J} does prove to be an intragenic triplication then the Johnson type (genotype Hp^{2J}/Hp^{1S}) provides an excellent example and a possible explanation at the molecular level of the stable position effect, since the Johnson phenotype is readily distinguished from Hp 2-2, in which the same genetic material is distributed equally between the two chromosomes.

Other unusual serum samples very similar to but not identical with the Johnson type have also been found and sent to us for testing. Unfortunately, all had been shipped considerable distances and were not freshly collected, so that the observed small differences are difficult to evaluate. However, differences would be expected in terms of the triplication hypothesis, since there should be eight different forms of a triplicated haptoglobin gene (see later) and consequently sixteen heterozygous combinations with the genes Hp^{1F} and Hp^{1S}.

Synapsis in heterozygotes Hp^2/Hp^{1F} and Hp^2/Hp^{1S} can occur in two ways (Fig. 5 II and III), as a result of the duplicate nature of the gene Hp^2. Crossing-over within the locus (which will always be unequal) should therefore lead eventually to the occurrence in the gene pool of all the four possible types of Hp^2. Thus, if we assume that the original Hp^2 gene was FS, then intragenic crossing-over in heterozygotes will lead to the formation of Hp^2 genes which are FF, SS, and SF. The relative chances of finding these types is difficult to predict, since we have insufficient knowledge about the frequency of the corresponding unequal crossing-over, and of the selective forces involved, to be able to estimate the equilibrium frequencies of the different genes. However, we may already have had some samples of hp 2α from individuals who are $Hp^{2(FF)}/Hp^{2(FF)}$ or $Hp^{2(FS)}/Hp^{2(FF)}$, as three out of fifteen single donor hp 2α preparations showed complete, or almost complete absence of the peptide S characteristic of hp $1S\alpha$ (Fig. 1), but clearly showed the corresponding F peptide. In any event, we predict that four types of Hp^2 gene are possible, and are undertaking a search for them.

In summary, we conclude that the haptoglobin system provides examples of the effect on the structure of a single polypeptide chain of both a 'point' mutation and chromosomal rearrangements. We suggest that proteins with radically changed properties can be formed as a consequence of the single genetic event of a chromosomal rearrangement involving non-integral numbers of genes. Chromosomal rearrangements of this type appear to provide a mechanism for achieving more rapid and extensive changes in protein structure during evolution than are possible by point mutations, even when preceded by gene duplication. New genes formed by chromosomal rearrangements need not be accompanied by loss to the organism of any pre-existing genes.

This work was supported in part by grants from the U. S. National Science Foundation, and the Medical Research Council, Canada. We thank Dr. W. E. Nance for his help during the preparation of the manuscript and acknowledge many helpful discussions of the work with him, Drs. J. F. Crow, N. E. Morton, and L. Sandler.

Hereditary Serological Human Serum Groups*

R. GRUBB

A. B. LAURELL

The discovery and elucidation of inherited variation among human gamma globulins represents an aspect of human genetics which has considerable potential importance to the study of immunity. The observations of Grubb, reprinted here, provide the beginning by which inherited differences can be recognized through a serologic reaction. This reaction occurs between an antigen, in this instance gamma globulin present in the form of incomplete anti-Rh serum adsorbed on erythrocytes, and an antibody, viz., an anti-gamma globulin present in the serum of certain subjects with rheumatoid arthritis. The resulting agglutination can be inhibited by prior incubation of rheumatoid serum with normal gamma globulin. A variety of gamma globulin phenotypes can be detected through selection of certain combinations of rheumatoid and incomplete anti-Rh sera.

The reprinted investigations of Harboe and his colleagues and of Franklin and his colleagues assign the function of two different genetic loci to distinct portions of the gamma globulin molecule. The relationship between gene and molecular sub-unit thus established forms a striking parallel to that which has developed in the study of human hemoglobin. It is important to recognize that in each case these developments have depended upon genetical analysis for the recognition of genes and upon many disciplines for the description of gene products.

As known, most rheumatoid arthritic sera agglutinate sheep red cells that have absorbed non-agglutinating doses of rabbit anti-sheep hemolysin, the Waaler-Rose test.

Heller *et al.* (1954, 1955) modified this test and obtained a potentiation

* Reprinted by R. Grubb's and publisher's permission from Acta Pathologica et Microbiologica Scandinavica. 1956. **39:** 390-398.

of the agglutination in the presence of selected normal sheep sera. In this special test 11 out of 28 normal human sera inhibited the agglutination. The inhibitor was located in the gamma-globulin fraction. Studies on the influence of normal human serum or fractions thereof in a conventional Waaler-Rose test have been made with contradictory results (Ziff *et al.* 1954, 1956; Svartz & Schlossman 1955).

It was recently found (Grubb 1956 b) that some rheumatoid arthritic sera agglutinate Rh-positive human red cells coated with certain "incomplete" anti-Rh. The agglutination obtainable by some of these rheumatoid arthritic sera was inhibited by a percentage of normal human sera. Human sera could thus be subdivided into two groups by serological methods.

This paper is concerned with the description of some observations on these human serum groups.

EXPERIMENTAL

MATERIAL AND METHODS

Diluent: Phosphate buffered saline pH 7.2 (3 parts 0.85 per cent saline + 1 part Sörensen phosphate buffer m/15) was used throughout as a diluent and for washing.

Sera containing incomplete anti-Rh: Anti-Rh sera of a titre of at most 1:4 in saline and 1:512 or more against trypsinized Rh-positive cells were used in most experiments. Seventeen sera of this kind were studied. The sera were from women immunized by pregnancy or by transfusion and pregnancy. (As to the selection of anti-Rh sera for the purpose described see Discussion and Grubb 1956 c).

Red cells of group O C+ D+ E— c— were preferably used. Four volumes of blood were mixed with one volume of citrate and, if not used immediately, was stored at +4° C for not more than 3 days.

Coating of red cells with anti-Rh: 0.4 ml of packed group ORh+ red cells, which had been washed 3 times, were incubated at 37° C with 5 ml of serum dilution for 2 hours and then washed 4 times, each time with about 10 ml of the phosphate buffered saline. The anti-Rh sera were usually diluted 1:20 for coating. It was checked that the coated red cells were quickly and strongly agglutinated by rabbit anti-human globulin serum.

The rheumatoid arthritic sera were selected from specimens collected from patients with active rheumatoid arthritis. It was practice not to heat the sera at 56° C. Most sera were still fairly active after heating at 56° C for 20 minutes. The sera were stored at −20° C. (As to the selection of rheumatoid arthritic sera for the inhibition test see Discussion and Grubb 1956 c).

Human gamma-globulin prepared from retroplacental blood by a Cohn procedure was kindly supplied by A.-B. Kabi, Stockholm. The product was stated to be pure, as judged by electrophoresis.

Normal human sera were secured from the laboratory personnel, from healthy sailors (samples sent in for routine Wassermann tests), from blood donors and from primigravidae in at least the fourth month of pregnancy. (Primigravidae were chosen to avoid selection with regard to Rh groups, Rh-negatives being over-represented among samples sent to the laboratory from multiparous women). Sera from 74 Esquimos were available. They were from the Holsteinsborg district. Most of the individuals were not closely related.

FAMILY MATERIAL

Twenty-eight families with 94 children were studied. Twenty-three were from southern Sweden and 5 were Danish. In 18 of the families the fathers were physicians. Children below 5 years of age were not included. Families with several children were given some preference.

Agglutination tests were performed in round-bottomed tubes measuring 80 mm by 3 mm. The volumes used were 0.25 ml serum dilution and 0.25 ml of an approximately 0.4 per cent suspension of coated Rh-positive cells. A saline control of the coated Rh-positive cells was included as was also a tube with serum dilution and the above Rh-positive cells which had not been coated with anti-Rh. In general the serum dilutions 1:10 through 1:320 were tested.

The tubes were allowed to stand for 4-6 hours at room temperature. The results were read by inspecting the pattern of the settled cells with the naked eye before and after gentle shaking.

In the saline control tube the coated Rh-positive cells did not generally settle to form a perfect "button" but were slightly spread out. Gently shaking dispersed the cells. In the presence of diluted normal human serum the coated cells were "stabilized" to form a perfect button upon settling (cf. experience with tannin treated red cells, Boyden 1951 *a. o.*). This stabilizing effect was obtained with most normal human sera up to a dilution of about 1:200. In order not to complicate the system a special "stabilizing" serum dose was not added. Furthermore, human serum is of course present in these titrations and with some practice the reading of the results offers no difficulty.

AGGLUTINATION—INHIBITION TESTS

The general technique was the same as in the agglutination test. 0.12 ml of the solution to be assayed for its content of inhibitor (normal serum or gamma-globulin) were mixed with 0.12 ml of selected rheumatoid arthritic sera diluted to contain 10-20 agglutinating doses. With the rheumatoid arthritic sera used this amounted to a 1:15 to a 1:30 dilution. After 15 min. 0.25 ml of the 0.4 per cent suspension of coated cells was added and the results were read as described. The normal sera tested as inhibitors were diluted 1:4, 1:12 and 1:36. The following controls were included: (1) 0.12 ml of the normal serum diluted 1:4 plus 0.12 ml buffered saline, (2) 0.12 ml rheumatoid arthritic serum of the dilution used in the test plus 0.12 ml buffered saline, (3) 0.25 ml buffered saline. To all control tubes 0.25 ml of the suspension of coated cells was added.

All solutions tested for their content of inhibitor were assayed against two rheumatoid arthritic sera. Experience on more than a hundred specimens has been gained for three selected rheumatoid arthritic sera. One of these was used throughout as a reference serum. The other two sera reacted like the reference serum.

Serum fractionation was made by paper electrophoresis by the method described by Laurell (1955).

RESULTS

TYPICAL EXAMPLES

Sera from two normal persons and pooled human gamma-globulin were tested for their power to inhibit the agglutinating action of two selected rheumatoid arthritic sera on Rh-positive red cells coated with a chosen incomplete anti-Rh. The results are given in Table 1.

Table 1. POOLED HUMAN γ-GLOBULIN AND TWO NORMAL HUMAN SERA AS INHIBITORS OF THE AGGLUTINATION OF COATED RH-POSITIVE CELLS BY SELECTED RHEUMATOID ARTHRITIC SERA

Gamma-globulin %	1	1/2	1/4	1/8	1/16	1/32	1/64	1/128
R. a. 1	—	—	—	—	—	.+.	.+.	+
R. a. 2	—	—	—	—	—	—	—	(—)
Normal serum 1.	1/3	1/6	1/12	1/24	1/48	1/96		
R. a. 1	—	—	—	—	+	⧣		
R. a. 2	—	—	—	—	—	(+)		
Normal serum 2.	1/3	1/6	1/12	1/24	1/48	1/96		
R. a. 1	⧣	⧣	⧣	⧣	⧣	⧣		
R. a. 2	(—)	.+.	+	+	+	+		

Controls	Gamma-globulin (1 %) + saline + coated cells: —
	Normal serum 1. 1/3 + saline + coated cells: —
	Normal serum 2. 1/3 + saline + coated cells: —
	R. a. 1 + saline + coated cells: ⧣
	R. a. 2 + saline + coated cells: +
	Saline + coated cells: .—.

R. a. = Rheumatoid arthritic serum agglutinating coated Rh-positive cells. The degrees of agglutination are recorded.

The table shows that small amounts of pooled human gamma-globulin inhibited this agglutinating action of both rheumatoid arthritic sera. One of the two normal sera was inhibitory at a 1:24-48 dilution, whereas the serum of the individual was but weakly inhibitory.

CHARACTERIZATION OF THE INHIBITOR

Seven normal human sera which inhibited the agglutination of the coated red cells by the rheumatoid arthritic sera were subjected to paper electrophoresis as were also two normal sera which did not inhibit this agglutination. The fractions obtained were then tested in agglutination inhibition tests. Inhibition was obtained by the gamma-globulin fractions of all seven inhibitory sera. None of the fractions of the non-inhibitory sera inhibited the agglutination. As was shown above pooled gamma-globulin prepared by a Cohn procedure was also inhibitory. The inhibitor proved non-dialysable.

NOMENCLATURE

On the basis of the above observations it was assumed that the inhibitor is located in the gamma-globulin fraction. The phenotypes of the serum groups are referred to below as Gm (a+) and Gm (a−), where Gm stands for Gamma-globulin. Gm (a+) denotes the group that inhibits the agglutinating effect of the rheumatoid arthritic sera on coated Rh-positive cells. Gm^a denotes the corresponding gene. The gene symbol Gm without a superscript denotes the gene (genes) at the same locus, not being Gm^a. Gene (genes) Gm is thus at present presumed. The notation was chosen in some accordance with symbolism used in blood group serology (Andresen *et al.* 1949).

FREQUENCY OF THE SERUM GROUPS

The Gm serum groups of healthy adults from southernmost Sweden was determined on a material consisting of 184 males and 144 female non-pregnant blood-donors and 32 pregnant women. These figures include the parents of the family material (see farther down). The results of these determinations are given in Table 2.

Table 2. FREQUENCY OF GM GROUPS IN HEALTHY ADULTS

	Gm (a+)	Gm (a−)	n	Percentage Gm (a+)
Men	113	71	184	61.4
Non-pregnant women	85	59	144	59.0
Pregnant women	17	15	32	53.1
Total	215	145	360	59.7

The differences between the three categories were not statistically significant and the Gm serum groups did not vary with sex or pregnancy. The frequency group Gm (a+) was about 60 per cent. The gene frequencies as calculated on the basis of these figures give Gm^a = 0.3653 and Gm = 0.6347.

In a few cases the Gm groups could not be found out until after cold-agglutinins and blood-group antibodies had been absorbed. The Gm groups of two persons could not be determined. The serum of one of these individuals agglutinated the coated Rh positive cells, the other was considered "intermediate." These two persons, from whom new samples could not be secured, were not included in the figures.

ABO and D groups were determined for all samples and their frequencies were found not to differ from those in random sampling in Sweden. In about 30 cases the C, E, c, MNS, P, Kell, Le (a), Le (b), Lu (a) and secretor characters were known. No close correlation was found between any of these factors and the Gm groups.

Of 54 consecutive sera containing anti-Rh studied, 33 proved Gm (a+) and 21 Gm (a−). The distribution was thus very similar to the one found in normals. Twenty of the samples had first to be absorbed with Rh-positive cells. Twelve of these 20 samples proved Gm (a+).

Sera from 70 out of 74 Esquimos were Gm (a+). This distribution significantly differs from the one found in the southern Swedish population.

FAMILY DATA

The result of the Gm group determinations in the 28 families studied are summarized in Table 3. The gene frequencies used for the calculations were those computed above *i.e.* Gm^a = 0.3653 and Gm = 0.6347. The calculations were made on the assumptions of unifactorial inheritance and of Gm^a being detectable in a single dose.

The observed frequency of mating classes came close to expectation.

Table 3. THE GM SERUM GROUPS OF 28 FAMILIES

Matings				Children				
	Number			Gm (a+)		Gm (a−)		
Type	Obs.	Exp.	Total	Obs.	Exp.	Obs.	Exp.	x^2
Gm (a+) × Gm (a+)	9	10	33	30	28.0	3	5.0	0.94
Gm (a+) × Gm (a−)	14	13.5	37	25	22.6	12	14.4	0.65
Gm (a−) × Gm (a−)	5	4.5	24	0	0.0	24	24.0	
								1.59
								for 2 d.f.
								0.95 > p > 0.1

Among the children, all phenotypes theoretically expected were observed. All 24 children from the matings Gm (a−) × Gm (a−) were Gm (a−). The distribution of the Gm group frequencies among the children did not significantly differ from that expected.

The family data did not suggest close linkage between the Gm and the ABO or D genes. Nor did the evidence indicate partial sex-linkage of the Gm genes.

More detailed information of the Gm groups in these 28 families is given in Table 4, where the families are classified according to mating type, family size and the presence or absence of Gm (a−) children.

Table 4. FAMILY MATERIAL SUBDIVIDED ACCORDING TO MATING CLASS, FAMILY SIZE AND THE OCCURRENCE OF PHENOTYPE GM (A—)

| Mating | | | Children | | Mating | | | Children | |
Father	Mother	No.	Gm (a+)	Gm (a−)	Father	Mother	No.	Gm (a+)	Gm (a−)
Gm (a+)	Gm (a+)				Gm (a−)	Gm (a+)			
		2	2	—			3	2	—
		3	3	—			1	4	—
		1	4	—	Gm (a+)	Gm (a−)			
		1	8	—			1	—	2
Gm (a+)	Gm (a+)						1	2	2
		1	3	1			1	1	3
		1	2	2	Gm (a−)	Gm (a+)			
Gm (a+)	Gm (a−)						1	—	1
		2	2	—			2	1	2
		1	3	—	Gm (a−)	Gm (a−)			
		1	5	—			5	—	24

MISCELLANEOUS OBSERVATIONS

The Gm groups of several Gm (a+) and Gm (a−) healthy people were determined on a number of samples collected at different occasions over a period of five months. All samples from one and the same person have been of the same Gm group.

Inhibition was obtained with sera stored for several years at −20° C. Gm (a+) sera did not lose their inhibitory power after exposure to 63° C for 25 minutes. This procedure, however, destroyed the agglutinating action of rheumatoid arthritic sera on coated Rh-positive cells.

Sera from five persons classified as cases of agamma-globulinemia on the basis of results obtained in paper electrophoresis were available. The amount of gamma-globulin in these sera as determined by the inhibition of the agglutinating action of rabbit anti-human-globulin serum on coated Rh-positive red cells (Wiener 1955, Grubb 1956 a), was found to range from

0.15 to 10 per cent of normal. These 5 sera did not inhibit the agglutinating action of the rheumatoid arthritic sera when tested in the same dilutions as normal human sera.

DISCUSSION

There are at least 9 well established blood group systems and our knowledge of the antigenic composition of the human erythrocyte is well advanced. In contrast, known individual differences outside the "blood groups" in body fluids and tissue cells are rare. This discrepancy may be more apparent than real and may be due to the fact that erythrocytes can be conveniently used in agglutination test whereas tissue cells and secretions cannot. The serum groups described here were determined by a red cell agglutination technique.

At present the demonstration of these serum groups depends upon the availability of two types of reagents *i.e.* selected rheumatoid arthritic sera and selected "incomplete" anti-Rh sera. As to the selection of rheumatoid arthritic sera, the first conditions for acceptance are of course that the serum should agglutinate coated Rh-positive cells and that the agglutination should be inhibited by pooled human gamma-globulin. Most of these agglutinating rheumatoid arthritic sera are inhibited by pooled human gamma-globulin. The serum should also preferably be potent and not show zoning. Furthermore, experience has shown that rheumatoid arthritic sera satisfying the above requirements are not all equally suited to make the distinction described. Despite these limitations useful rheumatoid arthritic sera will be found if some effort is made. In our experience some per cent of them make useful reagents. If desired, a primary selection can be made by the Waaler-Rose test because all sera hitherto used proved to agglutinate sheep cells "sensitized" with rabbit anti-sheep cell hemolysin. As to the selection of incomplete anti-Rh about half the number of hightitred incomplete anti-Rh can be used. This aspect of the subject will be dealt with in a future paper.

Hereditary group differences of serum are known, the ABO-Secretor —Lewis group differences being reflected also in serum. Hereditary differences between beta-globulins of strains of inbred mice have been found (Thompson *et al.* 1954). Hereditary human serum groups identifiable by zone electrophoresis have recently been described (Smithies 1955 a, b). The group differences of Smithies are referable to alpha-2-globulins and therefore it does not seem likely that they are identical with the Gm groups. Neither do the frequency figures argue for identity between these two group systems. An investigation aiming at a direct comparison is in progress.

The present family material, although small, shows that the Gm groups are hereditary and the observations do not argue against the assumption of autosomal unifactorial inheritance. The distinction between Gm (a+) and

Gm (a−) people offers little difficulty in normal adults provided appropriately selected reagents are used. The Gm groups in infancy and in disease have as yet not been studied.

Some evidence that the gamma-globulins are under genetical control has been adduced by familial occurrence of cases of agamma-globulinemia in boys (Kulneff *et al.* 1955 a.o.). Environmental factors, however, undoubtedly also influence the gamma-globulins, one pertinent finding being that rats which had been reared germ-free from birth to the age of 4 months had less than 25 per cent of the amount of gamma-globulins found in the control animals (Gustafsson & C.-B. Laurell, 1956).

The inhibitor on which the concept of the Gm groups is based is either a gamma-globulin or a substance of similar electrophoretic mobility and solubility. It should perhaps be stressed that the red cells used in the indicator system are coated with anti-Rh, which presumably is a gamma-globulin. The finding that the sera of the five persons with "agamma-globulincmia" did not contain appreciable amounts of inhibitor are compatible with an assumption that the inhibitor is a gamma-globulin. The absence of inhibition may however be due to the fact that those five persons are genetically Gm Gm.

It is of interest to note that Cutbush *et al.* (1955) observed that rabbit anti-humanglobulin serum absorbed with red cells coated with one anti-Rh may, after absorption, agglutinate cells coated with some other anti-Rh.

The observations made may suggest that gamma-globulins in different persons may contain differing serological determinant groupings. This is seemingly not in accord with the observations made in the immunoelectrophoretic analysis of human gamma-globulin made by Williams & Grabar (1955). Williams and Grabar used rabbit anti-human-globulin serum for their analysis. It is possible that one set of determinative groupings may be antigenically predominantly active in one species and that other specific groupings may determine the character of the antibody specificity in another species. To make an example: Anti-Rh produced in animals and man differ (Fisk & Foord 1942) and preparations from dd human red cells may give rise to anti-D in guinea-pigs (Murray & Clark, 1952). As is well-known the antibodies distinguishing the other factors of the Rh complex are human antibodies and cannot, at least not regularly, be produced by injection of corresponding antigens into animals. Evidence indicating the presence of several determinants in gamma-globulin has been found in studies of the relationship between myeloma proteins and normal gamma-globulin (see for example Korngold & Lipari 1956 a, b).

SUMMARY

1. Despite considerable dilution certain rheumatoid arthritic sera agglutinated group O Rh-positive red cells coated with selected "incomplete" anti-Rh antibodies.

2. Human serum could be grouped by agglutination-inhibition tests in this system.

3. The inhibitor was located in the gamma-globulin fraction. The serum group phenotypes were designated Gm (a+) and Gm (a−).

4. The Gm group frequencies in 360 healthy Swedish adults was found to be Gm (a+):59.7 per cent and Gm (a−):40.3 per cent.

5. The Gm serum groups were not found to be correlated with sex, pregnancy or various blood group factors studied.

6. Of 54 sera containing anti-Rh 61 per cent were Gm (a+).

7. Of sera from 74 Esquimos 95 per cent were Gm (a+).

8. The Gm groups were studied in a family material comprising 28 families with 94 children. The groups were found to be hereditary and the family data do not argue against an assumption of autosomal, unifactorial inheritance.

9. Sera from 5 patients with considerable hypogamma-globulinemia were not inhibitory in the system.

REFERENCES

(1) P. H. Andresen, S. T. Callender, R. A. Fisher, R. Grubb, W. T. J. Morgan, A. E. Mourant, M. M. Pickles and R. R. Race. 1949. A notation for the Lewis and Lutheran blood group systems. Nature. 163: 580.

(2) S. V. Boyden. 1951. The adsorption of proteins on erythrocytes treated with tannic acid and subsequent hemagglutination by anti-protein sera. J. Exper. Med. 93: 107-120.

(3) M. Cutbush, H. Crawford and P. L. Mollison. 1955. Observations on anti-human globulin sera. Brit. J. Haematol. 1: 410-421.

(4) R. T. Fisk and A. G. Foord. 1942. Observations on the Rh agglutinogen of human blood. Am. J. Clin. Path. 12: 545.

(5) R. Grubb. 1956a. A method for demonstrating minute amounts of human γ-globulin. Acta Path. Microbiol. Scand. 38: 339-346.

(6) R. Grubb. 1956b. Acta Path. Microbiol. Scand. 39: 195-197.

(7) R. Grubb. 1956c.

(8) B. E. Gustafsson and C.-B. Laurell. 1956. Personal communication.

(9) G. Heller, S. A. Jacobson, M. H. Kolodny and W. H. Kammerer. 1954. The haemagglutination test for rheumatoid arthritis. 2. The influence of human plasma fraction II (gamma-globulin) on the reaction. J. Immunol. 72: 66-78.

(10) G. Heller, M. H. Kolodny, I. H. Lepow, A. S. Jacobson, M. E. Rivera and G. H. Marks. 1955. The hemagglutination test for rheumatoid arthritis. 4. Characterization

Acknowledgements: Our thanks are due to Dr. Friedenreich and Dr. Friesleben of the State Serum Institute, Copenhagen, for supplying anti-Rh sera; to Dr. Henningsen and Dr. Galatius of the University Institute of Forensic Medicine, Copenhagen, for sera from 5 families and for sera from Esquimos supplied by Professor Laughlin, Madison.

of the rheumatoid agglutinating factors by analysis of serum fractions prepared by ethanol fractionation. J. Immunol. **74:** 340.

(11) L. Korngold and R. Lipari. 1956c. Multiple myeloma proteins. 1. Immunological studies. Cancer. **9:** 183-192.

(12) L. Korngold and R. Lipari. 1956b. Multiple myeloma proteins. 3. The antigenic relationship of Bence Jones proteins to normal gamma-globulin and multiple-myeloma serum proteins. Cancer. **9:** 262-272.

(13) N. Kulneff, K. O. Pedersen and J. Waldenström. 1955. Drei Fälle von agamma-globulinämie. Schweiz. Med. Wchnschr. **85:** 363-368.

(14) A.-B. Laurell. 1955. On antibodies separated by paper electrophoresis. Acta Path. Microbiol. Scand. Suppl. 103.

(15) J. Murray and E. C. Clark. 1952. Production of anti-Rh in guinea-pigs from human erythrocytes. Nature. **169:** 886-887.

(16) O. Smithies. 1955. Zone electrophoresis in starch gels. Group variations in the serum proteins of normal human adults. Biochem. J. **61:** 629-641.

(17) O. Smithies and N. F. Walker. 1955. Genetic control of some serum proteins in normal humans. Nature. **176:** 1265-1266.

(18) N. Svartz and K. Schlossmann. 1955. Cold precipitable haemagglutinating factor in serum from patients with rheumatoid arthritis. Ann. Rheumat. Dis. **14:** 191-194.

(19) S. Thompson, J. F. Foster, J. W. Gowan and D. E. Tauber. 1954. Hereditary differences in serum proteins of normal mice. Proc. Soc. Exp. Biol. & Med. **87:** 315-317.

(20) A. S. Weiner. 1955. Serological test for human gamma-globulin. 2. Application in diagnosis and treatment of agammaglobulinemia. Am. J. Clin. Path. **25:** 595-597.

(21) C. A. Williams and P. Grabar. 1955. Immunoelectrophoretic studies on serum proteins. 3. Human gamma-globulin. J. Immunol. **74:** 404-410.

(22) M. Ziff, P. Brown, J. Badin and C. McEwen. 1954. Bull. Rheumat. Diseas. **5:** 75-76.

(23) M. Ziff, P. Brown, J. Lospalutto, J. Badin and C. McEwen. 1956. Agglutination and inhibition by serum globulin in the sensitized sheep cell agglutination reaction in rheumatoid arthritis. Am. J. Med. **20:** 500-509.

Localization of Two Genetic Factors to Different Areas of γ-Globulin Molecules*

M. HARBOE

C. K. OSTERLAND
Fellow of the Canadian Arthritis Society

H. G. KUNKEL
The Rockefeller Institute

[*Abstract. Gm(a) and Gm(b) factors are present in 7S γ-globulin molecules and absent in 19S γ-globulins, β₂ₐ-globulins and Bence-Jones proteins, whereas the Inv(b) factor was demonstrated in all four kinds of proteins. The Inv type was identical in isolated 7S and 19S γ-globulins of six normal sera. After papain splitting of 7S γ-globulin, Gm determining sites were present only in the fast (F) split product and Inv determining sites were present only in the slow (S).*]

Recent observations on human γ-globulin have indicated that a variety of genetic types occur in different individuals. Of the seven factors known, only four are considered in this paper: the Gm(a) factor is present in 52.6 percent of the American white population, and the Gm(b) factor is present in 91.5 percent. The responsible genes, Gm^a and Gm^b, behave as codominant alleles. The Inv(a) factor is present in about 20 percent and the Inv(b) factor in about 99 percent of the same population; the responsible genes also behave as codominant alleles apparently being present at another independent locus (1-4).

All determinations were made by the hemagglutination inhibition reaction using red cells coated with incomplete anti-D and agglutinators of well-known and high degree of specificity. The Gm types were determined by a slide technique using anti-Gm(a) Smejsa with anti-D J.J., and anti-Gm(b) A.Berg with anti-D N.B. The Inv types were determined by a tube technique using anti-Inv(a) Travnikova with anti-D Roehm, and anti-Inv(b) Lucas with anti-D Ham. All readings were performed with a blind technique, and the results were easily reproducible.

* Reprinted by author's and publisher's permission from Science. 1962. **136**: 979-980.

Myeloma proteins were purified by starch block electrophoresis and classified immunologically as belonging to the more complete or more deficient 7S γ-globulin type or to the β_{2A} class. Macroglobulins were similarly purified from sera of patients with macroglobulinemia Waldenström. The macroglobulins and isolated Bence-Jones proteins were tested for purity by ultracentrifugation and immunological methods.

Four myeloma proteins were selected for splitting by papain because they fell into the antigenically more complete 7S γ-globulin type and were of relatively low electrophoretic mobility. Isolated γ-globulin of low electrophoretic mobility from a selected normal serum (45502) was used in one experiment. After treatment with papain (5), two main antigenic fragments were distinguished by immunoelectrophoresis (6) and subsequently separated by starch block electrophoresis. The degree of separation of the slow moving (S) and the fast (F) split products varied somewhat. A high degree of purity was, however, obtained in the segments corresponding to the slowest portion of S and the fastest portion of F. A typical example of a test for purity, using double diffusion in agar, is shown in Fig. 1. The slightly curved lines of both S and F isolated split products fused with marked spur formation with the straight lines of unsplit material. The S and F lines passed through each other with no evidence of cross-reaction. Each of the split products gave a single line indicating that there was very little or no contamination with unsplit material or the other split fraction.

None of the purified S preparations inhibited anti-Gm(a) Smejsa in the highest concentration tested (1 mg/ml). The isolated F split product of those proteins which possessed the Gm(a) character inhibited the agglutination completely in seven or eight successive, twofold serial dilutions, starting at the same protein concentration. If the starting material was of type

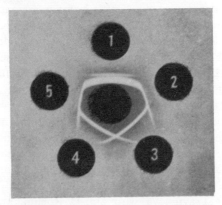

Fig. 1. Control of purity of isolated S and F fragments after papain splitting of 7S γ-globulin. Center well: Rabbit antihuman 7S γ-globulin No. 509; well 1, whole split; wells 2 and 5, unsplit; well 3, isolated slow (S) and well 4, isolated fast (F).

Gm(a−), none of the split fractions showed inhibition. Tests with two additional anti-Gm(a) sera (1604 and Kouba) gave virtually identical results. Preparation 45502 was Gm(b+); again the inhibiting capacity was confined to the F fragment. Neither of the split fragments of two Gm(b−) preparations had any inhibiting capacity.

Inv(a) testing of preparation 45502 showed that the inhibiting capacity was present in the S fragment, whereas F did not inhibit. One of the myeloma proteins was Inv(a+); again the inhibiting capacity was confined to the S fragment. Three of the myeloma proteins and preparation 45502 were Inv(b+). In all cases the inhibiting capacity was present in the S fragment and absent in F. In the Inv tests, the F fragments had no inhibiting capacity at a concentration of 1 mg/ml, whereas the S fragments inhibited the agglutination completely in at least three doubling dilutions starting at the same protein concentration.

The double diffusion tests in agar indicated that the purified preparations did not contain unsplit material. Ultracentrifugation, using a 5 to 10 per cent sucrose density gradient, gave more direct evidence that the inhibition was caused by components with a sedimentation coefficient smaller than 7S. Ten fractions were obtained from each tube, and inhibiting activity was recovered from top fractions of the split material, while corresponding fractions of control tubes with unsplit 7S γ-globulin contained no protein or inhibiting activity.

The β_{2A} myeloma protein was isolated from ten sera. Tests for purity were made by double diffusion tests in agar and showed that the preparations' contamination with 7S γ-globulin were less than 2 per cent of the total protein content. All ten β_{2A}-globulins were clearly Gm(a−b−), whereas seven possessed the Inv(b) character. Five isolated 19S γ-globulins from macroglobulinemia sera were all Gm(a−b−), whereas two of them were Inv(b+). Finally, six Bence-Jones proteins were Gm(a−b−), whereas two of them possessed the Inv(b) character.

Since the 19S γ-globulins possessed the Inv(b) character, it seemed of interest to isolate these from individual normal sera to determine whether they were of the same type as the 7S γ-globulins. Euglobulin preparations were dissolved in glycine HCl buffer at pH 3.0 and subjected to density gradient ultracentrifugation. Selected fractions were carefully dialyzed against saline and tested immunologically for purity before Gm and Inv typing. Bottom fractions were obtained from six individuals with 19S γ-globulins free of 7S γ-globulin; the corresponding top fractions contained 7S γ-globulin and no 19S material. The Gm characters were present in the 7S fraction, whereas the fractions containing 19S γ-globulins all were Gm(a−b−). Two of the 7S γ-globulin fractions were Inv(a+b+) and four Inv(a−b+). Identical results were obtained in Inv typing of the fractions containing 19S γ-globulins.

It has previously been known that Gm and Inv determining sites are present on 7S γ-globulin molecules (2, 3). Evidence has also been presented which indicates that 19S γ-globulins and β_{2A}-globulins lack the Gm characters (7). No evidence has been available concerning the presence of Inv determining sites on these proteins.

The present experiments confirmed that Gm determining sites are present only in 7S γ-globulins, whereas Inv determining sites are present also in 19S γ-globulins, β_{2A}-globulins, and Bence-Jones proteins. These findings and the results of the splitting experiments provide evidence for a common genetic makeup of a part of all four types of proteins. This is particularly interesting as this part of the 7S γ-globulin molecule is known to contain the antibody combining sites (8). The findings are in agreement with previous evidence from this laboratory (9) and elsewhere (10) which indicates that the immunological cross-reaction between 7S γ-globulin and the three other proteins is due to common antigenic determinants present on the S fragment after papain splitting of 7S γ-globulin, whereas antigenic determinants present on the F fragment appear not to be shared by the other proteins.

After papain splitting of 7S γ-globulin, the Gm determining site was found in one of the fragments only and the Inv site in the other. Irrespective of the precise action of papain on the 7S γ-globulin molecule, these findings indicate that the sites are present on different parts of the native molecule. The results with the highly homogeneous myeloma proteins are particularly relevant in this connection where the same myeloma protein contained the two sites in the different papain fragments. The molecules of 7S γ-globulin appears to consist of several polypeptide chains linked by disulfide bonds (11), and it is possible that the present findings correspond to the current concept of "one gene–one polypeptide chain" as exemplified by hemoglobin. However, this remains to be proved. At any rate, one gene, which also has the code of the Gm-determining site, might control the structure of one portion of the molecule. An independent gene may control the structure of another part of the molecule which contains the antibody combining sites (8) and also the Inv-determining site(s) (12).

REFERENCES AND NOTES

(1) R. Grubb and A.-B. Laurell. 1956. Acta Path. Microbiol. Scand. **39:** 390.

(2) R. Grubb and A.-B. Laurell. 1961. Arthritis and Rheumatism. 1961. **4:** 195.

(3) C. Ropartz, J. Lenoir and L. Rivat. 1961. Nature. **189:** 586.

(4) A. G. Steinberg, J. Wilson and S. Lanset. Nature. In press.

(5) R. R. Porter. 1959. Biochem. J. **73:** 119.

(6) G. M. Edelman, J. F. Heremans, M.-Th. Heremans and H. G. Kunkel. 1960. J. Exp. Med. **112:** 203.

(7) L. Martensson. Acta Med. Scand. Suppl. 367. 170: 87; J. L. Fahey and S. D. Lawler. 1961. J. Natl. Cancer. Inst. **27:** 293.

(8) E. C. Franklin. 1960. J. Clin. Invest. **39**: 1933; J. H. Morse and J. F. Heremans. 1962. J. Lab. Clin. Med. **59**: 891.

(9) J. F. Heremans and M.-Th. Heremans. 1961. Acta Med. Scand. Suppl. 367. **170**: 27.

(10) E. C. Franklin and D. R. Stanworth. 1961. J. Exp. Med. **114**: 521.

(11) G. M. Edelman and M. D. Poulik. 1961. J. Exp. Med. **113**: 861.

(12) We are grateful to O. Hartman, P. Herzog, J. C. Nielsen, C. Ropartz, and A. G. Steinberg for generous provision of reagents which made this work possible, and to A. G. Steinberg who kindly confirmed the Inv(b) character for two of the isolated proteins. This work was aided by a grant from the National Foundation.

13 January 1962.

The Structural Basis for Genetic Variations of Normal Human γ-Globulins*

EDWARD C. FRANKLIN

HUGH FUDENBERG

MARTIN MELTZER

DENIS R. STANWORTH

Departments of Medicine, New York University School of Medicine and the University of California School of Medicine

Communicated by Colin M. MacLeod, April 5, 1962

Genetic differences (allotypes) in γ-globulins have been noted in rabbits,[1,2] mice,[3] guinea pigs,[4] and humans.[5-11] Since the initial observation by Grubb[5]

* Reprinted by senior author's and publisher's permission from Proceedings of the National Academy of Sciences. 1962. **48**: 914-922.

[1] J. Oudin. 1956. C. R. Acad. Sci., Paris. **242**: 2489, 2606.

[2] S. Dray and G. O. Young. 1959. Science. **129**: 1023.

[3] A. Kelus and J. K. Moor-Jankowski. 1961. Nature. **189**: 586.

[4] B. Benacerraf and P. G. H. Gell. 1961. Nature. **189**: 586.

[5] R. Grubb. 1956. Acta Path. Microbiol. Scand. **39**: 195.

[6] M. Harboe. 1959. Acta Path. Microbiol. Scand. **47**: 191.

[7] M. Harboe and J. Lundevall. 1959. Acta Path. Microbiol. Scand. **45**: 357.

[8] B. Brandtzaeg, H. H. Fudenberg and J. Mohr. 1961. Acta Genet. **11**: 170.

[9] G. Ropartz, J. Lenoir and L. Rivat. 1961. Nature. **189**: 586.

[10] A. G. Steinberg, U. Wilson and S. Lanset. To be published.

[11] A. G. Steinberg, B. D. Giles and R. Stauffer. 1960. Am. J. Hum. Genet. **13**: 44.

that human γ-globulins differ in their ability to inhibit the agglutination, by selected sera containing rheumatoid factor, of Rho (+) cells coated with incomplete anti D antibody, seven genetically determined variants in human γ-globulins have been described.[5-11] In Caucasians, two loci segregating independently control the production of 6 well defined factors. Genes at the Gm 1 locus determine the production of two main factors known as Gm 1 (*a*) and (*b*) which are inherited as simple codominant non-sex-linked alleles,[5,6] and two minor ones known as Gm 1 (x)[7] and (r).[8] The second locus (In V or Gm 2) also determines the production of two codominant allelic factors known as In V (*a*)[9] and (*b*).[10] The seventh factor, "Gm like" is absent from Caucasian subjects.[11] It is not linked to the In V factors and its relationship to the Gm 1 factors has not yet been clarified.[11] These γ-globulins can by distinguished from each other only by differences in their capacity to inhibit the agglutination of cells by selected sera containing substances serologically similar to, if not identical to, "rheumatoid factors," and to date no other characteristic chemical or structural differences have been found between them.

Studies of 3.5S units prepared from human 7S γ-globulin with papain and cysteine[12,13] have shown them to consist of two fragments of slow electrophoretic mobility (A and C), each containing a single antibody combining site, and a third, more rapidly migrating fragment (B) which is devoid of antibody combining activity. The latter differs from the other two also in its antigenic properties[12] and the type of carbohydrate associated with it.[14] The determinant group(s) responsible for the cross-reaction of 7S γ-globulin with the other two immune globulins (19S γ and γ_{1A} globulins), as well as with the closely related pathologic myeloma proteins, macroglobulins, and Bence-Jones proteins, are associated with the part of the molecule containing the antibody combining site, while the antigenic specificity of 7S γ-globulin resides primarily in fragment B.[15,16]

The existence of two nonlinked genetic factors, together with the finding of two major chemically and immunologically distinct subunits of human 7S γ-globulin suggested the possibility of a separate genetic control of each subunit. The results of the present studies present support for this concept in that Gm factors controlled by the two Gm loci reside in separate parts of the molecule; Gm 1 activity has been found only in fragment B, while In V activity was associated only with fragments A and C. In addition, In V activity, but not Gm 1 activity, has been found also in the 19S γ-globulins, γ_{1A} globulins, and certain Bence-Jones proteins.

[12] E. C. Franklin. 1960. J. Clin. Inv. **39**: 1933.

[13] G. M. Edelman, J. F. Heremans, M.-Th. Heremans and H. G. Kunkel. 1960. J. Exp. Med. **112**: 203.

[14] E. C. Franklin and Z. Dische. 1962. Fed. Proc. **21**: 33.

[15] E. C. Franklin and D. Stanworth. 1961. J. Exp. Med. **114**: 521.

[16] J. F. Heremans and M.-Th. Heremans. 1961. Acta Med. Scand. Suppl. 367. **170**: 27.

MATERIALS AND METHODS. SERA

Twenty to thirty ml of fresh normal serum were obtained on one or more occasions from 13 normal subjects chosen from a larger number on the basis of their Gm types. As shown in Table 1, they include each of the possible combinations of the 4 major groups at the Gm 1 and In V loci. Only the (a) and (b) factors at each locus were examined and Gm (x), (r), and "Gm like" factors were not analyzed further in this study. Six of the sera were examined on two or three separate occasions, and in each instance γ-globulin was freshly prepared from a new aliquot of serum and separately digested and analyzed.

ISOLATION OF γ-GLOBULINS AND PAPAIN FRAGMENTS FROM 7S γ-GLOBULIN

7S γ-globulin was isolated in the majority of experiments by batch chromatography on DEAE cellulose.[17] The preparations so obtained contained only 7S γ-globulins and were free of 19S γ and $γ_{1A}$ globulins on immunoelectrophoresis. In three experiments, starch zone electrophoresis was employed for isolating the γ-globulins.[18] 3.5S fragments were prepared from 7S γ-globulin by digestion with papain, cysteine, and EDTA[12,19] at 37°C for 15 hr. The reaction was stopped by dialyzing against phosphate buffer pH 8, $μ$ 0.01 at 4°C. The two univalent fragments (A and C) were separated from fragment B by chromatography on DEAE cellulose.[12] Under the conditions employed, fragments A and C did not attach to the exchanger and came off the column together with the starting buffer (phosphate, pH 8, $μ$ 0.01), while fragment B remained on the column and was subsequently eluted with the same buffer containing 0.3 M NaCl. In most of the experiments, A and C were not separated from each other because structurally as well as functionally they appear to be closely related to each other and may even represent similar fragments derived from γ-globulin molecules of different mobility.[12,20,21] In four instances, Fractions A and C were separated from each other by chromatography on carboxymethyl cellulose.[12] In each case, as illustrated with fractions from two sera in Table 2, they gave similar results in the Gm 1 (a) and (b) and In V (a) and (b) systems. Purity of the fragments was checked in each experiment by immunoelectrophoresis and Ouchterlony analysis, as described previously.[12] In no instance were fractions employed which contained more than an estimated 10 per cent contamina-

[17] D. R. Stanworth. 1960. Nature. **188**: 156.

[18] H. G. Kunkel. 1954. D. Glick (editor). Methods of biochemical analysis. New York, Interscience Publishers. **1**: 141.

[19] R. R. Porter. 1959. Biochem. J. **73**: 119.

[20] J. L. Palmer, W. J. Mandy and A. Nisonoff. 1962. Proc. Nat. Acad. Sci. (U.S.). **48**: 49.

[21] H. H. Fudenberg. To be published.

Table 1. Inhibitory Capacity of Fragments A and C and B from 7S γ-Globulin from Normal Subjects on Gm 1 and In V Agglutination Systems

Subject	Gm 1 Locus — a Serum	a A and C	a B	b Serum	b A and C	b B	In V Locus — a Serum	a A and C	a B	b Serum	b A and C	b B
S.W. 1*	+	Neg.	<0.05	−	(Neg.)	(Neg.)	+	0.12	Neg.	+		Neg.
S.W. 2	−	0.125†	0.002									
B.F. 1*	+	(Neg.)	(Neg.)	+	Neg.	0.5	+	<0.1	Neg.	+	<0.1	Neg.
B.F. 2	−	(Neg.)	(Neg.)		Neg.	0.25		<0.1	Neg.			
H.F. 1*	+	Neg.	0.05	+	Neg.	0.5	−	(Neg.)	(Neg.)	+	<0.1	Neg.
H.F. 2	+	Neg.	0.03		Neg.	1.0		(Neg.)	(Neg.)			
D.A. 1	+	(Neg.)	(Neg.)	+	Neg.	1.0	−	(Neg.)	(Neg.)	+	<0.1	Neg.
D.A. 2	+	(Neg.)	(Neg.)		Neg.	0.25		(Neg.)	(Neg.)		<0.1	Neg.
D.A. 3	−	(Neg.)	(Neg.)		Neg.	0.5		(Neg.)	(Neg.)			
E.P. 1	+	0.1†	0.005	−	(Neg.)	(Neg.)	−	(Neg.)	(Neg.)	+	0.03	0.5†
E.P. 2	+	Neg.	0.015		(Neg.)	(Neg.)		(Neg.)	(Neg.)		<0.1	Neg.
M.D.	+	Neg.	<0.1	+	Neg.	0.5	−	(Neg.)	(Neg.)	+		
H.S.	+	Neg.	<0.03	+	Neg.	0.5	−	(1.0)	(Neg.)	+	0.03	0.5†
A.K.	−	(Neg.)	(Neg.)	+	Neg.	0.5	−	(Neg.)	(Neg.)	+	0.1	Neg.
S.L. 1	+	Neg.	0.02	+	Neg.	0.5	+	<0.1	Neg.	+	<0.1	Neg.
S.L. 2	+	Neg.	0.06		Neg.	1.0		<0.1	Neg.		0.03	Neg.
N.O.	+	Neg.	<0.1	+	Neg.	0.5	+	<0.1	1.0†	−	(0.25)	(Neg.)
F.A.	+	Neg.	0.01	−	(Neg.)	(Neg.)	+	<0.1	Neg.	+	0.06	0.5†
N.E.	+	Neg.	0.03	+			−	(Neg.)	(Neg.)	+		
R.G.	+	Neg.	0.06	+			+	0.12	Neg.	+		

Numerals = minimum concentration needed for inhibition (mg/ml). † 10–15% contamination by immunoelectrophoresis. Neg. = no inhibition at 2 mg/ml. (Neg.) = expected negative, found negative at 2 mg/ml. ( ) = unexpected (false) positive.
* Electrophoretic separation.

Table 2. Titration of Gm 1 (*a*) and In V (*a*) Activity of 7S γ-Globulin and Papain Fragments from 2 Sera

Serum	Fraction added	Gm 1 (*a*) (mg/ml)					In V (*a*) (mg/ml)			
		2	0.5	0.125	0.031	0.0078	2	0.5	0.125	0.031
S.L.										
Gm 1 (*a* +)	7S	0	0	0	+++	+++	0	0	0	+++
In V (*a* +)	A and C	+	+++	+++	+++	+++	0	++	++	+++
	A	+++	+++	+++	+++	+++	+	++	+++	+++
	C	+++	0	0	0	+++	0	++	+	+++
	B	0	+++	+++	+++	+++	+	+	+	+++
D.A.										
Gm 1 (*a* −)	7S γ	+++	+++	+++	+++	+++	+++	+++	+++	+++
In V (*a* −)	A and C	+++	+++	+++	+++	+++	+++	+++	+++	+++
	A	+++	+++	+++	+++	+++	+++	+++	+++	+++
	C	+++	+++	+++	+++	+++	+++	+++	+++	+++
	B	+++	+++	+++	+++	+++	+++	+++	+++	+++
Control	None	+++					+++			

0 to +++ refers to degree of agglutination.

tion. In the early experiments, completeness of digestion was checked further by analytical ultracentrifugation. Subsequently, it was noted that undigested γ-globulin could be detected also by immunoelectrophoresis. In none of the preparations employed were traces of native 7S γ-globulin detected. γ_{1A} globulins were isolated from pooled normal plasma by the procedure of Heremans[22] and 19S γ-globulins by repeated preparative ultracentrifugation as discussed in detail previously.[23] Neither preparation contained more than 5 per cent contaminating proteins.

Bence-Jones proteins from the urines of 8 patients with multiple myeloma and one subject with Macroglobulinemia of Waldenström were studied initially. In 8 instances, sera were also available. Four of these had a γ myeloma spike, two had normal patterns, one was hypogammaglobulinemic, and one had a macroglobulin in the slow α_2 globulin region. The Bence-Jones proteins were isolated by precipitation with 40–50 per cent saturated ammonium sulfate. They were redissolved in water and freed of salt by dialysis. Eight of the proteins gave only a single line on immunoelectrophoresis, which migrated with the γ or β globulins and, in one instance, with the α_2 globulins (ME). One (Bu) contained a second precipitin line. Each protein could be placed into one of two distinct antigenic groups by the Ouchterlony technique.[24] As demonstrated previously[24] and shown in Figure 1, these two classes of myeloma proteins differ from each other in antigenic structure, but each cross-reacts with fragments A and C and not with fragment B of 7S γ-globulin.[15] Thirteen additional Bence-Jones proteins kindly supplied by Dr. E. Osserman were examined to confirm the results obtained with these proteins. In the latter instances, serum samples were not available for comparison.

TYPING METHOD AND REAGENTS

Two per cent washed 0 Rho positive red cells suspended in pH 7.2 phosphate buffered saline were sensitized at 37°C for one hr. with an equal volume of anti Rho serum containing 160 "units" of antibody activity. (One unit is defined as the minimal amount of the anti Rho antiserum detected by the indirect Coombs' test.) The sensitized cells were washed three times with saline and reconstituted to a 1.5 per cent suspension in phosphate buffered saline pH 7.2.

One volume of serial dilutions (made with separate pipettes to prevent carry-over) of sera or fractions to be tested for inhibitory activity were added

[22] J. F. Heremans. 1960. Les Globulines Sériques de Système Gamma, Brussels. Arscia, Sa.

[23] C. A. Reisner and E. C. Franklin. 1961. J. Immunol. **87**: 654.

[24] L. Korngold and R. Lipari. 1956. Cancer. **9**: 262. We would like to thank Dr. Leonard Korngold for studying two of these proteins for us.

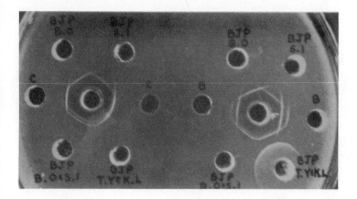

Fig. 1. Comparison of the antigenic properties of Bence-Jones proteins of types A & B and mixtures of these with fragments B or C of humans 7S γ-globulin. Antiserum to 7S γ-globulin in the center wells.

to an equal volume of a standard dilution of a rheumatoid serum of known specificity for one or another of the Gm or In V factors. The mixture was incubated in a 10 × 75 mm test tube at room temperature for 30 min. Then one volume of the sensitized cell suspension was added. After a 3-hr period of incubation at room temperature, the tubes were centrifuged for 45 sec. in a serological centrifuge (Serofuge) and read for agglutination with a hand lens. Agglutination was graded from 0 to 3+ depending on the degree of clumping. In all studies, appropriate controls were used to insure that agglutination was not due to the test serum or the added fractions rather than the "rheumatoid factor."

The test sera and red cell coating sera employed were similar to those used previously.[25] Each fraction was tested for inhibitory activity with at least two separate sets of reagents for each Gm factor with the exception of In V (b), for which only one set of reagents exists to date. In some of the later experiments, tests for In V (b) activity were not possible since the reagent was no longer available.

Inhibitory activity (+) or lack of inhibition (−) varies with the quality of the reagents used for the various test systems. For Gm 1 (a), the difference is striking and varies by a factor of at least 32 with both sets of reagents used. For In V (a), the difference is 8- and 16-fold with the two reagents used. For In V (b), the difference is 8-fold, and in the Gm 1 (b) system the difference between a positive and a negative serum is 4- to 8-fold with two sets of test reagents.

[25] H. H. Fudenberg and H. G. Kunkel. 1961. J. Exp. Med. **114:** 257.

RESULTS

Recovery of Gm activity with whole 7S γ-globulins isolated by starch zone electrophoresis or chromatography was good in all instances. Gm 1 (*a*) activity was obtained at a concentration of 0.06 mg/ml; Gm 1 (*b*) was active at a concentration of 0.25-0.50 mg/ml, while In V (*a*) and (*b*) inhibited agglutination of the appropriate cells at concentrations of 0.125 mg/ml and 0.25 mg/ml respectively. In no instance was γ-globulin from a negative serum able to inhibit agglutination by the appropriate test serum following isolation. Results with papain fragments of 7S γ-globulin obtained from sera of varying combinations of Gm 1 and In V activity are summarized in Table 1. Following papain digestion and chromatographic separation of the fragments, Gm 1 (*a*) activity, i.e. the ability to inhibit agglutination of appropriately sensitized cells by an anti Gm (*a*) serum, was recovered only in fragment B, and in most experiments the inhibitory capacity per mg of protein was equal to or as much as two times greater on a weight basis than that of the native 7S γ-globulin from the same subject prior to digestion. No inhibition greater than expected on the basis of incomplete separation was ever noted in fragments A and C even when tested in concentrations 10 to 100 times greater than the minimal amount necessary for inhibition by the active fragment B. In the earlier experiments using small amounts, Gm 1 (*b*) activity could not be recovered in any of the fragments. When larger amounts of the fractions were used, inhibition was also observed only with fragment B. However, with one exception a concentration of 0.5-1.0 mg/ml of protein, or approximately twice the concentration of the native 7S protein, was required to inhibit. As was the case in Gm 1 (*a*) activity, inhibition was never associated with fragment A and C in concentrations as high as 4.0 mg/ml, nor was it recovered from Gm 1 (*b*) negative sera. While recovery of activity was poor and inconstant, the results suggest that it was present only in fragment B. The reason for the poorer recovery is not certain, but may be in part due to destruction of Gm activity by papain.[26]

In contrast to the results obtained with Gm 1 activity, In V activity (*a*) as well as (*b*) was not associated with fragment B but always found on fragments A and C. Here, too, activity recovered in fragment B could be explained by small amounts of contaminating proteins. In general, the fragments were less active than native 7S γ-globulin, and in two instances In V activity was found in fragments prepared from a serum initially devoid of In V inhibitory activity when tested at high concentration. The reason for these discrepancies and for the somewhat lower inhibitory efficiency of the fragments compared to the native protein remains to be explained. As noted above, it may be in part due to changes during digestion and the fractionation procedures.[26]

[26] R. Grubb. 1958. In, P. Grabar and P. Miescher. Immunopathology, first international symposium. Basle, Benno Schwabe: 359.

Detailed results of one titration with two sera, S. L. Gm 1 $(a+)$ and In V $(a+)$ and D. A. Gm 1 $(a-)$ In V $(a-)$ are shown in Table 2. These demonstrate clearly the separation of the two activities controlled by these two loci and illustrate that fragments A and C behave similarly.

While it has been recognized that Gm 1 activity is found only on 7S γ-globulin and not on any of the other immune globulins,[21,27,28] there are no reports as to the location of In V activity. In view of the previously demonstrated cross-reaction of fragments A and C with γ_{1A}, and 19S γ-globulins and Bence-Jones proteins, and the present finding of In V activity associated with these fragments, attempts were made to determine if In V activity also resided in these proteins. Examination of a preparation of pure 19S γ-globulin obtained from a pool of 20 donors and a pure γ_{1A} globulin preparation isolated from pooled plasma from 10 donors revealed In V activity to be associated with each of these fractions. Similar results have also been obtained with γ_{1A} myeloma proteins and pathologic macroglobulins by ourselves[29] and by Harboe, Osterland, and Kunkel.[30] The results with Bence-Jones proteins are of particular interest in that they appear to permit more precise localization of In V activity. Figure 1 confirms the existence of two major types of Bence-Jones proteins[24] each of which cross-reacts with fragments A and C but which are antigenically distinct from each other when tested with an antiserum to 7S γ-globulin. Even when mixed, they do not contain all the antigenic determinant groups present in fragments A and C. Studies with four Bence-Jones proteins of Group B and five of Group A indicated that each of the type B proteins possessed In V activity while only one of the five type A proteins was able to inhibit. The latter (Bu) gave a second band on immunoelectrophoresis although it sedimented as a single peak in the ultracentrifuge. The In V activities of these proteins and the In V type of seven of the sera are listed in Table 3. It is likely that most of the sera were In V $(b+)$ but sufficient reagents were not available for complete typing.

Confirmatory studies with the remaining 13 Bence-Jones proteins where appropriate serum samples were not available are also shown in Table 3. Of eight proteins in Group B, five were definitely positive, one intermediate in reactivity, and two were negative. Of five Group A proteins, none showed In V (a) or In V (b) activity. It seems possible that other Type B proteins (especially 010, 014) also had In V (b) activity since only two out of eight Type B proteins were tested. The findings could not be related to the electrophoretic mobilities of the proteins. Although an insufficient number of sera were available for testing, it seems unlikely that these results reflect differences in the In V types of the sera, since differences between the normal

[27] L. Mårtensson. 1961. Acta Med. Scand. Suppl. 367. **170:** 87.

[28] J. L. Fahey and S. D. Lawler. 1961. J. Nat. Cancer. Inst. **27:** 973.

[29] H. F. Deutsch and H. H. Fudenberg. To be published; H. H. Fudenberg. 1962. P. Kallós (editor). Progress in allergy. Basle, Karger. **6.**

[30] M. Harboe, C. K. Osterland and H. G. Kunkel. 1962. Science. **136:**979.

Table 3. INHIBITORY ACTIVITY OF BENCE-JONES PROTEINS OF DIFFERENT IMMUNOLOGIC TYPES[24]

Name and diagnosis	Serum In V (a)	BJP, Type B		Name and diagnosis	Serum In V (a)	BJP, Type A	
		In V (a)	In V (b)			In V (a)	In V (b)
G.L. MM¹ 0	+	+	−	S.I. MM		−	−
T.Y. MM 0	−	−	+	K.L. MM γ	−	−	−
B.O. MM γ	+	+	−	F.E. MM Hypo γ	−	−	−
R.O. MM γ	Aggl.	+	−	B.U. MM γ		−	+
				M.E. MG² α₂	−	−	−
02		−	+	01		−	−
04		−	Int +	03		−	−
05		+		06		−	−
08		+		07		−	−
09		+		013		−	
010		−					
012		+					
014		−					
No. Tested		12	6	No. Tested		10	9
No. Pos.		7	3	No. Pos.		0	1
% Pos.		58	50	% Pos.		0	11

¹ MM = multiple myeloma and type-O no spike. 2 MG = Macroglobulinemia (α_2 globulin).

proteins and the myeloma proteins in the same serum have also been noted in patients with multiple myeloma.[26,29,30]

DISCUSSION

Complex molecules the size of γ-globulins do not yet lend themselves readily to precise structural analyses similar to those successfully employed in determining the structure of smaller proteins such as ribonuclease[31,32] and insulin.[33] However, several approaches in recent years have aided in partially clarifying the structure of some of these proteins. Thus, chemically well defined reductive cleavage has provided evidence for the existence of several chains in γ-globulins from a number of species[34] and has detected differences in the primary structure of various paraproteins and pure antibodies.[34,35] The less well defined breakdown with enzymes such as papain, trypsin, and

[31] C. H. W. Hirs, W. H. Stein and S. More. 1958. A. Neuberger (editor). Symposium on protein structure. New York, John Wiley & Sons, Inc.: 211.

[32] C. B. Anfinsen. 1958. A. Neuberger (editor). Symposium on protein structure. New York, John Wiley & Sons, Inc.: 223.

[33] J. I. Harris, F. Sanger and M. A. Naughton. 1956. Arch. Biochem. Biophys. 65: 427.

[34] G. M. Edelman and M. D. Poulik. 1961. J. Exp. Med. 113: 861.

[35] G. M. Edelman, B. Benacerraf, Z. Ovary and M. D. Poulik. 1961. These Proceedings. 47: 1751.

pepsin has yielded fragments about one fourth to one third the size of native proteins which are biologically active[12,13,19,36-38] and each of which may contain one or more of the chains making up the native protein.

The results of the present studies on normal human γ-globulins isolated from individuals of different genetic γ-globulin groups (Gm groups) and similar studies on myeloma proteins by ourselves[29] and by Harboe and collaborators[30] present strong evidence that the Gm factors, controlled by two distinct Gm loci, reside in separate parts of the γ-globulin molecule and suggest that the two major genetic loci affect different parts of the protein. Gm 1 activity, which is found only in 7S γ-globulin, resides in fragment B, which is unique to 7S γ-globulin. On the other hand, In V activity, which is also found in the 19S γ and $γ_{1A}$ globulins as well as some Bence-Jones proteins, resides in that part of the molecule which carries the determinant groups responsible for the cross-reaction of all of these proteins and also the antibody combining site. While the exact location of the In V activity on these fragments cannot yet be determined, the observation that many Bence-Jones proteins of one antigenic type carry In V activity while few of those belonging to the other type are In V-positive can probably not be explained by differences in the Gm types of the sera and suggests that comparison of these two types of proteins and further controlled chemical or enzymatic degradation of these proteins may permit better delineation of these factors, possibly on individual chains of the molecule. The recent finding by Putnam[39] that the peptide pattern of Type B Bence-Jones proteins differs from that of Type A proteins and resembles that of 7S γ-globulin more closely is consistent with this. Of particular interest in further evaluating the possible mode of action of these genes is the observation of Harboe et al.[30] that in six individuals studied, the In V activity associated with the 7S fraction was similar to that in the 19S γ-globulin.

From the data currently available, it is not possible to determine the exact site of action of each of the genes, since the fragments may well contain one or more of these chains or even parts of chains. Similar studies of these better defined entities have not yet been possible because of the virtually complete loss of all biologic activities during their preparation. However, the excellent correlation between the two genetic factors and a variety of other structural properties of these fragments employed suggest that while they may not be the ultimate genetically defined units they must at least contain them. A similar type of genetic control appears to exist in the case of the hemoglobins,[40] where each chain is controlled by a separate gene, and may also be found in other proteins.

[36] A. Nisonoff, F. C. Wissler and D. Woernley. 1960. Arch. Biochem. Biophys. **88**: 241.

[37] A. Taranta, E. C. Franklin and Z. Ovary. 1961. Science. **134**: 1981.

[38] A. Taranta, E. C. Franklin, and Z. Ovary. 1962. Fed. Proc. **21**: 21.

[39] F. W. Putnam. Personal communication.

[40] V. M. Ingram. 1958. Biochim. Biophys. Acta. **28**: 539.

At present, there are no other techniques available to distinguish the various genetically distinct γ-globulins from each other. However, the results obtained with the different types of Bence-Jones proteins, as well as preliminary studies employing "fingerprint" techniques,[39] suggest that further controlled enzymatic degradation and analyses may succeed in detecting the chemical basis of the specificity.

SUMMARY

3.5S fragments prepared from 7S γ-globulins from sera of a variety of Gm types were assayed for their Gm 1 (*a*) and (*b*) and In V (*a*) and (*b*) activities. These two activities, which are controlled by two distinct genetic loci, were found on different parts of the γ-globulin molecule. In V activity was always recovered with fragments A and C, while Gm 1 activity was always associated with fragment B. In V activity, but not Gm 1 activity, was also associated with 19S γ-globulins, γ_{1A} globulins, and the majority of Group B Bence-Jones proteins. All of these proteins cross-react with fragments A and C of 7S γ-globulin. The finding of two activities which are under separate genetic control on different parts of the γ-globulin molecule suggests that these genes may control individual chains of the γ-globulin molecules.

The authors would like to thank D. Ropartz, A. Steinberg, C. Podliachouk, and S. H. Boyer for some of the reagents.

Cytogenetics

Part Four

In the years preceding the report of Tjio and Levan the chromosomal number of man was presumed to be 48. The demonstration that the human chromosomal complement was in fact 46 provided not only a baseline for judging abnormality but also indicated an adequate and comparatively simple means for examining human chromosomes. The first demonstration of variation from normal was made by Lejeune with the discovery that persons with Mongoloid idiocy have 47 chromosomes. This signal accomplishment was rapidly followed by the observations of Jacobs and Strong and then by those of Ford and his colleagues to the effect that both Klinefelter's and Turner's syndromes respectively are explicable on the basis of alteration in sex chromosome complement. In their inception these latter observations owe much to a decade of interest which followed Barr and Bertram's discovery (1), in 1949, of the nuclear sex chromatin body in female cats. The subsequent finding that most individuals with Turner's syndrome were male-like, that is, lacked a nuclear sex chromatin body, while those with Klinefelter's syndrome possessed a sex chromatin body and were thus female-like provided a spur to the hunt culminating in these papers.

The four reports, reprinted below, are those of the pioneers in what is now a burgeoning field of interest. The utility of these developments to diagnosis is obvious. The utility of such studies to genetics at large is perhaps less obvious since the principle of chromosomal aberration in number and form was established in other species long ago. However, in its details the study of human chromosomes has provided information of interest to all geneticists. For example, the role of the Y chromosome has advanced from its formerly assigned inactive role to an active one by virtue of the fact that individuals with XXY Klinefelter's syndrome appear male rather than female in the external view. Here again the success of human genetics has depended upon correlation with disease.

Of perhaps even greater general interest is the recent hypothesis advanced by Lyon and independently by Beutler (2). In this hypothesis, a

*discussion of which is reprinted here, normal mammalian females are
presumed to be X-chromosome mosaics and any one cell has presumably
only one operative X-chromosome.*

(1) M. L. Barr and E. A. Bertram. 1949. A morphological distinc-
    tion between neurones of the male and female, and the
    behaviour of the nucleolar satellite during accelerated nucleo-
    protein synthesis. Nature. **163:** 676-677.

(2) E. Beutler, Mary Yeh and V. F. Fairbanks. 1962. The normal
    human female as a mosaic of X-chromosome activity: Studies
    using the gene for G-6-PD deficiency as a marker. Proc.
    Nat. Acad. Science. **48:** 9-16.

The Chromosome Number of Man*

JOE HIN TJIO
Estacion Experimental de Aula Dei, Zaragoza, Spain
ALBERT LEVAN
Cancer Chromosome Laboratory, Institute of Genetics, Lund, Sweden

While staying last summer at the Sloan-Kettering Institute, New York, one
of us tried out some modifications of Hsu's technique (1952) on various
human tissue cultures carried in serial *in vitro* cultivation at that institute.
The results were promising inasmuch as some fairly satisfactory chromosome
analyses were obtained in cultures both of tissues of normal origin and of
tumours (Levan, 1956).

Later on both authors, working in cooperation at Lund, have tried still
further to improve the technique. We had access to tissue cultures of human
embryonic lung fibroblasts, grown in bovine amniotic fluid; these were very
kindly supplied to us by Dr. Rune Grubb of the Virus Laboratory, Institute
of Bacteriology, Lund. All cultures were primary explants taken from human
embryos obtained after legal abortions. The embryos were 10-25 cm in
length. The chromosomes were studied a few days after the *in vitro* explantation had been made.

* Reprinted by senior author's and publisher's permission from *Hereditas*. 1956.
42: 1-6.

In our opinion the hypotonic pre-treatment introduced by Hsu, although a very significant improvement especially for spreading the chromosomes, has a tendency to make the chromosome outlines somewhat blurred and vague. We consequently tried to abbreviate the hypotonic treatment to a minimum, hoping to induce the scattering of the chromosomes without unfavourable effects on the chromosome surface. Pre-treatment with hypotonic solution for only one or two minutes gave good results. In addition, we gave a colchicine dose to the culture medium 12-20 hours before fixation, making the medium 50×10^{-9} mol/l for the drug. The colchicine effected a considerable accumulation of mitoses and a varying degree of chromosome contraction. Fixation followed in 60% acetic acid, twice exchanged in order to wash out the salts left from the culture medium and from the hypotonic solution that would otherwise have caused precipitation with the orcein. Ordinary squash preparations were made in 1% acetic orcein. For chromosome counts the squashing was made very mild in order to keep the chromosomes in the metaphase groups. For idiogram studies a more thorough squashing was preferable. In many cases single cells were squashed under the microscope by a slight pressure of a needle. In such cases it was directly observed that no chromosomes escaped.

THE CHROMOSOME NUMBER

With the technique used exact counts could be made in a great number of cells. Figs. 1 *a* and *b* represent typical samples of the appearance of the chromosomes at early metaphase (*a*) and full metaphase (*b*), showing the ease with which the counting could be made. In Table 1 the numbers of counts made from the four embryos studied are recorded.

Table 1. NUMBER OF EXACT CHROMOSOME COUNTS MADE

Embryo No.	Number of cultures	Number of counts
1	5	15
2	10	98
3	3	119
4	4	29
Total	22	261

We were surprised to find that the chromosome number 46 predominated in the tissue cultures from all four embryos, only single cases deviating from this number. Lower numbers were frequent, of course, but always in cells that seemed damaged. These were consequently disregarded just as were the solitary chromosomes and the groups with but a few chromosomes, which

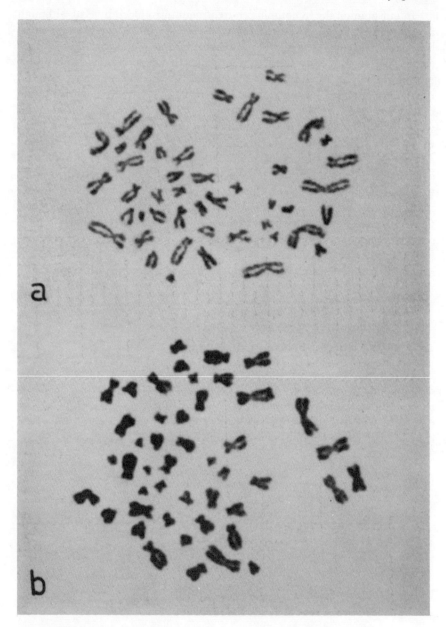

Fig. 1. Colchicine-metaphases of human embryonic lung fibroblasts grown *in vitro*. *a*: early metaphase, *b*: full metaphase. The two
cells are from embryos 2 and 3 (Table 1), respectively. — ×2300.

were frequent. In some doubtful cases the numbers 47 and 48 were counted (in four cases not included in the table). This may be due to one or two solitary chromosomes having been pressed into a 46-chromosome plate at the squashing. It is also possible that deviating numbers may originate through non-disjunction, thus representing a real chromosome number variation in the living tissue. This kind of variation will probably increase as a consequence of the change in environment for the tissue involved in the *in vitro* explantation. Hsu (1952) reports a certain degree of such variation in his primary cultures. LEVAN (1956), studying long-carried serial subcultures, found hypotriploid stemline numbers in two of them, and a near-diploid number in a third culture. In this culture one cell with 48 chromosomes was analysed. Naturally, at that time, this was thought to represent the normal diploid number.

CHROMOSOME MORPHOLOGY

Some data on the chromosome morphology of the 46 human chromosomes will be communicated here. The detailed idiogram analysis will be postponed, however, until we are able to study individuals of known sex, the sex of the present embryos being unknown. The comparative study of germline chromosomes in spermatogonial mitoses constitutes an urgent supplement to the present work.

In Fig. 2 four cells are analysed ranging from late prophase (*a*) to late c-metaphase (*d*). The chromosomes of metaphases with moderate colchicine contraction vary in length between 1 and 8 μ (Fig. 2 *b*), but the entire range of variation of Fig. 2 is from 1 to 11 μ. The chromosome morphology is roughly concordant with the observations of earlier workers, as, for instance, the idiogram of Hsu (1952). The chromosomes may be divided into three groups: M chromosomes (median-submedian centromere; index long arm:short arm $1-1,_9$), S chromosomes (subterminal centromere; arm index $2-4,_9$), and T chromosomes (nearly terminal centromere; arm index 5 or more).

The M and S chromosomes are present in about equal numbers (twenty of each), while six T chromosomes are found. The classification of the three groups is arbitrary, of course, since gradual transitions of arm indices occur between the three groups. Certain submedian M chromosomes are hard to distinguish from some of the S chromosomes, and the most asymmetric S chromosomes approach the T group.

. The chromosomes are easily arranged in pairs, but only certain of these pairs are individually distinguishable. Thus, the M chromosomes include the three longest pairs, which can always be identified. The two longest pairs are different: the second having a decidedly more asymmetric location of its centromere. The two or three smallest M pairs are also recognizable.

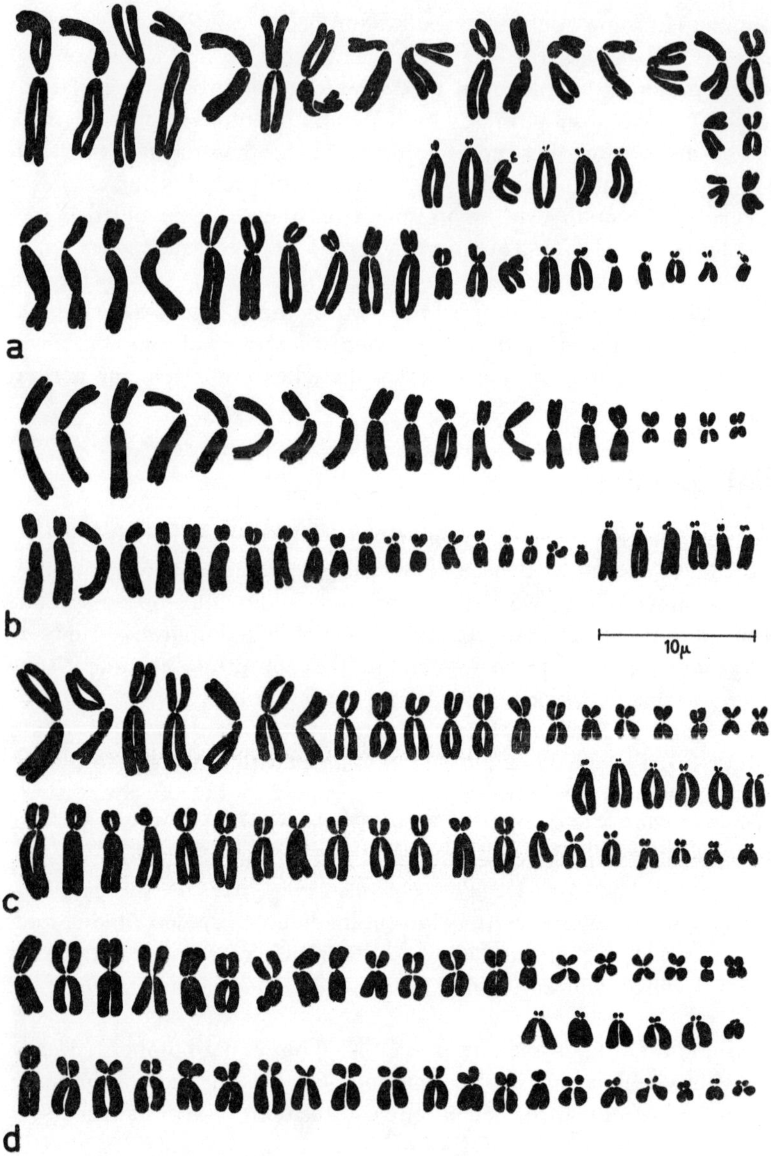

Fig. 2. Four idiogram analyses of human embryonic lung fibroblasts grown *in vitro*. The chromosomes have been grouped in three classes: M (top row), S (bottom row), and T (in between, except in *b*, where T is at the end of the S row). Within each class the chromosomes have been roughly arranged in diminishing order of size. — ×2400.

Between the three longest and the three shortest pairs there are four intermediate pairs that cannot be individually recognized.

The S chromosomes are hardly identifiable, since they form a series of
gradually decreasing length. The largest pair, however, is characteristic.
Certain chromosomes were seen to have a small satellite on their short arms.
Secondary constrictions, too, have been observed now and then, so that it
may be hoped that the detailed morphologic study will lead to the identification of more chromosome pairs. The T chromosomes are recognizable; they
constitute three pairs of middle-sized chromosomes. Unlike the mouse chromosomes, the human T chromosomes evidently have a small shorter arm.

CONCLUSION

The almost exclusive occurrence of the chromosome number 46 in one
somatic tissue derived from four individual human embryos is a very unexpected finding. To assume a regular mechanism for the exclusion of two
chromosomes from the idiogram at the formation of a certain tissue is
unlikely, even if this assumption cannot be entirely dismissed at this stage of
inquiry. Our experience from one somatic tissue in mice and rats, *viz.*, regenerating liver, speaks against this assumption. The exact diploid
chromosome set was always found in regenerating liver.

After the conclusion had been drawn that the tissue studied by us had
46 as chromosome number, Dr. EVA HANSEN-MELANDER kindly informed us
that during last spring she had studied, in cooperation with Drs. YNGVE
MELANDER and STIG KULLANDER, the chromosomes of liver mitoses in
aborted human embryos. This study, however, was temporarily discontinued
because the workers were unable to find all the 48 human chromosomes in
their material; as a matter of fact, the number 46 was repeatedly counted
in their slides. We have seen photomicrographs of liver prophases from this
study, clearly showing 46 chromosomes. These findings suggest that 46 may
be the correct chromosome number for human liver tissue, too.

With previously used technique it has been extremely difficult to make
counts in human material. Even with the great progress involved in HSU's
method exact counts seem difficult, judging from the photomicrographs
published (HSU, 1952 and elsewhere). For instance, we think that the excellent photomicrograph of HSU published in DARLINGTON's book (1953,
facing p. 288) is more in agreement with the chromosome number 46 than
48, and the same is true of many of the photomicrographs of human chromosomes previously published.

Before a renewed, careful control has been made of the chromosome
number in spermatogonial mitoses of man we do not wish to generalize our
present findings into a statement that the chromosome number of man is
$2n = 46$, but it is hard to avoid the conclusion that this would be the most
natural explanation of our observations.

Acknowledgements: We wish to express our sincere thanks to the Swedish Cancer Society for financial support of this investigation, and to Dr. RUNE GRUBB for supplying us with tissue cultures.

SUMMARY

The chromosomes were studied in primary tissue cultures of human lung fibroblasts explanted from four individual embryos. In all of them the chromosome number 46 was encountered, instead of the expected number 48. Since among 265 mitoses counted all except 4 showed the number 46, this number is characteristic of the tissue studied. The possible bearing of this result on the chromosome number of man is discussed.

Institute of Genetics, Lund, January 26, 1956.

LITERATURE CITED

(1) C. D. DARLINGTON. 1953. The facts of life. London.

(2) T. C. HSU. 1952. Mammalian chromosomes *in vitro*. The karyotype of man. J. Hered. **43:** 167-172.

(3) A. LEVAN. 1956. Chromosome studies on some human tumors and tissues of normal origin, grown *in vivo* and *in vitro* at the Sloan-Kettering Institute. Cancer. Philadelphia. 648-666.

Étude des chromosomes somatiques de neuf enfants mongoliens*
(Study of the Somatic Chromosomes of Nine Mongoloid Idiot Children)

JEROME LEJEUNE

MARTHE GAUTIER

RAYMOND TURPIN

The culture of fibroblasts from nine Mongoloid children reveals the presence of 47 chromosomes, the supernumerary chromosome being a small telo-

* Reprinted by senior author's and publisher's permission from Comptes rendus des séances de l'Académie des Sciences. 1959. **248:** 1721-1722.

centric one. The hypothesis of chromosome determination of Mongolism is considered.

The study of mitosis of fibroblasts in culture from nine Mongoloid children recently (1) permitted us to establish with regularity the presence of 47 chromosomes. The observations made in these nine cases (five boys and four girls) are recorded in the table below.

The number of cells counted in each case may seem relatively small. This is due to the fact that only the pictures that claim a minimum of interpretation have been retained in this table.

NUMBER OF CELLS EXAMINED IN EACH CASE

Number of chromosomes	Diploid cells						Tetraploid cells			
	"Doubtful" cells			"Perfect" cells			"Perfect" cells			Total
	46	47	48	46	47	48	—	94	—	—
Boys { Mg 1	6	10	2	—	11	—	—	1	—	30
Mg 2	—	2	1	—	9	—	—	—	—	12
Mg 3	—	1	1	—	7	—	—	2	—	11
Mg 4	—	3	—	—	1	—	—	—	—	4
Mg 5 *	—	—	—	—	8	—	—	—	—	8
Girls { Mg A	1	6	1	—	5	—	—	—	—	13
Mg B	1	2	—	—	8	—	—	—	—	11
Mg C	1	2	1	—	4	—	—	—	—	8
Mg D	1	1	2	—	4	—	—	—	—	8
	10	27	8		57			3		105

* This child is the product of a twin pregnancy. His normal twin, examined at the same time, possesses 46 chromosomes, of which 5 are small telocentric ones.

The apparent variation in the chromosome number in the "doubtful" cells, that is to say, cells in which each chromosome cannot be noted individually with certainty, has been pointed out by several authors (2). It does not seem to us that this phenomenon represents a cytologic reality, but merely reflects the difficulties of a delicate technique.

It therefore seems logical to prefer a small number of absolutely certain counts ("perfect" cells in the table) to a mass of doubtful observations, the statistical variance of which rests solely on the lack of precision of the observations.

Analysis of the chromosome set of the "perfect" cells reveals the presence in Mongolian boys of 6 small telocentric chromosomes (instead of 5 in the normal man) and 5 small telocentric ones in Mongoloid girls (instead of 4 in the normal woman).

The "perfect" cells of non-Mongoloid individuals never present these characteristics (1) and therefore it seems legitimate to conclude that there exists in Mongoloids a small supernumerary telocentric chromosome, accounting for the abnormal figure of 47.

DISCUSSION

To explain the sum total of these observations, the hypothesis of non-disjunction of a pair of small telocentric chromosomes at the time of meiosis can be considered. It is known that in Drosophila non-disjunction is greatly influenced by maternal aging, such a mechanism accounting for the increase in frequency of Mongolism as a function of the advanced age of the mother.

It is, however, not possible to say that the supernumerary small telocentric chromosome is indeed a normal chromosome and at the present time the possibility cannot be discarded that a fragment resulting from another type of aberration is involved.

REFERENCES

(1) J. Lejeune, M. Gautier and R. Turpin. 1959. Comptes rendus. **248:** 602.

(2) P. A. Jacobs and J. A. Strong. Nature. 1959. **183:** 302-303.

A Case of Human Intersexuality Having a Possible XXY Sex-determining Mechanism*

PATRICIA A. JACOBS

DR. J. A. STRONG

Medical Research Council Group for Research on the General Effects of Radiation and Department for Endocrine and Metabolic Diseases, Western General Hospital and University of Edinburgh

Recent improvements in techniques for the examination of human somatic chromosomes have made possible the study of the chromosome complement of human intersexes; consequently, it is now practicable to investigate the relationship in these cases between sex as determined by direct chromosome

* Reprinted by senior author's and publisher's permission from Nature. 1959. **183:** 302-303.

study, and sex as inferred from the study of 'nuclear sex chromatin' of the type described by Barr and Bertram.[1] This report is concerned with one of a series of patients with gonadal dysgenesis who are under investigation, and the particular feature of interest is the occurrence of 47 somatic chromosomes in contrast with the normal number of 46 in man.

In recent years the diploid chromosome number of 46 has been recorded in a large number of instances. In addition to the 60 cases cited in a previous publication[2] we have recorded a diploid number of 46 in bone marrow preparations from a further 40 European subjects. Kodani, on the other hand, has recently published results of counts made on testicular material from 36 Japanese and 8 American white males.[3,4] He claims that in 16 Japanese and 1 American there was a diploid number of 48; in 2 Japanese a diploid number of 47, and that in the remaining 13 Japanese and 7 whites the number was 46. He suggests that 46 is the basic diploid chromosome number for man, but in some instances there are additional "supernumerary chromosomes." The occurrence of this type of supernumerary chromosome, however, has not been reported previously among the vertebrates and awaits confirmation by other workers.

Our patient, an apparent male aged twenty-four, was presented as a case of gonadal dysgenesis with gynæcomastia and small testes associated with poor facial hair-growth and a high-pitched voice. Biopsy examination of testicular tissue showed the seminiferous tubules to be extremely hyalinized and atrophic. and also an apparent increase in the number of interstitial cells. Chromosome studies were attempted on part of this material, but no spermatogonial mitotic or meiotic divisions were seen. Smears made from both the buccal mucosa and the blood were examined by Dr. B. Lennox of the Department of Pathology, Western Infirmary, Glasgow, and found to demonstrate typical female morphology with regard to their nuclear sex chromatin.

Material obtained by sternal marrow puncture was used for investigating the somatic chromosomes. The technique used for culturing the material in the presence of calchicine and for making squash preparations has already been described.[2]

The chromosomes were counted in 44 cells in metaphase and the results are shown in Table 1.

Table 1.

Chromosome No.	45	46	47	48	49
No. of cells	2	7	29	5	1

[1] M. L. Barr and E. G. Bertram. 1949. Nature. **163**: 676.
[2] C. E. Ford, P. A. Jacobs and L. G. Lajtha. 1958. Nature. **181**: 1565.
[3] M. Kodani. 1957. Proc. U. S. Nat. Acad. Sci. **43**: 285.
[4] M. Kodani. 1958. Am. J. Genet. **10**: 125.

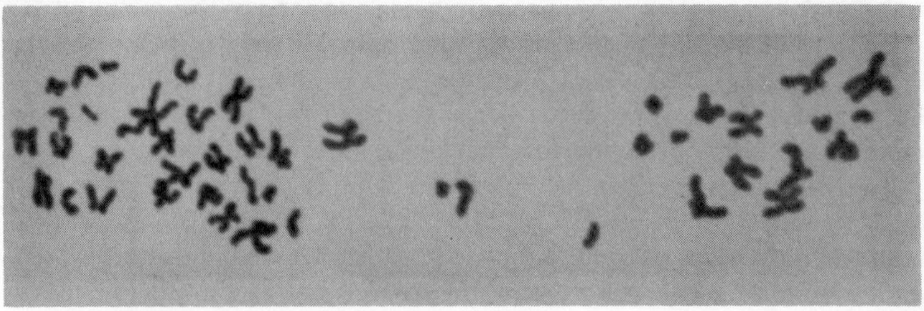

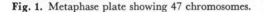

Fig. 1. Metaphase plate showing 47 chromosomes.

The majority of the cells contained 47 chromosomes, and in all those cells where the chromosomes were well fixed and spread, the count was undoubtedly 47 (Fig. 1). The apparent variation is in all probability due to technical errors. Fragments of cells containing chromosomes may become lost during the squashing process so that counts lower than the diploid number are obtained; and occasionally chromosomes split at the centromere and individual chromatids may be counted as chromosomes, giving a count higher than the diploid number.[2]

A study of the chromosome morphology in 8 cells of a suitably high standard showed that each of these had a normal male complement with the Y chromosome present, but that there was also an extra chromosome having a sub-median centromere occurring in the medium size range. In the normal male there are 15 chromosomes in this range, and in the female 16, all having sub-terminal or sub-median centromeres.[2] Owing to the slight variations in their size and morphology these chromosomes have proved difficult to pair, and it is in this category that the X chromosome is to be found.

There are strong grounds, both observational and genetic,[5,6] for believing that human beings with chromatin-positive nuclei are genetic females having two X chromosomes. The fact that this patient is chromatin-positive and has an additional chromosome within the same size range as the X, as well as an apparently normal Y, makes it seem likely that he has the genetic constitution XXY. The possibility cannot be excluded, however, that the additional chromosome is an autosome carrying feminizing genes.

The presence of the extra chromosome might have been due to one or other of the parents having 47 chromosomes, and, therefore, chromosome studies were made on marrow specimens from both parents. Both were found to have a diploid number of 46 (Table 2), and analysis of cells of suitable quality showed the morphology of the chromosomes to be normal.

The occurrence of the extra chromosome therefore may be due to non-

[5] M. M. Grumbach and M. L. Barr. 1958. Recent progress in hormone research. **14:** 255.

[6] P. E. Polani, P. M. F. Bishop, B. Lennox, M. A. Ferguson-Smith, J. S. S. Stewart and A. Prader. 1958. Nature. **182:** 1092.

Table 2.

Father	Chromosome No.	44	45	46	47	48	49
32 cells counted	No. of cells	2	3	26	—	—	1

Mother	Chromosome No.	44	45	46	47	48	49
39 cells counted	No. of cells	1	3	33	2	—	—

disjunction at either mitosis or meiosis during gametogenesis in one or other parent. Alternatively, it may be due to non-disjunction occurring during the patient's very early embryological development, in which case there is a possibility that the patient may be a mosaic. Unfortunately, it is not possible with the techniques at present available to examine the chromosomes of tissues arising from different germ layers of the embryo.

We would like to thank Dr. B. Lennox of the Department of Pathology, Western Infirmary, Glasgow, for checking the nuclear sex of the preparations of buccal mucosa and blood and Miss M. Brunton for technical assistance.

A further report of this and other cases will follow.

A Sex-Chromosome Anomaly in a Case of Gonadal Dysgenesis (Turner's Syndrome)*

C. E. FORD

K. W. JONES
Of the Medical Research Council Radiobiological Research Unit, Atomic Energy Research Establishment, Harwell, Berks

P. E. POLANI

J. C. de ALMEIDA

J. H. BRIGGS
Of Guy's Hospital, London, S.E.1

* Reprinted by senior author's and publisher's permission from Lancet. 1959. i: 711-713.

Gonadal dysgenesis (ovarian agenesis, gonadal dysplasia) is a clinical syndrome usually presenting as a failure of secondary sex characteristics at puberty in girls whose gonads are absent or rudimentary. It is often associated with other congenital malformations such as small stature, digital anomalies, and, more rarely, webbed neck, congenital heart-disease, renal anomalies, intellectual subnormality, and other developmental errors. The more extreme expressions are often referred to as Turner's syndrome.

A considerable proportion of patients with gonadal dysgenesis are chromatin-negative (Décourt, Sasso, Chiorboli, and Fernandes 1954, Polani, Hunter, and Lennox 1954, Wilkins, Grumbach, and Van Wyck 1954), although chromatin-negativity (Barr and Bertram 1949) is an invariable feature of normal males. One possible explanation is that gonadal dysgenesis in man is due to castration while an embryo, since the experimental castration of embryonic rabbits results in the production of animals of female phenotype irrespective of the genetic sex-constitution of the embryo (Jost 1947). However, in abnormal individuals chromatin negativity or positivity ("nuclear sexing") may not necessarily indicate true chromosomal sex (*Lancet* 1956, Polani, Lessof, and Bishop 1956). An alternative explanation for the findings in gonadal dysgenesis might be abnormal sex differentiation following anomalous sex determination in the zygote.

Two approaches to the problem of certainly identifying the sex chromosomes present in Turner's syndrome suggested themselves: direct cytological observation, and the study of colour-blindness, which is a sex-linked recessive character and an X-chromosome marker. The results obtained by the second method agreed with the simple interpretation of the "nuclear sexing" results: chromatin-negative patients with gonadal dysgenesis seemed to have only one X chromosome (Polani et al. 1956). The presence or absence of the Y chromosome could not be determined and it was thought likely that the patients had an XY sex-chromosome constitution, although the possibility that they might be XO was also considered. Danon and Sachs (1957) also suggested that some patients with gonadal dysgenesis might have an XO sex-chromosome constitution, but that other patients might be examples of somatic mosaicism in respect of their sex-chromosome constitution. A study of the blood-groups of three patients with gonadal dysgenesis (Platt and Stratton 1956) supplied evidence that these individuals were not haploid— i.e., were not XO merely because all their chromosomes were unpaired.

Technical developments have recently made it possible to obtain accurate information regarding the somatic chromosomes of human patients, either in bone-marrow cells briefly incubated in vitro (Ford, Jacobs, and Lajtha 1958) or in cells from tissue cultures (Tjio and Puck 1958). In consequence the normal number of human chromosomes and their normal morphology are now reasonably well known. The subject of this report is a chromatin-negative case of Turner's syndrome whose bone-marrow cells proved to contain 45 chromosomes only, instead of the normal number of 46, and whose sex-chromosomal constitution is determined to be XO.

CASE REPORT

The patient presented at the age of 14 with a short stature, primary amenorrhœa, and absence of secondary sex characteristics. In addition she was backward at school.

Family history. Parents healthy. Father 5 ft. 4 in., mother 5 ft. 2 in. A maternal aunt, who died at the age of 21, was dwarfed and had had only two scanty periods; she was known to have pernicious anæmia. Two brothers 6 and 10 years old and one sister aged 9 were all healthy.

Personal history. Maternal health good during pregnancy, and delivery normal. Birth weight 5 lb. 4 oz. Early development normal.

On examination, height 51 in., lower segment 25 in., arm-span 50 in. Weight 4 st. 13 lb.

There was slight facial asymmetry, low implantation of the ears, and a small chin. There was a high arched palate, a short broad neck without webbing, slight funnel deformity of the chest, cubitus valgus, pes cavus, and digital deformities. Cardiovascular system normal. Blood-pressure 110/70. Normal femoral pulses. There was no evidence of puberty.

INVESTIGATIONS

Examination of skin biopsy and blood smear showed a chromatin-negative pattern.

Follicle-stimulating hormone positive to 32 mouse units 17-ketosteroids 10.8 mg. per day.

Radiographically chest, heart, intravenous pyelography normal. Radiological assessment of bone age corresponded to the chronological age.

No defect in colour-vision (Ishihara) in patient or parents.

The marrow cells, obtained by a routine marrow puncture, were suspended in a mixture of glucose-saline and serum from the patient herself, and were sent to Harwell for cytological processing. After incubation the cells were exposed to colchicine for one hour, then fixed and stained by the Feulgen procedure. Squash preparations were made and the chromosomes were studied in cells arrested in the metaphase of mitosis by the action of the colchicine.

The chromosomes were counted in 102 cells of which 99 cells were found to have 45 chromosomes only. The remaining 3 cells contained fewer than 45 chromosomes and previous experience suggests that the deficiency is likely to be a consequence of damage to the cells during the making of the preparations. 14 cells were selected for detailed study. In every one of them 4 small acrocentric chromosomes were present, as in a normal female: in a normal male there are 5 of these chromosomes, one being the Y chromosome. All the selected cells also contained 15 medium-length metacentric chromosomes, as in a normal male—a normal female having 16 which include the two X chromosomes (Ford et al. 1958). These observations of themselves strongly suggest that the chromosome constitution is XO.

The individual recognition of the X and Y chromosomes may be a matter of some difficulty. However Tjio and Puck (1958) assert that X and Y chromosomes can be recognised individually in their preparations made from tissue cultures. We agree that the Y chromosome can be distinguished in favourable cells of normal males, but we have not yet been able to identify the X chromosome (or chromosomes) unequivocally in bone-marrow preparations. Nevertheless in many of the selected cells of the present patient it was possible to make a reasonably satisfactory classification of the chromosomes into 22 pairs and one odd chromosome. A photograph of one of these cells is reproduced in fig. 1. In fig. 2 the chromosomes from the same cell are

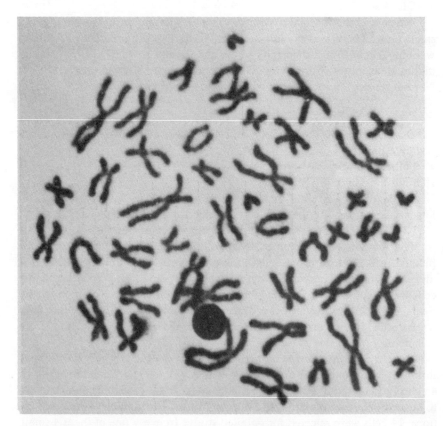

Fig. 1. Chromosomes (45) of the patient with Turner's syndrome discussed in the text. Colchicine-arrested metaphase in a bone-marrow cell. Feulgen squash preparation (× 2200). The round black body is probably an oil droplet.

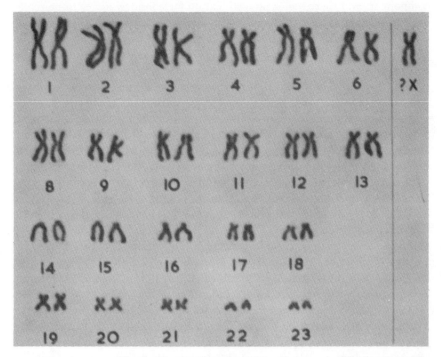

Fig. 2. Chromosomes from the cell shown in Fig. 1 arranged in pairs (× 2200).

shown arranged in pairs. Suspicion that the odd chromosome is the X·is inevitable, but this chromosome and the two members of pair 6 are very similar in length and arm-ratio and their true relationships remain uncertain. The probability that one of the three is X is strengthened by the good agreement of their proportions with those of undoubted X-chromosomes in X-Y bivalents at metaphase in primary spermatocytes (Ford and Hamerton 1956). Experience of numerical chromosomal abnormalities in animals and plants (Swanson 1957) suggests that it is very improbable that a human individual who has only 45 chromosomes as the result of the loss of a large or medium-sized autosome would be viable, but that an XO zygote might well develop to maturity. We therefore conclude that the sex-chromosome constitution of the patient is XO.

DISCUSSION

These observations are of interest not only with reference to Turner's syndrome. Here is an individual who is female anatomically and psychologically, whose cells are "male" as judged by nuclear sexing, and whose chromosomes are neither male nor normally female. However, as judged by her chromosomes she has no male component, but half a normal female component, and there seems no justification for considering her to be really male in any sense. It must therefore be accepted that chromatin negativity does not necessarily imply maleness and it would probably be best if the phrase "nuclear sexing" were dropped from the vocabulary and the more accurate if less striking terms, chromatin negativity or positivity, were always used instead. The very real clinical reasons for doing this have already been stressed.

An explanation of the origin of the sex chromosome anomaly in gonadal dysgenesis can be sought in the process of non-disjunction, best known as an abnormality of oogenesis in *Drosophila melanogaster* (Morgan, Bridges, and Sturtevant 1925). Non-disjunction of the sex-chromosomes in the female fly implies the migration of two X chromosomes to one pole of the spindle during one of the two meiotic anaphases. Thus the ovum comes to contain either the haploid number of autosomes plus *two* X chromosomes, or only the haploid number of autosomes *without* X chromosomes. Fertilisation of an ovum of the latter type by a Y-bearing sperm results in a non-viable YO zygote; fertilisation by an X-bearing sperm yields an XO zygote which develops into a sterile male. Our findings suggest that in man an XO zygote develops into a sterile "agonadal" individual whose phenotype is female.

Fertilisation of the other type of abnormal ovum (XX) by an X-bearing sperm gives, in drosophila, an XXX zygote with poor viability, but which occasionally survives pupation and then emerges as a fly with accentuated female secondary sexual characteristics, technically called a "super-female"; fertilisation by a Y-bearing sperm yields an XXY zygote which develops into a fertile female. In man the XXX state is as yet unknown, but evidence that the XXY individual appears as a chromatin-positive case of Klinefelter's syndrome has been presented (Ford, Polani, Briggs, and Bishop 1959, Jacobs and Strong 1959). The evidence in favour of the occurrence of non-disjunction in man is thereby strengthened.

Non-disjunction has so far been considered as occurring during oogenesis only. Family colour-vision studies in cases of gonadal dysgenesis suggest that it may also occur during spermatogenesis. If an O ovum is fertilised by an X sperm and the resultant individual has a major red-green colour-vision defect, the father should also show the colour-vision defect. But in four families where patients with gonadal dysgenesis (chromatin-negative) have a major red-green colour-vision defect this was not the case (Lenz 1957, Stewart 1958 personal communication; and two of our families, see Bishop et al. 1959). It would appear that in these patients the X-chromosome with the anomalous colour-vision gene was not of paternal origin but was derived from a heterozygous (carrier) mother. These patients have not been examined cytologically, but, if they are XO, it will follow that they developed from zygotes arising from the fertilisation of normal X-bearing ova by sperm carrying neither X nor Y. Such sperm would arise as a result of non-disjunction during spermatogenesis. Evidence that this is by no means unlikely is provided by the observation that X and Y chromosomes are sometimes unpaired at metaphase in first spermatocytes (Ford and Hamerton 1956). Both chromosomes would then be expected to migrate to the same pole in approximately 50% of the ensuing anaphases.

In conclusion it should be emphasised that the XO patient should not be referred to as an instance of "sex-reversal," as a "chromosomal male," or as a "genetic male": she is a female, with an abnormal genotype.

We wish to thank Dr. P. M. F. Bishop for permission to study a patient under his care. We acknowledge the skilful technical assistance of Mr. G. D. Breckon, Miss P. A. Moore, and Miss S. R. Wakefield.

REFERENCES

(1) M. L. Barr and E. G. Bertram. 1949. Nature, London. **163**: 676.

(2) P. M. F. Bishop, M. H. Lessof and P. E. Polani. 1959. C. R. Austin (editor). Memoir no. 7. London, Society for Endocrinology.

(3) M. Danon and L. Sachs. 1957. Lancet. **ii**: 20.

(4) L. Décourt, W. da S. Sasso, E. Chiorboli and J. M. Fernandes. 1954. Rev. Assoc. Med. Brazil. **1**: 203.

(5) C. E. Ford and J. L. Hamerton. 1956. Nature, London. **178**: 2020.

(6) C. E. Ford, P. A. Jacobs and L. G. Lajtha. 1958. Nature, London. **181**: 1565.

(7) C. E. Ford, P. E. Polani, J. H. Briggs, P. M. F. Bishop. 1959. Nature, London. **183**: 1030-1032.

(8) P. A. Jacobs and J. A. Strong. 1959. Nature, London. **183**: 302.

(9) A. Jost. 1947. C. R. Soc. Biol., Paris. **141**: 126.

(10) Lancet, 1956. **2**: 127.

(11) W. Lenz. 1957. Acta Genet. Med. Gemollol. **6**: 231.

(12) T. H. Morgan, C. B. Bridges and A. H. Sturtevant. 1925. Bibliog. Genet. **2**: 1.

(13) R. Platt and F. Stratton. 1956. Lancet. **ii**: 120.

(14) P. E. Polani, W. F. Hunter and B. Lennox. 1954. Lancet. **ii**: 120.

(15) P. E. Polani, M. H. Lessof and P. M. F. Bishop. 1956. Lancet. **ii**: 118.

(16) J. S. S. Stewart. 1958. Personal communication.

(17) C. P. Swanson. 1957. Cytology and cytogenetics. Englewood Cliffs, N. J., Prentice-Hall, Inc.

(18) J. H. Tjio and T. T. Puck. 1958. Proc. Nat. Acad. Sci. **12**: 1229.

(19) L. Wilkins, M. M. Grumbach and J. J. Van Wyck. 1954. J. Clin. Endocrin. **14**: 1270.

Sex Chromatin and Gene Action in the Mammalian
X-Chromosome*

MARY F. LYON
M. R. C. Radiobiological Research Unit,
Harwell, Didcot, Berkshire, England

This paper describes in greater detail a hypothesis, which has already been put forward briefly, concerning gene action in the X chromosome of the mouse (*Mus musculus* L.) (Lyon, 1961-a), and at the same time extends it to cover the X chromosomes of mammals generally. The hypothesis was formed by the welding together of facts recently described in the two fields of mouse genetics and mouse cytology.

FACTS AND HYPOTHESIS

The cytologic evidence was provided by Ohno and Hauschka (1960), who showed that in cells of various tissues of female mice one chromosome was heteropyknotic. They interpreted this chromosome as an X chromosome and suggested that the so-called sex-chromatin was composed of one hetero-pyknotic X chromosome.

The hypothesis formulated on the basis of this and the genetic facts was that (1) the heteropyknotic X chromosome was genetically inactivated, (2) that it could be either paternal or maternal in origin in different cells of the same animal, and (3) that the inactivation occurred early in embryonic development.

The genetic facts used in formulating the hypothesis were: first, that mice of the chromosomal type XO are normal, fertile females (Welshons and Russell, 1959), showing that only one active X chromosome is necessary for normal development of the female mouse, and second, that female mice heterozygous for sex-linked genes affecting coat color have a mosaic phenotype. Several mutant genes of this type have been described under the names

* Reprinted by author's and publisher's permission from American Journal of Human Genetics. 1962. **14:** 135-148.

mottled, brindled, tortoiseshell, dappled, and 26K (Fraser, Sobey and Spicer, 1953; Dickie, 1954; Welshons and Russell, 1959; Lyon, 1960; Phillips, 1961). Some or all of them may be allelic with each other. In each case the coat of the heterozygous female has patches of white, normal color and an intermediate color. Most of these mutants are lethal when hemizygous, but brindled males live long enough to show that their coat is white. Thus the coat of heterozygous females may be considered to consist of patches of mutant color and of wild-type color. A similar phenotype, described as variegated or flecked, is seen in females heterozygous for autosomal coat color genes whose normal alleles have been translocated onto the X chromosome. Four such sex-linked translocations are so far known: one in which part of linkage group VIII including the normal allele of the gene brown (b) is translocated to the X chromosome, and three in which parts of linkage group I, including the loci of the genes chinchilla, c^{ch}, and pink-eye, p, are so translocated (Russell and Bangham, 1959, 1961; Cattanach, 1961). The color of the patches in each case corresponds to that of the mutant concerned. The distribution of the patches in these sex-linked conditions differs from that seen in mutants causing white spotting in the mouse. All the spotting mutants, including s, bt, W, Sp, Sl, Mi^{wh} and Va, have a certain basic similarity of pattern, in that certain regions of the body are more susceptible to spotting and tend to be affected first. These regions include the tail, feet, belly, forehead, nose and the dorsal lumbar region (Grüneberg, 1952). In heterozygotes for sex-linked color genes, however, the white regions seem to be distributed more or less evenly over the body. Characteristic features are that both the mutant and the fully pigmented patches rarely cross the mid-dorsal or mid-ventral line, and that the edges of the patches tend to be ill defined. In these features the pattern resembles that resulting from somatic mutation. Russell and Major (1957), studying radiation-induced somatic mutation, remarked on the ill defined edges of the mutant patches and the mingling of mutant and normal-colored hairs. They gave a diagram of the distribution of the mutant patches which seems to indicate that these rarely cross the midline. Cases of spontaneous somatic mutation include that of Dunn (1934) at the c-locus, in which the animal had several small areas of the mutant color on its back and head, with the gonads also partly affected, and a similar animal found recently by Lyon (1959) which carried a spontaneous gonosomic mutation from c^{ch} to c. On a background of color $aa\ c^{ch}\ c^{ch}$, patches of the mutant color, $aa\ c^{ch}c$, were scattered over the body, with ill defined edges and mingling of hairs of the two types. The animal bred as though the gonads were entirely of the type $c^{ch}c$.

This resemblance of the pattern of mottled, dappled, etc., females to that of somatically mosaic animals suggested that some event happened early in development which determined whether the normal or mutant gene should act in any particular cell (Lyon, 1960). This event is now thought to be the inactivation of one X chromosome. It is postulated that the pigment cells of the normal-colored patches are descended from cells in which the chromosome carrying the mutant gene was inactivated, and those of the mutant-colored patches from cells with the normal gene inactivated. Patches of intermediate color would arise by cell mingling in development, and the shape of the patches would depend on cell movement during growth. The proportions of active normal or mutant chromosomes would be expected to vary from one individual to another by chance.

TESTS OF THE HYPOTHESIS

Various expectations can be formulated from the hypothesis and used to test it.

The first is that all sex-linked color genes of the mouse, and all autosomal color genes translocated to the X chromosome should show the mottling effect in heterozygous females. This is obeyed so far.

A second expectation is that in female mice of chromosomal type XO the single X chromosome would not be inactivated, and therefore neither sex-chromatin nor mottling should occur in XO females. Both of these expectations are fulfilled. Ohno, Kaplan, Kinosita, and Welshons (1960) found no heteropyknotic X chromosome in XO females, and Cattanach (1961) and Russell and Bangham (1960, 1961) have reported that females carrying a sex-linked translocation and lacking one X do not show variegation. Similarly, males of the chromosomal type XXY would be expected to have one X chromosome inactivated and therefore to show variegation, and this also is obeyed in males with a translocation (Cattanach, 1961). In this respect variegation in mice differs from the V-type position effect in Drosophila. Sex-linked translocations in Drosophila may cause color variegation, but this still occurs in flies with a single X chromosome (Lewis, 1950), whereas two X chromosomes are essential for its expression in mice.

Another expectation, which it has not been possible to test so far, is that females heterozygous for two different color genes, one on each X chromosome, should show no normal-colored patches. They should also show no doubly mutant patches, but this might be more difficult to score. It is hoped to test this point using sex-linked translocations.

Rather more diffuse expectations can be formulated concerning the expression of sex-linked genes other than color genes in heterozygous females. Any gene with localized action would be expected to show a similar mosaic effect. This would include genes affecting hair and coat structure, of which there are two, tabby *Ta*, and scurfy, *sf* (Table 1). Tabby heterozygotes do show a mosaic effect. Males hemizygous and females homozygous for this gene have an abnormal coat structure, while heterozygous females have a striped appearance which gives the mutant its name. Falconer (1953) showed that the normal-colored regions of the coat had a normal hair structure, while the black regions had a structure resembling that of the tabby homozygotes

Table 1. Sex-linked Genes in the Mouse

Color	Skin	Other
Mottled	Tabby	Bent-tail
Brindled	Scurfy	Jimpy
Tortoiseshell		Gyro
Dappled		
Dappled-2		
26K		
4 translocations involving:		
Brown		
Albino alleles		
Pink-eye		

and hemizygotes. The gene scurfy, on the other hand, does not express itself in heterozygous females (Russell, Russell, and Gower, 1959).

Where the phenotype is not the result of localized gene action, heterozygous females might show various types of effect. Except in rare cases, the cells in which the gene action takes place will include both the type with the normal gene active and that with the mutant gene active, and the proportions of the two types will vary by chance. Thus, it may be that the phenotype of the heterozygotes will be intermediate between those of the two homozygous types, or the presence of any normal cells may be enough to insure a normal phenotype (so that the gene behaves as a recessive), or the phenotype of heterozygotes may vary as the proportion of cells with active normal or mutant genes varies, leading to incomplete penetrance and variable expression. The gene bent-tail (Garber, 1952), is probably an example of this last type. The hemizygous males have bent and shortened tails; in the heterozygotes the expression of the defect varies from nearly normal to nearly equal to the hemizygotes, and the penetrance is only 80 to 85 per cent (Falconer, 1954; Grüneberg, 1955). The gene jimpy, jp, behaves as a recessive, but as mentioned in the earlier publication, there has been one exceptional jimpy female, heterozygous for tabby (Ta), which may represent an example of the rare case in which, by chance, all the cells responsible for the jimpy phenotype have the normal gene inactivated. Gyro, (Gy) (Lyon, 1961-b) gets its name from the circling behavior of the affected animals. The males in addition are small, sterile, and have abnormal bone development. The female heterozygotes show a low penetrance of the circling behavior, but no other abnormalities have been detected.

In general the hypothesis predicts that females heterozygous for sex-linked genes with nonlocalized gene action will show incomplete penetrance, and variable gene expression, as the proportion of active normal and mutant chromosomes varies. This prediction is borne out. There is, of course, no need to invoke a similar explanation for incomplete penetrance of autosomal genes, since genetic theory has always allowed that variable gene manifestation might have many different causes in different instances.

Thus, so far, the hypothesis stands up to test in the mouse.

CAN THE HYPOTHESIS BE EXTENDED TO OTHER MAMMALS?

One obvious question is whether this phenomenon is peculiar to the mouse or is general in mammals.

Sex-chromatin is found generally in female mammals, and Ohno and colleagues have reported that it is formed from a single heteropyknotic X chromosome not only in the mouse, but also in the rat, opossum, and man (Ohno, Kaplan, and Kinosita 1959, 1960; Ohno and Makino, 1961). Thus the cytologic evidence suggests that inactivation of one X is the typical method of dosage compensation in female mammals. Does the genetic evidence point in the same direction?

The only other mammalian species in which an appreciable number of sex-linked genes are known is man. In mammals other than man there are only yellow, in the cat, and hemophilia, in the dog. As mentioned in the earlier publication the mosaic phenotype of the tortoiseshell cat is in accord with the hypothesis; hemophilia in the dog strongly resembles that in man except that no heterozygous effect has yet been recorded (Brinkhous and Graham, 1950).

To test the hypothesis for man, the two aspects of human genetics which have to be considered are the phenotype of XO individuals, and that of females heterozygous for color genes. An important fact in relating the hypothesis to the mouse was that mice of type XO are normal fertile females. In man the XO type is female, but not normal; women of this chromosome type have Turner's syndrome, which includes small stature and gonadal dysgenesis (Ford *et al.*, 1959). Thus, in man one cannot say that only one active X chromosome is necessary for normal female development. However, it is still possible that inactivation of one X does take place in man, but that it differs in some way from the process in the mouse, e.g., it might occur later in embryogeny. Therefore, it is worthwhile to consider the second part of the evidence, the phenotype of heterozygous females. Only one sex-linked gene affecting color is at present known in man: sex-linked ocular albinism. Males carrying this gene lack retinal epithelial pigment, while the stromal pigmentation of the iris and choroid are normal. Heterozygous females have irregular retinal pigmentation, with patches of pigment and patches lacking pigment, so that the fundus has a stippled appearance (Falls, 1951; Francois and Deweer, 1953; Waardenburg and van der Bosch, 1956). Thus, the only color gene available for study shows the expected mosaic effect in heterozygotes. The further predictions of the hypothesis should now be considered.

Any other genes with localized action would also be expected to give the mosaic effect, while heterozygotes for genes with nonlocalized action would be expected to show incomplete penetrance and variable expression. The effects observed in heterozygotes for genes for which there is good evidence of sex-linkage (based on the progeny of affected males or linkages with a known sex-linked gene), and which are known by more than one pedigree, are shown in Table 2. This table has been compiled from a study of the literature on human genetics including Gates (1946), Sorsby (1951-a), Stern (1960), and recent papers. In six conditions the heterozygotes typically show an intermediate effect, and in two of these, choroideremia and chronic hypochromic anemia, the effect is visibly mosaic. In choroideremia the hemizygous males have a pale grayish white eye fundus, while the heterozygotes have patches of paleness with overlying pigment, attributed by McCulloch and McCulloch (1948) to disruption of patches of the pigment epithelium. In chronic hypochromic anemia the males have abnormally shaped hypochromic red cells and an enlarged spleen. The heterozygous females have a small proportion (5 to 20 per cent) of typically abnormal red cells, the remainder appearing normal. This leaves nine conditions for which no typical heterozygous effect is recorded, but of these, eight have reports of partial, occasional, or rare heterozygous expression, leaving only one condition, ichthyosis vulgaris, out of the fifteen mentioned which, according to the literature, is completely recessive.

The frequency and degree of heterozygous expression varies greatly from one disease to another, as would be expected. Diseases with relatively common heterozygous expression include nystagmus in which the percentage manifestation varies from zero to 78 per cent in different families; keratosis follicularis, in which many partly affected females are recorded in one of the two known pedigrees showing sex-linkage; and vitamin D-resistant rickets with hypophosphatemia, in which twelve out of forty-eight females showed the bony deformities which are characteristic in the male. In diseases in which heterozygous expression is rare, including both hemophilia and color blindness, some authors have in the past expressed doubt that it occurs at all. These doubts are well justified since there are several other possible explanations for the manifestation of a sex-linked disease in a female. These explanations include:

1. The female is homozygous for the gene concerned, either as a result of mutation or of consanguineous mating.

2. The disease has been mistaken for a closely similar but autosomally inherited one. This possibility is especially important in hemophilia, which with modern methods of diagnosis can be separated into several different "hemophilioid states" (Brinkhous and Graham, 1954).

3. The female does not have the normal XX chromosome complement. As would be expected, women with the chromosome constitution XO manifest any sex-linked mutant genes that they carry, to the same degree as the corresponding XY male. Similarly, women with the

Table 2. Effects in Heterozygotes for Various Human Sex-linked Genes

| Condition | Heterozygous effect | | References |
	Frequency	Type of effect	
Color blindness Protanopia series	Typical	Schmidt's sign (decreased sensitivity to red light)	Schmidt (1934); Pickford (1947); both referred to by Walls & Mathews (1952)
	Occasional	Partial manifestation	Walls & Mathews (1952)
	Rare	Complete manifestation	Jaeger (1951)
Deuteranopia series	Rare	Complete manifestation	Jaeger (1951, 1952)
Retinitis pigmentosa	Typical	Tapetal reflex	Falls & Cotterman (1948); Sorsby (1951-b)
	Occasional	Complete manifestation	Sorsby (1951-b)
Choroideremia	Typical	Fundus has pale patches with overlying pigment	Goedbloed (1942) McCulloch & McCulloch (1948)
	Occasional	Partial night blindness and reduced visual field	Goedbloed (1942)
Nystagmus	Occasional	Penetrance in 0-73% heterozygotes of different families Penetrance 5.6-78) in different families	Cuendet & Streiff (1957) Franceschetti (1961)
Night blindness with myopia	Occasional	Manifestation	Gates (1946)
Megalocornea	Occasional	Manifestation	Gates (1946)
Ichthyosis vulgaris		None	Levit (1936) Gates (1946)
Keratosis follicularis spinulosa	Frequent	Partial expression	Levit (1936)
Anhidrotic ectodermal dysplasia	Occasional	Partial expression: missing teeth, dry skin	Levit (1936); Seagle (1954); Bowen (1957)
		One report of mosaic patches on skin	Roberts (1929)
	Rare	Complete manifestation reported but not genetically proven	Seagle (1954)
Hemophilia A	Occasional	Mild bleeding in a proportion of carriers	Merskey & Macfarlane (1951); Fantl & Margolis (1955); Taylor & Biggs (1957); Biggs & Macfarlane (1958)

Table 2. (*Cont'd.*)

| Condition | Heterozygous effect | | References |
	Frequency	Type of effect	
		Abnormal laboratory findings in some carriers	Merskey & Macfarlane (1951); Graham *et al.* (1953); Biggs & Macfarlane (1958)
	Rare	Complete manifestation reported but not genetically proven	Wilkinson *et al.* (1957) Mellman *et al.* (1961)
Christmas disease	Occasional	Abnormal laboratory findings in some carriers	Ramot *et al.* (1955) Pitney & Dacie (1955)
	Rare	Complete manifestation reported but not genetically proven	Hardisty (1957)
Chronic hypochromic anemia	Typical	Small proportion of abnormal red cells	Rundles & Falls (1946)
Glucose-6-phosphate-dehydrogenase deficiency	Typical	Reduced enzyme activity Much individual variation	Childs *et al.* (1958); Beutler (1959)
Vitamin D-resistant rickets with hypophosphatemia	Typical	Hypophosphatemia	Graham, McFalls & Winters (1959)
	Occasional	Bony deformities	
Diabetes insipidus	Occasional	Sometimes slight signs or symptoms	Forssman (1955)
Duchenne type muscular dystrophy	Rare	One partly affected mother of affected sons	Kryschowa & Abowjan (1934)
		Out of 107 cases, 2 were females not genetically tested, and 1 was an XO female	Walton (1957)

condition of "testicular feminization" and the chromosome constitution XY manifest sex-linked genes as does a male. The literature on color blindness in such individuals has recently been reviewed by Palani (1961), while hemophilia in an XY girl has been reported by Nilsson *et al.* (1959). Turner's syndrome in an XO individual may be diagnosed fairly easily while the child is still young. Testicular feminization, and other types of chromosome anomaly, however, are often not suspected until adult life, when primary amenorrhea results (Jacobs *et al.*, 1961). Moreover, some women with this type of chromosome abnormality have been color-blind (Lindsten, 1961; Stewart, 1961), suggesting that perhaps the locus of color blindness had been deleted from the abnormal chromosome.

In view of all these possible alternative explanations for manifestation of a sex-linked gene in a female, the necessary criteria that must be fulfilled before she can be interpreted with reasonable certainty as a manifesting hetero-zygote are quite formidable. These criteria are: (1) The condition must have been diagnosed recently with modern methods for distinguishing closely related diseases. (2) The woman must be fertile and have produced both normal and affected sons, showing that she is neither homozygous nor hemizygous at the locus concerned.

With these criteria there are no instances known to the present writer of severe hemophilia in a manifesting heterozygote. Snyder (1932) found hemo-philic women with normal sons, but it cannot now be known from what type of hemophilia they suffered. Wilkinson *et al.* (1957) knew the type of hemo-philia, hemophilia A, of the two affected female cousins that they studied, but unfortunately since these children were aged only 4 and 2 years, it will be some time before their genotypes can be ascertained from their sons. Hardisty (1957) reported typical Christmas disease in a young woman whom he considered heterozygous. She had normal menstruation but had not yet married. On the other hand, there appears to be ample evidence of mild hemophilia in heterozygotes. Merskey and Macfarlane (1951) examined twenty-one mothers of hemophilic sons and compared them with normal controls. They found no test which would reliably distinguish the hetero-zygotes from the normals, but they stated that 47 per cent of the known carriers had excessive bleeding after tooth extractions as compared with 5 per cent of normals, and there were "three positive results out of 21 known carriers examined by the prothrombin consumption test." All these three bled excessively after tooth extraction. A large pedigree with fourteen males showing a very mild form of hemophilia, with bleeding only after injuries such as tooth extraction or tonsillectomy, was studied by Graham *et al.* (1953). Several females were genetically ascertained from their sons to be heterozygous, and they fell into two groups: some with plasma antihemo-philic factor values in the normal range and others with values intermediate between normal and those of the affected males of this pedigree. None of them showed any abnormal bleeding. Similar instances of abnormal labora-tory findings in otherwise unaffected heterozygous women have been reported for Christmas disease. One woman who was proved heterozygous by her normal and affected sons had a definitely abnormal thromboplastin generation test and "recalled having bled profusely after hysterectomy and also after a tooth extraction" (Ramot *et al.*, 1955). To sum up, the general picture among heterozygotes for hemophilia seems to be one of considerable variation in expression, which is in accord with the present hypothesis.

In color blindness it does seem possible to find instances of genetically proven manifesting heterozygotes. Jaeger (1951) gave the pedigree of two sisters who from their ancestry would have been expected to be doubly heterozygous for genes of the protanopia and deuteranopia series, on opposite chromosomes. (Such double heterozygotes usually have normal color vision.) One of these sisters manifested deuteranomaly and had both a protanopic and a deuteranomalous son; the other manifested protanopia and had a deuteranomalous son. In another pedigree Jaeger (1952) found a deuter-anomalous woman who was the mother of one normal and one deuter-anomalous son. She also had a bilateral macular degeneration which he thought might have precipitated the manifestation of color blindness. Walls (1959) considered that when one of a pair of monozygotic female twins is color-blind the manifesting twin may safely be considered heterozygous, and gave examples, including two of the Dionne quintuplets. This seems open to the objection, however, that X chromosome loss during cleavage might well occur in one only of a pair of twins, and they might still be regarded as monozygotic. As with hemophilia, although fully manifesting heterozygotes for color blindness seem very rare, partially affected ones are quite frequently found, especially for genes of the protanopia series. Walls and Mathews (1952) mentioned the sister of a protanopic male who considered herself color blind but was only partly affected by their standards, and they reviewed the work of Pickford and Schmidt who have both shown that slight deviations from normality are common in the relatives of color-blind males.

Thus, the general picture concerning heterozygotes for sex-linked genes in man is one of variable expression, which accords with the predicted result of random inactivation of one or the other X chromosome. Moreover, in a few conditions the effect in heterozygotes is visibly mosaic.

Another prediction of the hypothesis is that if a female carries two non-allelic mutant genes affecting the same cells, one on each X chromosome, she should have no normal cells of this type. This fact would only be demon-strable for genes with localized effects. Since most of the conditions mentioned in Table 2 are very rare the hope of finding two suitable ones together in the same pedigree is slight. Color blindness and glucose-6-phosphate-dehydrogenase deficiency, however, are both sufficiently common to occur in pedigrees together with other sex-linked diseases. Franceschetti (1961) has reviewed such pedigrees involving color blindness. A very interesting one is that described by Falls and Cotterman (1948). In a family with sex-linked retinitis pigmentosa they were able to detect the heterozygotes by a glistening property of the tapetum, the tapetal reflex. A heterozygous woman had three daughters by a color-blind man. Two daughters showed themselves hetero-zygous for retinitis pigmentosa by the tapetal reflex and these two both manifested the color blindness for which they were heterozygous; the third daughter did not show the tapetal reflex and did not manifest color blindness though she was presumed heterozygous like her sisters. The explanation of this, according to the present hypothesis, would be that in the sisters hetero-zygous for retinitis pigmentosa all the retinal cells were affected either by retinitis pigmentosa or by color blindness, so that the two sisters had no normal cells and were necessarily color-blind. However, until more pedigrees can be found showing two suitable sex-linked diseases, this particular example can only be considered an interesting one. Franceschetti mentions also one pedigree involving nystagmus and color blindness and one with night blindness and color blindness. In both instances the two mutant genes were carried on the same X chromosome, and so the point is not tested. In the night blindness pedigree one woman is shown as being a repulsion heterozygote, but from her ancestry this seems unlikely. The usually normal color vision of double heterozygotes for genes of the protanopia and deuteranopia series seems at first contrary to expectation, but it can be explained by the complementary nature of the two defects; the protanopic cones are normal for green light, and the deuteranopic ones normal for red.

RELATION OF THE HYPOTHESIS TO RECENT FINDINGS CONCERNING SEX CHROMOSOMES AND SEX CHROMATIN IN MAN

Recent progress in the understanding of sex chromosome abnormalities in man has been very rapid (Miller, 1960; Polani, 1961), and it is obviously important to consider how the new hypothesis fits in with these findings.

It is postulated that in a normal female with two X chromosomes one of the two is inactivated and forms a sex chromatin body, and that when there is only one X, as in a normal male or an XO female, it is not inactivated. This agrees with the finding that XO women are sex chromatin negative, and also with the fact that XXY males, with Klinefelter's syndrome, are sex chromatin positive. Recently, individuals have been found with three and four X chromosomes (Jacobs *et al.*, 1959; Ferguson-Smith *et al.*, 1960; Fraccaro and Lindsten, 1960; Miller *et al.*, 1961) and in each instance the maximum number of sex chromatin bodies present has been one less than the number of X chromosomes. This means that the hypothesis may be extended to postulate that all X chromosomes in excess of one normal one are inactivated. This would explain some hitherto rather puzzling features of cases such as the males with XXXXY chromosomes: that the Y chromosome has been able to produce a male phenotype in opposition to so many X's, and that the abnormalities of an individual with three extra chromosomes are not much greater than those of an XXY male with only one extra chromosome. These observations are readily understandable if the three additional X's are inactive. If the findings of small sex chromatin bodies in women with a partly deleted X, and large ones in a woman with presumptive isochromosome X, are substantiated (Jacobs *et al.*, 1961) this would indicate that if one of two X's is deficient, then the normal one remains active in all cells, with the abnormal one forming the sex chromatin body. This would provide an alternative explanation for the manifestation of color blindness in women with this type of chromosome abnormality, if they carry the gene for color blindness on the normal, active X. Stewart (1961) has suggested the explanation of deletion of the locus of color blindness.

Facts that remain unexplained are that an XO female and an XXY male show any abnormality, and that an XO female in man differs in phenotype from that in the mouse. There seem at least two possible explanations for these facts. The first is that the abnormal phenotype of XO etc. individuals in man is due to abnormal action of the sex-chromosomes before the time in development at which inactivation of one X occurs. Park (1957) found that sex-chromatin in human embryos was first detectable at sixteen days gestation, and became more easily detectable up to eighteen days. Thus, one must presume that before this stage all X chromosomes are active. No similar observations are available for the mouse, but in the rat, which has an embryology similar to that of the mouse, sex chromatin is first detectable at seven days gestation (Zybina, 1960). This is an early egg cylinder stage, and probably corresponds to a rather earlier stage than that of the sixteen-day human embryo, which is just forming the primitive streak. Thus it seems quite possible that inactivation of X chromosomes takes place at a developmentally earlier stage in the mouse than in man.

The other possible explanation is that the X chromosome of man has a short pairing segment, that this is not normally inactivated, and that it is duplication or deficiency of this region which gives rise to the abnormal phenotypes observed. Controversy still remains concerning the presence or absence of a pairing segment in the sex chromosomes of particular mammalian species (Hamerton, 1958).

No other general hypothesis concerning the behavior of sex-linked genes in mammals has been put forward. However, simultaneously with the original publication of the present hypothesis, Russell (1961) put forward a very similar but more limited one concerning the variegation due to sex-linked translocations in the mouse. She considered that this variegation was "presumably a heterochromatic effect," and from the fact that two X chromosomes were essential for its expression, together with cytologic evidence, postulated that "in mammals, genic balance requires the action of *one* X in a manner which precludes realization of its heterochromatic potentialities, so that only *additional* X's present assume the properties characteristic of heterochromatin."

CONCLUSION

Although it would be desirable to have far more evidence, that which has been collected already seems sufficient to warrant extending the hypothesis to cover gene action in the X chromosome of man and mammals in general. Efforts to obtain more evidence about mosaicism in heterozygotes, phenotypes of double heterozygotes, the appearance of sex chromatin in embryology, etc., will be pressed forward.

SUMMARY

The hypothesis is put forward that the normal method of dosage compensation in mammals, including man, is inactivation of one of the two X chromosomes of females. It is postulated that the inactive X forms the sex chromatin body, that either one of the two X's may be inactivated in different cells of the same animal, and that the inactivation occurs early in development. In adult life this leads to patches of cells some with one and some with the other X chromosome inactivated and hence to the mottled appearance characteristic of female mammals heterozygous for sex-linked color genes. The hypothesis stands up so far to test against the predictions which can be made from it, but more evidence is needed. Recent discoveries concerning sex chromosome abnormalities in man suggest that in such cases all X chromosomes in excess of one normal one are inactivated. The hypothesis thus explains some hitherto puzzling facts, such as the viability of XXXXY individuals with three extra chromosomes.

REFERENCES

(1) E. Beutler. 1959. The hemolytic effect of primaquine and related compounds: a review. Blood. **14:** 103-139.

(2) R. Biggs and R. G. Macfarlane. 1958. Haemophilia and related conditions: a survey of 187 cases. Brit. J. Haemat. **4:** 1-27.

(3) R. Bowen. 1957. Hereditary ectodermal dysplasia of the anhidrotic type. South. M. J. **50:** 1018-1021.

(4) K. M. Brinkhous and J. B. Graham. 1950. Hemophilia in the female dog. Science. **111:** 723-724.

(5) K. M. Brinkhous and J. B. Graham. 1954. Hemophilia and the hemophilioid states. Blood. **9:** 254-257.

(6) B. M. Cattanach. 1961. XXY mice. Genet. Res. **2:** 156-160.

(7) B. Childs, W. Zinkham, E. A. Browne, E. L. Kimbro and J. V. Torbert. 1958. A genetic study of a defect in glutathione metabolism of the erythrocyte. Bull. Johns Hopkins Hosp. **102:** 21-37.

(8) J. F. Cuendet and E. B. Streiff. 1957. La relativité des notions mendéliennes classiques de dominance et de récessité. Acta genet., Basel. **7:** 75-79.

(9) M. M. Dickie. 1954. The tortoise shell house mouse. J. Hered. **45:** 158-159.

(10) A. S. Douglas and I. A. Cook. 1957. Deficiency of antihaemophilic globulin in heterozygous haemophilic females. Lancet. **2:** 616-619.

(11) L. C. Dunn. 1934. Analysis of a case of mosaicism in the house mouse. J. Genet. **29:** 317-326.

(12) D. S. Falconer. 1953. Total sex-linkage in the house mouse. Z. indukt. Abstamm. u. Vererblehre. **85:** 210-219.

(13) D. S. Falconer. 1954. Linkage in the mouse: the sex-linked genes and "rough." Z. indukt. Abstamm. u. Vererblehre. **86:** 263-268.

(14) H. F. Falls. 1951. Sex-linked ocular albinism displaying typical fundus changes in the female heterozygote. Am. J. Ophthalmol. Supp. **34:** 41-50.

(15) H. F. Falls and C. W. Cotterman. 1948. Choroidoretinal degeneration, a sex-linked form in which heterozygous women exhibit a tapetal-like retinal reflex. Arch. Ophth. **40:** 685-703.

(16) P. Fantl and J. Margolis. 1955. Alpha-prothromboplastin deficiencies (haemophilia) of differing degrees in a mother and son. Brit. M. J. **1:** 640.

(17) M. A. Ferguson-Smith, A. W. Johnston and S. D. Handmaker. 1960. Primary amentia and micro-orchidism associated with an XXXY sex-chromosome constitution. Lancet. **2:** 184-187.

(18) C. E. Ford, K. W. Jones, P. E. Polani, J. C. De Almeida and J. H. Briggs. 1959. A sex-chromosome anomaly in a case of gonadal dysgenesis (Turner's syndrome). Lancet. **1:** 711-713.

(19) H. Forssman. 1955. Two different mutations of the X-chromosome causing diabetes insipidus. Amer. J. Hum. Genet. **7:** 21-27.

(20) M. Fraccaro and J. Lindsten. 1960. A child with 49 chromosomes. Lancet. **2:** 1303.

(21) A. Franceschetti. 1961. Acquisitions récentes concernant les troubles congenitaux du sens chromatique et leurs relations avec les aberrations chromosomiques. Arch. Julius Klaus-Stiftung. **35:** 322-412.

(22) J. Francois and J. P. Deweer. 1953. Albinisme oculaire lié au sexe et altérations caractéristiques du fond d'oeil chez les femmes hétérozygotes. Ophthalmologica. **126:** 209-221.

(23) A. S. Fraser, S. Sobey and C. C. Spicer. 1953. Mottled: a sex-modified lethal in the house mouse. J. Genet. **51:** 217-221.

(24) E. D. Garber. 1952. "Bent-tail," a dominant, sex-linked mutation in the mouse. Proc. Nat. Acad. Sci. **38:** 876-879.

(25) R. R. Gates. 1946. Human genetics. New York, Macmillan.

(26) J. Goedbloed. 1942. Mode of inheritance in choroideremia. Ophthalmologica. **104:** 308-315.

(27) J. B. Graham, V. W. McFalls and R. W. Winters. 1959. Familial hypophosphatemia with Vitamin D-resistant rickets II. Three additional kindreds of the sex-linked dominant type with a genetic analysis of four such families. Amer. J. Hum. Genet. **11:** 311-332.

(28) J. B. Graham, W. W. McLendon and K. M. Brinkhous. 1953. Mild hemophilia: an allelic form of the disease. Am. J. Med. Sc. **225:** 46-53.

(29) H. Grüneberg. 1952. The genetics of the mouse. The Hague, Martinus Nijhoff.

(30) H. Grüneberg. 1955. Genetical studies on the skeleton of the mouse. XVII Bent-tail. J. Genetics. **53:** 551-562.

(31) J. L. Hamerton. 1958. Mammalian sex chromosomes. D. Robertson Smith and W. M. Davidson (editors). Symposium on nuclear sex. London, Heinemann.

(32) R. M. Hardisty. 1957. Christmas disease in a woman. Brit. Med. J. **1:** 1039.

(33) P. A. Jacobs, A. G. Baikie, W. M. Court-Brown, T. N. MacGregor, N. Maclean and D. G. Harnden. 1959. Evidence for the existence of the human "super female." Lancet. **2:** 423-425.

(34) P. A. Jacobs, D. G. Harnden, K. E. Buckton, W. M. Court-Brown, M. J. King, J. A. McBride, T. N. MacGregor and N. Maclean. 1961. Cytogenic studies in primary amenorrhoea. Lancet. **1:** 1183-1188.

(35) W. Jaeger. 1951. Gibt es Kombinationsformen der verschiedenen Typen angeborener Farbensinnstörung? Graefe Arch. Ophth. **151:** 229-248.

(36) W. Jaeger. 1952. Werden die angeborenen Störungen des Rotgrünsinns ausnahmslos recessiv-geschlechtsgebunden vererbt? Graefe Arch. Ophth. **152:** 379-384.

(37) N. Kryschowa and W. Abowjan. 1934. Zur Frage der Heredität der Pseudohypertrophie Duchenne. Z. Ges. Neurol. **150:** 421-426.

(38) S. G. Levit. 1936. The problem of dominance in man. J. Genet. **33:** 411-434.

(39) E. B. Lewis. 1950. The phenomenon of position effect. Advance Genet. **3:** 73-115.

(40) J. Lindsten. 1961. New type of chromosomal mosaicism in ovarian dysgenesis. Lancet. **1:** 1228.

(41) M. F. Lyon. 1959. Private communication. Mouse News Letter. **21:** 39.

(42) M. F. Lyon. 1960. A further mutation of the mottled type in the house mouse. J. Hered. **51:** 116-121.

(43) M. F. Lyon. 1961-a. Gene action in the X-chromosome of the mouse (*Mus musculus* L.) Nature. **190:** 372-373.

(44) M. F. Lyon. 1961b. Private communication. Mouse News Letter **24:** 34.

(45) C. McCulloch and R. J. P. McCulloch. 1948. A hereditary and clinical study of choroideremia. Trans. Amer. Soc. Ophth. Oto. **52:** 160-190.

(46) W. J. Mellman, I. J. Wolman, H. A. Wurzel, P. S. Moorhead and D. H. Qualls. 1961. A chromosomal female with hemophilia A. Blood. **17:** 719-727.

(47) C. Merskey and R. G. Macfarlane. 1951. The female carrier of haemophilia, a clinical and laboratory study. Lancet. **1:** 487-490.

(48) O. J. Miller. 1960. L. S. Penrose (editor). Recent advances in human genetics, London, J. and A. Churchill, Ltd.

(49) O. J. Miller, W. R. Breg, R. D. Schmickel and W. Tretter. 1961. A family with an XXXXY male, a leukaemic male and two 21-trisomic mongoloid females. Lancet. **2:** 78-79.

(50) I. M. Nilsson, S. Bergman, J. Reitalu and J. Waldenstrom. 1959. Haemophilia in a "girl" with male sex-chromatin pattern. Lancet. **2:** 264-266.

(51) S. Ohno and T. S. Hauschka. 1960. Allocycly of the X-chromosome in tumors and normal tissues. Cancer Res. **20:** 541-545.

(52) S. Ohno, W. D. Kaplan and R. Kinosita. 1959. Formation of the sex chromatin by a single X-chromosome in liver cells of *Rattus norvegicus*. Exp. Res. **18:** 415-418.

(53) S. Ohno, W. D. Kaplan and R. Kinosita. 1960. The basis of nuclear sex difference in somatic cells of the opossum *Didelphis virginiana*. Exp. Cell Res. **19**: 417-420.

(54) S. Ohno, W. D. Kaplan, R. Kinosita and W. J. Welshons. 1960. Conditions which dictate allocyclic behavior of sex chromosomes in somatic or malignant cells. Proc. Amer. Ass. Cancer Res. **3**: 139.

(55) S. Ohno and S. Makino. 1961. The single X-nature of sex chromatin in man. Lancet. **1**: 78-79.

(56) W. W. Park. 1957. The occurrence of sex chromatin in early human and macaque embryos. J. Anat. **91**: 369-373.

(57) R. J. S. Phillips. 1961. '*Dappled*' a new allele at the *Mottled* locus in the house mouse. Genet. Res. **2**: 290-295.

(58) W. R. Pitney and J. V. Dacie. 1955. Haemophilia and allied disorders of blood coagulation. Brit. Med. Bull. **11**: 11-15.

(59) P. E. Polani. 1961. The sex chromosomes in Klinefelter's syndrome and in gonadal dysplasia. L. I. Gardner (editor). Molecular genetics and human disease. Springfield, Ill., C. C Thomas.

(60) B. Ramot, B. Angelopoulos and K. Singer. 1955. Variable manifestations of plasma thromboplastin component deficiency. J. Lab. Clin. Med. **46**: 80-88.

(61) E. Roberts. 1929. The inheritance of anhidrosis associated with anodontia. J. Am. Med. Assn. **93**: 277-279.

(62) R. W. Rundles and H. F. Falls. 1946. Hereditary (? sex-linked) anemia. Amer. J. Med. Sci. **211**: 641-658.

(63) L. B. Russell. 1961. Genetics of mammalian sex chromosomes. Science. **133**: 1795-1803.

(64) L. B. Russell and J. W. Bangham. 1959. Variegated-type position effects in the mouse. Genetics. **44**: 532.

(65) L. B. Russell and J. W. Bangham. 1960. Further analysis of variegated-type position effects from X-autosome translocations in the mouse. Genetics. **45**: 1008-1009.

(66) L. B. Russell and J. W. Bangham. 1961. Variegated-type position effects in the mouse. Genetics. **46**: 509-525.

(67) L. B. Russell and M. H. Major. 1957. Radiation-induced presumed somatic mutations in the house mouse. Genetics. **42**: 161-175.

(68) W. L. Russell, L. B. Russell and J. S. Gower. 1959. Exceptional inheritance of a sex-linked gene in the mouse explained on the basis that the XO sex-chromosome constitution is female. Proc. U. S. Nat. Acad. Sci. **45**: 554-560.

(69) J. B. Seagle. 1954. Anhidrotic hereditary ectodermal dysplasia: report of two cases in a brother and sister. J. Pediat. **45**: 688-691.

(70) L. H. Snyder. 1932. Hemophilia. Ohio J. Sci. **32**: 152-157.

(71) A. Sorsby. 1951a. Clinical genetics. London, Butterworth.

(72) A. Sorsby. 1951b. Genetics in ophthalmology. London, Butterworth.

(73) C. Stern. 1960. Principles of human genetics, 2nd ed. San Francisco, W. H. Freeman & Co.

(74) J. S. S. Stewart. 1961. Genetic factors on the X chromosome. Lancet. **2**: 104.

(75) K. Taylor and R. Biggs. 1957. A mildly affected female haemophiliac. Brit. Med. J. **1**: 1494-1496.

(76) P. J. Waardenburg and J. Van Der Bosch. 1956. X-chromosomal ocular albinism in a Dutch family. Ann. Hum. Genet. **21**: 101-122.

(77) G. L. Walls. 1959. Peculiar color blindness in peculiar people. Arch. Ophthalmol. **62**: 13-32.

(78) G. L. Walls and R. W. Mathews. 1952. New means of studying color blindness and normal foveal color vision. Univ. Calif. Pub. Psychol. **7**: 1-172.

(79) J. N. Walton. 1957. The inheritance of muscular dystrophy. Acta Genet., Basel. **7**: 318-320.

(80) W. J. Welshons and L. B. Russell. 1959. The Y-chromosome as the bearer of male-determining factors in the mouse. Proc. U. S. Nat. Acad. Sci. **45**: 560-566.

(81) J. F. Wilkinson, M. C. G. Israels, F. Nour-Eldin and R. L. Turner. 1957. Unusual transmission of the haemophilic gene. Brit. Med. J. 1528-1529.

(82) E. V. Zybina. 1960. (Translated title) Sex-chromatin in the trophoblast of young rat embryos. Dokl. Akad. Nauk U. S. S. R. **130**: 633-635.

Mutation

Part Five

The appearance of nuclear weapons and, to a lesser extent, the advent of science fiction have made mutation a word known but unwelcome in most households. It is perhaps not commonly appreciated that mutation in man, particularly as relating to causes and rates of mutation, is extraordinarily difficult to study. The papers included in this section illustrate some of the difficulties and provide some often ingenious circumventions. As a group these reports represent the adoption of various mathematical and statistical approaches and as such form a prominent aspect of human genetics.

In the paper by L. S. Penrose an attempt is made to delineate the causes of mutation by examining the influence of parental age. This short report is a model of simple but useful examination of comparatively crude data.

The paper by Schull and Neel deals with a much larger body of data and represents the summation of a considerable undertaking. Through examination of the sex ratio among children born to the survivors of Hiroshima and Nagasaki evidence is adduced for the probable occurrence of sex-linked lethal mutations.

Although not included in this collection, papers by Haldane (1), by Muller (2) and by Morton, Crow and Muller (3) in particular, further illustrate such approaches as well as emphasize the concern which surrounds the topic of mutation in our species. Crow (4) and Penrose (5) provide recent summaries of this topic.

(1) J. B. S. Haldane. 1935. The rate of spontaneous mutation of a human gene. J. Genetics. **31:** 317-326.

(2) H. J. Muller. 1950. Our load of mutations. Am. J. Hum. Genet. **2:** 111-176.

(3) N. E. Morton, J. F. Crow and H. J. Muller. 1956. An estimate of the mutational damage in man from data on consanguineous marriages. Proc. U. S. Nat. Acad. Sci. **42:** 855-863.

(4) J. F. Crow. 1961. Mutations in man. A. G. Steinberg (editor). Progress in medical genetics. New York, Grune and Stratton: 1-26.

(5) L. S. Penrose. 1961. Chapter 1. Mutation. L. S. Penrose and H. L. Brown (editors). Recent advances in human genetics. Boston, Little, Brown: 1-18.

Parental Age and Mutation*

L. S. PENROSE
Galton Professor of Eugenics in the University of London, at University College

In certain instances, human malformations are believed to originate by fresh mutation of single genes. Knowledge on this question has been summarised recently by Haldane (1949), Nachtsheim (1954), and Neel and Schull (1955).

Mutation is supposed to be constantly recurring, but only occasionally are conditions favourable for its detection. Achondroplasia, which is apparently due to a single gene in heterozygous state, usually occurs sporadically, as shown in the extensive survey by Mørch (1941), and in such cases it is believed to have arisen by fresh mutation. The incidence of this condition, however, has a marked association with parental age. Weinberg (1912) expressed the view that the high incidence of achondroplasia in lastborn children strongly suggested that mutation was the cause. It was natural to think that older germ-cells, possessed by older parents, might be more likely to show deterioration, in the form of genetical changes. On the other hand, in conditions such as epiloia, aniridia, neurofibromatosis, and retinoblastoma, which also are thought to arise from time to time by fresh mutation, no clear relationship has been found between incidence and either parental age or birth order.

Conversely, a disease in which the association with parental age is conspicuous—namely mongolism—seems not to be caused by a single gene mutation (Penrose 1954). This view is disputed by Kemp (1944), who considers that mongolism arises in the same way as achondroplasia. To decide

*Reprinted by author's and publisher's permission from Lancet. 1955. **ii**: 312-313.

which view is correct, more data need to be collected; but even on the basis
of existing material the question can be subjected to critical examination.

CAUSES OF SPONTANEOUS MUTATION

Spontaneous mutation in a cell in the germ line might be due to various
causes, of which the two most obvious are (1) failure to copy the gene correctly at cell division, and (2) irradiation from natural sources—i.e., cosmic
rays and terrestrial radioactive substances. Another cause may be (3) chemical mutagenic agents.

FAILURE TO COPY GENE

Let us consider the likely effects of type-1 mutation in relation to parental
age. There are very few cell divisions in the female germ line but many in the
male germ line since the spermatogonia are continually dividing. Thus the
incidence of mutation due to failure to copy a gene at cell division would be
unlikely to have any strong relation to maternal age; a marked increase of
defects with this origin, however, would be seen at late paternal ages. The
incidence of such a defect would increase with the father's age at first in a
fairly linear manner, presumably starting to do so at puberty, but perhaps
accelerating later.

IRRADIATION FROM NATURAL SOURCES

The effects of type-2 mutation, on the other hand, would be proportional
to total exposure of germ-cells to radiation, and this would be proportional
to the time irrespective of the number of cell divisions. The incidence of
diseases directly due to this cause would increase with parental age fairly
steadily; this would apply equally to fathers and to mothers. The relationship
between incidence and age of parents would not, however, be very marked
and consequently it would be difficult to detect. The theoretical increase in
mean age of parents of these fresh mutants, compared with the population
average, is easy to calculate. Suppose that m_0 is the mean maternal age in the
unmutated population, measured in years, and v the variance. Then m_1,
the mean maternal age for mutants, is obtained thus: * $m_1 = m_0 + (v/m_0.)$
In England, for example, the mean age of mothers, m_0, in the general population is 28.6 years, and the standard deviation is 6.0 years; thus, $m_1 =$
28.6 + 36.0/28.6 $\doteq$ 29.9 years. The same calculation can be made for age
of fathers, but with less confidence because of inadequate data. The mean,
p_0, is probably about 30.9 years, and the standard deviation is 6.6 years.
The expected mean age, p_1, of fathers of fresh mutants of this type, would
thus be 32.3 years.

* The formula is correct for all types of distributions of maternal ages.

CHEMICAL MUTAGENS

Under type 3, there is a possibility, suggested by Haldane (1955), that chemical mutagens might be produced as toxic by-products of normal metabolism. If they accumulated in the germ-cells such agents would affect ova more than sperms and would tend to cause diseases which appeared at late maternal ages, the incidence perhaps rising with the square of the age. In the case of mongolism, however, the increase of the incidence with the age of the mother is greater than this; it rises exponentially (Jenkins 1933). This suggests a different kind of causation. For example, the influence of a virus, or other such agent, growing and multiplying in the cytoplasm of the germ-cells could increase exponentially with time. It might act, conceivably, by way of gene mutation, but more probably it would infect the zygote directly through transfer of cytoplasm. In either case association with the father's age would not be significant. The frequency of cell division in the spermatogonia and the paucity of cytoplasm in the spermatozoa would both tend to mini-mise paternal transmission. A very sharp rise of incidence with maternal age is, of course, also consistent with many other explanations, such as hormonal mechanisms affecting the environment of the developing embryo.

DIFFERENCES BETWEEN PARENTS' AGES

The difference between mean ages of fathers and mothers $(p - m)$ for a particular condition is a sensitive and critical measurement. For example, if both means are raised because the condition is due to type-2 mutation, the difference between them would remain almost constant, increasing only very slightly. A number of observed means are listed in Table 1. In the case of mongolism, in spite of the greatly raised mother's age, exact calculations have repeatedly failed to demonstrate any independent effect of the father's age (Jenkins 1933, Penrose 1933, Øster 1953). The low value of the difference $(p - m)$ is an index of the same phenomenon. The very large effect, attrib-utable to mother's age alone, puts mongolism in rather a special category. A weaker effect, also purely maternal, is observed in dizygotic twinning (Dahlberg 1926), another trait which cannot reasonably be attributed to fresh mutation.

The situation regarding achondroplasia is strikingly different. Here the father's age is increased much more than the mother's, as shown by the large differences between means both in English and Danish data, 3.4 years and 6.6 years respectively. It seems not unlikely, however, that the associa-tion of the incidence with the father's age is the main factor, and that the raised mean age of the mother is only a reflection of it due to the very close correlation between father's and mother's ages in the general population (0.8). If so, the cause of mutation in achondroplasia may have to do with copying failure or special sensitivity of germ-cells during division (type 1).

Table 1. MEAN AGES, IN YEARS, OF UNAFFECTED PARENTS FOR SOME
CONGENITAL MALFORMATIONS

Condition, number of cases, and source*	Father's age (yr.) (p)	Mother's age (yr.) (m)	Difference (yr.) ($p - m$)
Data from England:			
Mongolism (215) *a*	37.7	36.0	1.7
Anencephaly (21) *b*	31.8	29.7	2.1
Hydrocephaly (43) *b*	33.6	31.3	2.3
Spina bifida with hydrocephaly (18) *b*..	34.8	32.1	2.7
Epiloia (12) *c*	31.7	28.9	2.8
Congenital heart-disease (386) *d*	32.0	28.9	3.1
Spina bifida (59) *b*	34.6	31.8	3.2
Achondroplasia (16) *e*	37.7	34.3	3.4
Control population	30.9	28.6	2.3
Trait with incidence proportional to parental age	32.3	29.9	2.4
Data from Denmark:			
Mongolism (369) *f*	38.6	35.1	3.5
Epiloia (21) *g*	33.7	29.1	4.6
Neurofibromatosis (49) *g*	34.2	29.4	4.8
Achondroplasia (97) *h*	38.7	32.1	6.6
Control population	33.3	28.6	4.7
Trait with incidence proportional to parental age	34.9	30.0	4.9

* *a*, Galton Laboratory data; *b*, Penrose (1946); *c*, Gunther and Penrose (1935); *d*, Polani and Campbell (1955); *e*, Krooth (1952); *f*, Oster (1953); *g*, Borberg (1951); *h*, Mørch (1941).

As previously demonstrated, phenomena attributable to mutations caused by natural radiation (type 2) would be associated with only slight increases in parental ages. Small increases are shown actually by epiloia and by neurofibromatosis, both of which are believed to arise by fresh mutation in the sporadic cases. The findings are suggestive, but, from the statistical point of view, insignificant like those given by Neel and Schull on retinoblastoma. A large group of sporadic malformations, probably due to fresh mutations in most instances, is provided by the material on microphthalmos collected by Sjögren and Larsson (1949). Table 2 gives the age-distribution of mothers. This was not considered by the investigators to be remarkable, but, as is clear from the relative-incidence column, there is a slight linear rise as the mother's age increases. The mean for microphthalmics, m_1, is 31.5 years, which differs from m_0, 30.1, by 1.4 years, a quantity which is just statistically significant. The expected difference, on the hypothesis of type-2 causation, would be $(6.8)^2/30.1 = 1.5$ years, which is in satisfactory agreement with

Table 2. MATERNAL AGE IN MICROPHTHALMOS (SJÖGREN AND LARSSON 1949)

Central maternal age (yr.)	Microph- thalmos	Expectation based upon control Swedish population	Relative incidence	
			Observed	Expected*
17	4	4.7	0.85	0.56
22	19	27.0	0.70	0.73
27	30	36.4	0.82	0.90
32	33	31.9	1.03	1.06
37	38	23.7	1.60	1.23
42	11	11.9	0.92	1.40
47	2	1.4	1.43	1.56
All ages	137	137.0	1.00	1.00
Mean	31.5	30.1	—	—

N.B.—The standard deviation of the control population is 6.8 years: thus, the difference, mean of the observed total (31.5) less mean of controls (30.1), is 1.4 years, that is, more than twice its standard error, 0.6 years.
  * On the basis of linear increase with age.

observation. Unfortunately information is lacking concerning ages of fathers in this series.

In other congenital defects which may sometimes arise as the result of fresh mutation it is not unreasonable to search for evidence of relationship to parental age. An example is acrocephaly, considered by Ferriman (1941) to be due to mutation in many instances. A significant increase in maternal age has been found for this condition (Penrose 1938). It is possible also that some of the elusive parental-age relationship observed for congenital hydro-cephaly, spina bifida, and anencephaly (Penrose 1946), may be evidence of the part played by fresh mutation. This suggestion would only be valid in so far as these malformations were due to dominant or sex-linked genes. Anencephaly, which sometimes has the appearance of a recessive trait (Böök and Rayner 1950), shows no appreciable association with either father's or mother's age (Record and McKeown 1949). The sample of 21 anen-cephalics in Table 1 has a slightly raised mother's age, and the 43 cases of hydrocephaly without spina bifida have a greater increase. In spina bifida, with or without hydrocephaly, and in congenital heart-disease, in so far as there is an increase in mean parental age it applies perhaps more to fathers than to mothers.

COMMENTS

These inconclusive data are cited to emphasise the need for accurate and comprehensive inquiry in this field. Yerushalmy (1939) produced evidence that, for constant maternal age-groups, the father's age was significantly associated with the general stillbirth-rate and with neonatal mortality. The influence of the father was less strong than that of the mother, but its independent existence seems to supply evidence for supposing that fresh mutations not uncommonly cause mortality in early life. It leaves open the question of the type to which such mutations might belong.

Another question which requires much further study is the effect of parental ages in sex-linked diseases such as haemophilia and the Duchenne type of muscular dystrophy. Haldane (1946) has suggested that mutation of the haemophilia gene may be much more likely to occur in males than in females—i.e., usually in the germ-cells of the maternal grandfather of the patient under observation. If this were so, the ascertainment of the grandfather's age at the mother's birth should be of special interest, but so far no data have been published on this point.

SUMMARY

It is assumed that the gene mutations, which are responsible for certain human diseases and malformations, can originate in several different ways.

An attempt is made to differentiate causes of mutation by examining their relationships to parental age.

The influence of the father's age is shown to be of critical significance. When the effect of the father's age on incidence is appreciable, as in achondroplasia, the hypothesis of fresh gene mutation as the cause is strengthened. When it is absent, as in mongolism, other mechanisms must be postulated.

Slight increase of both father's and mother's mean ages may be shown in conditions originating in mutations caused by radiation.

REFERENCES

(1) J. A. Böök and S. Rayner. 1950. Am. J. Hum. Genet. **2**: 61.

(2) A. Borberg. 1951. Op. Dom. Biol. Hered. Hum. Kbh. **23**.

(3) G. Dahlberg. 1926. Twin births and twins from a hereditary point of view. Stockholm.

(4) D. Ferriman. 1941. Acrocephaly and acrocephalosyndactyly. London.

(5) M. Gunther and L. S. Penrose. 1935. J. Genet. **31**: 413.

(6) J. B. S. Haldane. 1946. Ann. Eugen. London. **13**: 262.

(7) J. B. S. Haldane. 1949. Hereditas. London, Suppl. vol.: 267.

(8) J. B. S. Haldane. 1955. Personal communication.

(9) R. L. Jenkins. 1933. Am. J. Dis. Child. **45**: 506.

(10) T. Kemp. 1944. Acta Path. Microbiol. Scand. Suppl. **54**: 195.

(11) R. S. Krooth. 1952. The Ætiology of human malformations. Ph.D. thesis. University of London.

(12) E. T. Mørch. 1941. Op. Dom. Biol. Hered. Hum. Kbh. **3**.

(13) H. Nachtsheim. 1954. Caryologia. Suppl. **6**: 139.

(14) J. V. Neel and W. J. Schull. 1955. Human heredity. Chicago.

(15) J. Øster. 1953. Mongolism. Copenhagen.

(16) L. S. Penrose. 1933. J. Genet. **27**: 219.

(17) L. S. Penrose. 1938. Spec. rep. ser. med. res. coun. London. No. 229.

(18) L. S. Penrose. 1946. Ann. Eugen., London. **13**: 73.

(19) L. S. Penrose. 1954. Lancet. **ii**: 505.

(20) P. E. Polani and M. Campbell. 1955. Ann. Hum. Genet., London. **19**: 209.

(21) R. G. Record and T. McKeown. 1949. Brit. J. Soc. Med. **3**: 183.

(22) T. Sjögren and T. Larsson. 1949. Acta Psychiat. Kbh. Suppl. No. 56.

(23) W. Weinberg. 1912. Arch. Rass.-u. Ges. Biol. **9**: 710.

(24) Y. Yerushalmy. 1939. Hum. Biol. **11**: 342.

Radiation and the Sex Ratio in Man*
Sex Ratio Among Children of Survivors of Atomic Bombings Suggests Induced Sex-linked Lethal Mutations

WILLIAM J. SCHULL
JAMES V. NEEL
Department of Human Genetics University of Michigan Medical School

In species with an XX-XY type of chromosomal sex determination, such as man, the distribution to the offspring of radiation-induced, sex-linked mutations will differ according to the sex of the radiated parent. Furthermore, in the human species the nonhomologous nature of the X- and Y-

* Reprinted by senior author's and publisher's permission from Science. 1958. **128**: 343-348.

chromosomes, coupled with the genetic inertness of the Y, permits the more frequent manifestation of sex-linked recessive genes in the heterogametic sex—namely, the male. This difference in manifestation and distribution of sex-linked genes would lead us to expect a significant change in the sex ratio if human populations were sufficiently exposed to mutagenic factors such as X-rays, or the fallout from weapon testing. Specifically, if fathers alone were exposed, an increase in the frequency of male births would be expected because sex-linked lethal mutants induced by the exposure would be transmitted only to the exposed fathers' daughters. If mothers alone were exposed, a decrease in the frequency of male births would be expected because sex-linked recessive mutants would more frequently find expression in the sons rather than in the daughters of the exposed females. If both parents were exposed, and if the effects of parental exposure were additive although not necessarily equal, we would expect a decrease in the frequency of male births; the change, however, would not be expected to be as pronounced as when mothers alone were exposed.

ASSUMPTIONS

Several assumptions are implicit in postulating the changes just mentioned, and it seems important to state explicitly, at the outset, these assumptions, with a brief justification for each. Firstly, it is assumed that although autosomal lethal or semilethal mutations which are sex-limited may occur, their net effect is not such as to obscure the different effects on the sex ratio of paternal versus maternal radiation. Clearly, were this not so, the deviations postulated could be altered in degree or direction depending upon the relative frequencies of male-limited or female-limited mutants, or both. In view of the current state of knowledge of radiation genetics, it seems appropriate to assume that the predominant change in the sex ratio will stem from sex-linked rather than sex-limited effects.

Secondly, it has been assumed that the effect on the sex ratio of genes in the Y-chromosome is negligible, and that there exist no homologous portions of the X- and Y-chromosomes. The reasonableness of the former is supported by the knowledge that there is known, at present, no single, well-documented case of holandric inheritance, although this form of genetic transmission should be easy to recognize [for a discussion of Y-borne inheritance, see Stern (1)]. The legitimacy of the assumption that there is no homology between the X- and Y-chromosomes rests on the cytological work of Mathey (2) and Sachs (3).

Thirdly, and with reference to the exposure of both parents, it is assumed that sex-linked recessive mutants would outnumber sex-linked dominant mutations. The only animal for which data exist relevant to this assumption is *Drosophila melanogaster*, and here sex-linked recessives are estimated to be several times more common than sex-linked dominant mutants. In this connection, however, attention must be called to the evidence which suggests that sex-linked spontaneous mutation occurs more frequently in the human male than in the female (4, 5). The possibility must be entertained that the same may hold true for sex-linked induced mutations. If this is, in fact, true, then maternal exposure may not lead to a relatively greater effect on the sex ratio than paternal exposure. The directions of deviation of the sex ratio would not of course be altered even if induced sex-linked mutations occurred more frequently in the male than in the female. One other assumption which has been made in the analysis of the data presented below is that the increase in gene mutations with increasing radiation is linear over the measurable range of exposures. The linearity of the response in gene mutations to dose of radiation is one of the cornerstones of radiation genetics, and rests on a literature far too extensive to review here. Suffice it to say that since linearity obtains in all organisms thus far studied, it seems improbable that a different situation would obtain in man.

STUDIES OF THE SEX RATIO

To date, four studies on man have reported information on the sex ratio among infants born subsequent to parental exposure to ionizing radiations. These are the observations of Macht and Lawrence (6) on the offspring of American radiologists; of Kaplan (7) on the pregnancies occurring to women following the use of X-ray therapy to correct an apparent sterility; of Turpin, Lejeune, and Rethore (8) on the sex of children born to French men and women receiving X-ray therapy for sciatic neuralgia and a variety of other complaints; and, lastly, of Neel and Schull (9) on pregnancy terminations to survivors of the atomic bombings of Hiroshima and Nagasaki. We present in Table 1 a summary of the findings of Kaplan and of Macht

Table 1. Summary of the Findings of Kaplan (7) and of Macht and
Lawrence (6) with Regard to the Frequency of Male Births
Following Parental Exposure to Ionizing Radiations

Exposed parent	Estimated dose (r)	Total off-spring of known sex born after radiation	Male	Female	p
		Kaplan, 1956			
Mother	50-200	407	200	207	0.4914
		Macht and Lawrence, 1955			
Father	Unknown	4277	2198	2079	0.5139
None	Control	3491	1830	1661	0.5242

and Lawrence; in Table 2, the findings of Turpin, Lejeune, and Rethore; and in Tables 3 and 4, the findings of Neel and Schull. In the presentation of these data, we give, when it has been published, the author's estimate of the average exposure (or the range) sustained by the various groups of individuals. Let us be the first to recognize the tenuous nature of these estimates; however, since we shall be principally concerned with the direction of deviation of the sex ratio rather than the magnitude of the change, precise specification of the dose is less important, in a sense, than the proper ranking of the various exposure groups.

In a discussion of the data presented in Tables 1 to 4, one can deal rather briefly with the findings of Kaplan and of Macht and Lawrence (Table 1). In Kaplan's case, there does not exist a satisfactory unexposed control for his observations, nor have the data been presented in a fashion such that the proportion of male births could be regressed on different maternal exposures (generally Kaplan's cases received 200 roentgens, but some appear to have received less). In Macht and Lawrence's data, it is impossible to estimate the average exposure of radiologists in the United States as contrasted with physicians who are not radiologists. It is worth noting, however, that the direction of deviation in Kaplan's data would appear to be in keeping with genetic theory, for the frequency of male births is less than in the general population; this may not, however, be a meaningful comparison. The direction of deviation in Macht and Lawrence's data, on the other hand, is contrary to genetic theory; there are proportionately fewer, rather than more, males when the fathers were exposed.

Turpin, Lejeune, and Rethore's observations (Table 2) warrant somewhat more extended discussion. These authors selected for study, from the radiotherapy files of all the hospitals in and around Paris, 4428 individuals who had received radiotherapy between 1925 and 1952, a substantial majority having been treated between 1940 and 1952, and where the estimated skin dose was in excess of 300 roentgens. Two other restrictions were placed upon the cases to be selected—namely, the radiotherapy had to be for complaints of a noncancerous nature, and the exposed persons were to be adults less than 35 years of age, if female, and less than 40, if male. Repeated questionnaires were then sent to these individuals. In all, questionnaires were sent to 3579 males, of whom 37.4 percent (1334) responded, and 849 females, of whom 33.5 percent (284) responded. Turpin *et al.* do not present data which would afford some indication of how representative the respondents were of the whole group queried. This is, of course, a problem of real concern in all questionnaire surveys, and especially in those surveys where only a minority of those queried bother to respond.

Be this as it may, the irradiated males were divided by these authors into three groups (a) 368 cases where the X-ray was delivered high up on the lumbar region, or to the thigh, (b) 180 cases where irradiation was to the pelvic area but with the gonads probably shielded, and (c) 786 cases

Table 2. SUMMARY OF THE FINDINGS OF TURPIN, LEJEUNE, AND RETHORE (8) WITH REGARD TO THE FREQUENCY OF MALE BIRTHS FOLLOWING PARENTAL EXPOSURE TO IONIZING RADIATIONS

Exposed parent*	Estimated dose (r)	Reproductive performance before exposure					Reproductive performance after exposure				
		Total matings	Total children of known sex	Male	Female	p	Total matings	Total children of known sex	Male	Female	p
All cases											
Father (b)	Unknown	66	112	62	50	0.5536	52	96	42	54	0.4375
Father (C_1)	1295	284	465	242	223	0.5204	194	275	157	118	0.5709
Father (C_2)	1461	137	231	116	115	0.5022	95	130	68	62	0.5231
Mother	1360	154	236	130	106	0.5508	97	136	63	73	0.4632
Only cases having children before and after exposure											
Father (C_1)	1295	92	150	79	71	0.5267	92	119	66	53	0.5546
Father (C_2)	1461	42	67	30	37	0.4478	42	51	27	24	0.5294
Mother	1360	45	61	37	24	0.6066	45	51	26	25	0.5098

* An explanation of the subdivisions of paternal exposure will be found in the text.

Table 3. SUMMARY OF THE FINDINGS IN JAPAN WITH REGARD TO THE ASSOCIATION
OF THE FREQUENCY OF MALE BIRTHS AND PARENTAL EXPOSURE
Only one parent exposed

Father only exposed				Mother only exposed			
Total births	Male births	p	Estimated mean exposure (rep)	Total births	Male births	p	Estimated mean exposure (rep)
Neel and Schull, 1956 (1948-1953) (9), parents unrelated							
31,904	16,613	0.5207	0	31,904	16,613	0.5207	0
3,670	1,892	0.5155	8	14,684	7,681	0.5231	8
839	442	0.5268	75	2,932	1,474	0.5027	75
534	284	0.5318	200	1,676	850	0.5072	200
Neel and Schull, 1956 (1954-1955) (9), parents unrelated							
11,640	6,067	0.5212	0	11,640	6,067	0.5212	0
1,498	774	0.5167	8	4,926	2,512	0.5099	8
387	211	0.5452	75	1,026	562	0.5478	75
219	113	0.5160	200	592	311	0.5253	200
This article (1948-1953), parents related							
2,622	1,396	0.5324	0	2,622	1,396	0.5324	0
295	152	0.5153	8	963	466	0.4839	8
83	46	0.5542	100	258	134	0.5194	100

where the subjects were irradiated in the pelvic area under conditions making
protection of the gonads impossible. Turpin *et al.* present data on reproductive performance for groups (b) and (c), but not for group (a). In the
analysis of their data, group (b) is rejected because of the uncertainty
regarding the amount of radiation received by the group. The third group,
(c), was further subdivided into individuals treated for "sciatic neuralgia"
[517 cases (group c_1)], and for various other complaints [269 cases (group c_2)].

Turpin *et al.* use, as is apparent from Table 2, the reproductive performance of the exposed individuals prior to their exposure as the base of
reference with which to compare reproductive performance after exposure.
This procedure leads to a confounding of age and parity effects with those
due to radiation. The importance of this confounding is difficult to assess.
We know (i) that first-born children are more frequently males than children
in subsequent birth ranks (10), and (ii) that the frequency of male births
tends to decrease with advancing maternal or paternal age (11). It is not
clear whether the correlation between birth rank and frequency of male

Table 4. Summary of the Findings in Japan with Regard to the Association of the Frequency of Male Births and Parental Exposure
Both parents exposed

Total births	Male births	p	Estimated mean exposure (rep)	
			Mother	Father

Neel and Schull, 1956 (1958-1953) (9), parents unrelated

Total births	Male births	p	Mother	Father
5994	3053	0.5093	8	8
658	337	0.5122	8	75
422	225	0.5332	8	200
703	354	0.5036	75	8
615	319	0.5187	75	75
192	94	0.4896	75	200
318	165	0.5189	200	8
145	72	0.4966	200	75
145	71	0.4896	200	200

Neel and Schull, 1956 (1954-1955) (9), parents unrelated

Total births	Male births	p	Mother	Father
1474	806	0.5468	8	8
220	129	0.5864	8	75
174	101	0.5805	8	200
212	111	0.5236	75	8
107	53	0.4953	75	75
66	35	0.5303	75	200
89	48	0.5393	200	8
43	20	0.4651	200	75
33	18	0.5455	200	200

This article (1948-1953), parents related

Total births	Male births	p	Mother	Father
394	208	0.5279	8	8
69	38	0.5507	8	100
54	29	0.5370	100	8
43	21	0.4884	100	100

births is due wholly or in part to the correlation between birth rank and parental age. Conceivably this confounding could, then, lead to an overestimation of maternal exposure effects and an underestimation of paternal effects.

The extent of this over- or underestimation is in part a matter of speculation; however, Ciocco (10) has found that the sex ratio among first born is 0.5153 and that the sex ratio among fifth or higher order births is 0.5124. This change would be the equivalent of approximately 50 rep of maternal exposure, judging from the Japanese data (see below). It is not our purpose to present a critique of the data of Turpin *et al.*, but merely to indicate that this study, like all of the others, including our own, suffers from several deficiencies. One must, therefore, exercise considerable caution in any interpretation of the data on the sex ratio. Be this as it may, it is interesting to observe that of the four comparisons afforded by all of the data presented by Turpin *et al.*, three are in the direction which one would expect on genetic grounds.

JAPANESE DATA

Before we turn to a description of the Japanese data, it is important that one rather important fundamental difference between the study in Japan and those previously mentioned be pointed out. The data of Kaplan, Macht and Lawrence, and Turpin *et al.* involve observations on individuals whose exposure was distributed over some interval in time. Thus Macht and Lawrence's observations are on persons whose total dose may be appreciable, but this dose was incurred at relatively low levels and over a considerable period of time. Kaplan's individuals received three exposures of 50, 75, and 75 roentgens, and the interval intervening between successive exposures was 7 days. Turpin *et al.* do not state that the individuals in their study received repeated exposures; however, if the practice of radiotherapy in France is similar to that in the United States, this is undoubtedly so. The observations from Hiroshima and Nagasaki, on the other hand, are on individuals who received but a single exposure.

In the past, this distinction would perhaps not have been considered important since the data from *Drosophila*, for example, suggest that the critical factor is the total dose and not the period of time over which this dose occurred. Recently, however, Russell (12) has presented data on the mouse which suggest that the effect of chronic irradiation for a given dose and in terms of the frequency of the induction of specific locus mutations is less than the effect of acute irradiation. Russell states "Results obtained from an accumulated dose of 600 r given to spermatogonia at approximately 100 r/wk continuous irradiation show a much lower mutation rate than that obtained earlier with a 600 r acute dose of X-rays." The same also appears to be true at a total dose of 100 roentgens. If this finding is confirmed, and if the same phenomenon holds true in man, then there are reasons for believing that the Japanese data are not comparable to the studies in the United States and France.

The Japanese data concerning the effects of radiation on the sex ratio fall into three categories, as follows, two of which (i and ii) have been presented previously (9), but analyzed differently, one of which (iii) is presented here for the first time: (i) the sex ratio in infants born to *unrelated* parents in the years 1948-1953, these infants all examined by Japanese physicians; (ii) the sex ratio in infants born to *unrelated* parents in the years 1954-1955, sex reported by the parents but not verified by a physician examiner; (iii) the sex ratio in infants born to *related* parents in the years 1948-1953, these infants all examined by physician examiners [A description of the background of these children will be found in Schull's report (13)].

Detailed presentation of the method of data collection and the bases for the dosage estimates for the parents will not be attempted here, since this material has been described by Neel and Schull (9) and Schull (13). The present method of analysis was an outgrowth of an effort to integrate the findings on the offspring of related parents with those previously reported on the pregnancy terminations of unrelated parents. In the analysis to follow, we have treated the data as if they were the results from three separate, but similarly oriented, experiences. The decision to do this was based upon two considerations. Firstly, the information collected in the years 1948-1953 involved direct observations by physicians on newly born infants, whereas the information obtained in 1954-1955 was based upon municipal birth records supplemented by a questionnaire to the parents. The two methods of collecting data would seem sufficiently different to justify maintaining a distinction between the two bodies of data which were collected. Secondly, within the years 1948-1953, the division of the data into observations on the offspring of related and unrelated parents seems appropriate in view of the frequently voiced belief that the increased homozygosity of the inbred child may make it a more sensitive indicator of genetic damage, and direct combination of these data was not feasible because of the dissimilarity in the frequency of consanguineous marriages in the various exposure classes. Let us turn now to a brief description of how the data have been analyzed, and a presentation of the results which were obtained.

As we have indicated, we have, in effect, three experiences, and the information with respect to each of these three experiences can be further subdivided into three parts—namely, pregnancies where the mother was exposed but the father was not, where the father was exposed but the mother was not, and where both parents were exposed. Within each of these nine "experience-exposed parent(s)" groups, there exist three or more dosage levels. Thus it is possible to fit nine linear regressions of the frequency of male births on the dose of radiation received by the parent(s). Six of these regressions will be of the form

$$E(p_i) = \bar{p} + b(d_i - \bar{d}),$$

where $E(p_i)$ is the expected proportion of males in the ith exposure class, $\bar{p}$ is the mean proportion of males, d_i is the dose in the ith exposure class, $\bar{d}$ is the average dose, and b is the regression coefficient. Three of the regressions will be of the form

$$E(p_{ij}) = \bar{p} + b_1(F_i - \bar{F}) + b_2(M_j - \bar{M}),$$

where b_1 and b_2 are now partial regression coefficients, F_i and M_j are, respectively, the doses in the ith paternal and j^{th} maternal exposure groups, $\bar{F}$ and $\bar{M}$ are the mean paternal and maternal exposures, and $\bar{p}$ is, again, the mean proportion of male births. The regressions which were, in fact, fitted were weighted to allow for the differences in the numbers of observations at the various exposure levels. The weights which were used were the reciprocals of the variances (the information) of the proportions of males at the different dosage levels. The final weights were obtained by iteration, starting with the observed proportions as trial values. The intercepts and regression coefficients which were obtained are presented in Table 5. Several comments on these values are in order.

Table 5. MEANS AND REGRESSION COEFFICIENTS OBTAINED BY FITTING A WEIGHTED LINEAR REGRESSION OF THE PROPORTION OF MALE BIRTHS TO AVERAGE GROUP EXPOSURE IN THE JAPANESE DATA. THE VALUES IN PARENTHESES ARE THOSE OBTAINED WHEN UNEXPOSED PARENTS ARE REJECTED

References: Neel and Schull, 1956 (9); Schull and Neel, 1958 (this article)	Father only exposed		Mother only exposed		Both parents exposed			
					Father		Mother	
	$\bar{p}$	b *	$\bar{p}$	b	$\bar{p}$	b	$\bar{p}$	b
1948-1953								
Unrelated parents	0.5202	0.0058 (0.0094)	0.5213	−0.0101 † (−0.0111)	0.5102	0.0039	0.5102	−0.0037
Related parents	0.5307	0.0188 (0.0423)	0.5204	−0.0116 (0.0386)	0.5310	0.0024	0.5310	−0.0179
1954-1955								
Unrelated parents	0.5211	0.0039 (0.0047)	0.5186	0.0090 (0.0141)	0.5464	0.0137	0.5464	−0.0269
Common regression coefficients		0.0056		−0.0080		0.0036		−0.0042

* Regression coefficients are given as increase or decrease in proportion of male births per 100 rep.
† Significant at the 5-percent level.

1) It should be noted that no less than 11 of the 12 regression coefficients are of the sign anticipated by genetic theory—that is to say, the deviation is in the direction anticipated if sex-linked mutations have been induced by the exposure. The one nonconforming coefficient is that for mothers unrelated, 1954-1955. The prior probability that 11 or more of 12 regression coefficients will have signs in keeping with genetic theory, if the signs of these regression coefficients are, in fact, equiprobable, is approximately 1 in 341. Clearly the array of signs is significant.

2) Only one of the regression coefficients can be shown to be significantly different from zero, at the 5-percent level of significance, and, unfortunately none of the common regression coefficients for mothers only exposed, fathers only exposed, or both parents exposed differs significantly from zero. It should be mentioned here that substantially the same results are obtained if the arc sin transformation is used.

3) It will be noted from Table 3 that certain observations—namely, those where both parents were unexposed—occur more than once. This, of course, implies that the regression coefficient for "fathers only exposed,

1954-1955," say, is not wholly independent of the regression coefficient for "mothers only exposed, 1954-1955." It may, therefore, be argued that we are not, in fact, dealing with 12 independent regression coefficients since some data are scored twice. This difficulty can be avoided, at the expense of some observations, by omitting entirely the observations on both parents unexposed, and basing the regression coefficients on only those data where the "exposed" parent experienced some irradiation. When this is done, we find that 10 of these 12 estimates have the signs one would expect from genetic theory under these circumstances. A simple sign test reveals that approximately 2 times in 100 we would expect this distribution of signs, or one favoring genetic theory even more if, in fact, the null hypothesis were true.

ANALYSIS

The findings in the Japanese data pose two very interesting and important questions. (i) How much confidence can we place in these findings as evidence of radiation-induced genetic damage? (ii) If the changes in the sex ratio are, in fact, manifestations of genetic damage, why do we not find evidence for a radiation-induced change in the frequency of congenital malformations or one of the other attributes of a pregnancy termination? In this connection, it should be stated that an analysis of radiation effects in the consanguineous material with respect to malformation frequency and frequency of stillbirths and neonatal deaths, to be presented in detail elsewhere, fails to yield results comparable to those regarding sex ratio, in their negativity confirming the findings reported earlier for the children born to unrelated parents (9). Clearly a categorical answer to either of these questions is impossible; however, certain observations seem pertinent to any answer which one may arrive at.

With respect to the first of these two questions, we have indicated elsewhere (9) the interpretive difficulties which arise when one begins to select, in the Japanese data, specific cells or groups of cells on which to base comparisons. The present approach would, however, seem to avoid many of these difficulties since (i) all of the data are used, and (ii) the division of the data was based upon a priori considerations regarding parental exposure, relationship, and method of data collection alone, and did not involve value judgments regarding the extent to which one portion of data, collected at one time and in one manner, was *in pari materia* with another collected at the same time and in the same manner.

It must be pointed out, however, that the sex ratio, as a variable, leaves much to be desired, the elegant genetic argument which can be advanced for expecting changes in the sex ratio consequent to parental exposure notwithstanding. Any number of factors—for example, maternal age, paternal age, parity, war, and so forth—seem capable of altering the sex ratio, and though these effects are, in general, small, adequate explanation for the peculiar variations which occur due to these factors has not been advanced. Perhaps the greatest recommendation for accepting the observations with regard to the sex ratio as a manifestation of a real effect of parental exposure is the consistency of the findings. It is true, however, that one does not find within the Japanese data other evidence of sex-linked lethal genes which might logically be expected, such as an increase in the difference in frequency between inviable males and inviable females as maternal exposure increases. The significance of this absence of what might be termed "secondary effects" is not readily appraised since (i) the direct effect on the sex ratio is itself small and (ii) the sex difference in viability has been measured only for the period from approximately the 21st week of gestation onward. Thus, sex-linked lethal mutants leading to gametic death or to the early death of the zygote would not come within our ken.

A further possible recommendation for accepting the results as real is the apparent "reasonableness" of the change. The following rather simple calculation illustrates this: The average number of induced sex-linked lethal mutants at any given dose of radiation is equal to the product of the number of genetic loci at risk, the probability of inducing a mutant per unit dose, and the dose received. If we accept 0.0060 as the best estimate of the change in the sex ratio following 100 rep of maternal irradiation, and if we assume that the number of "targets"—that is, sex-linked lethal producing genetic loci on one X-chromosome—lies between 250 and 2500, then we find that the probability of a sex-linked lethal mutation per rep lies in the interval 2.4×10^{-7} and 2.4×10^{-8}. Current genetic thinking would tend to suggest that the number of loci at risk is rather nearer 250 than 2500, and hence that the sensitivity of human genes would be more likely to be of the order of 2.4×10^{-7}, a figure which agrees well with the findings for the only other mammal studied thus far, the mouse (14), but which suggests a significantly greater sensitivity than that observed in *Drosophila*.

With respect to the second of the two questions raised above, concerning the implications for the validity of the sex-ratio findings of the failure to demonstrate parallel changes with regard to the frequency of malformations or stillbirths or neonatal deaths, it should be pointed out that Neel (15) has recently suggested, on the basis of an analysis of certain aspects of the Japanese data and a comparison of the findings with those available for Caucasian populations, that a significant fraction of congenital malformations may be the segregants from complex homeostatic genetic systems. If this viewpoint is correct, then it follows that induced mutations at loci involved in these homeostatic systems, while ultimately resulting in an increase in malformation frequency, would not be expected to bear the same simple and immediate relationship to malformation frequency as sex-linked lethal mutations do to the sex ratio. It may well be, then, that no conflict of evidence is involved in the failure to demonstrate an effect of radiation exposure on malformation frequency in the first postbomb generation.

SUMMARY

An analysis of new data concerning the sex of children born to the survivors of the atomic bombings of Hiroshima and Nagasaki, together with a reanalysis of the data previously presented by Neel and Schull (9), reveals significant changes in the sex ratio of these children, changes in the direction to be expected if exposure had resulted in the induction of sex-linked lethal mutations (16).

REFERENCES

(1) C. Stern. 1957. Am. J. Hum. Genet. **9**: 147.

(2) R. Mathey. 1951. Advances in Genetics. **4**: 159.

(3) L. Sachs. 1954. Ann. Eugen. **18**: 255.

(4) J. B. S. Haldane. 1947. Ann. Eugen. **13**: 262.

(5) J. B. S. Haldane. 1956. Ann. Hum. Genet. **20**: 344.

(6) S. H. Macht and P. S. Lawrence. Am. J. Roentgenol. Radium Therapy Nuclear Med. **73**: 442.

(7) I. I. Kaplan. 1956. Indian J. Radiol. Souvenir no. 1.

(8) R. Turpine, J. Lejeune and M. O. Rethore. 1957. Proc. 1st Int. Cong. Hum. Genet. **1**: 204.

(9) J. V. Neel and W. J. Schull. 1956. The effect of exposure to the atomic bombs on pregnancy termination in Hiroshima and Nagasaki. Washington, D. C., National Academy of Sciences, National Research Council: xvi, 241.

(10) A. Ciocco. 1938. Hum. Biol. **10**: 36.

(11) E. Novitski. 1953. Science. **117**: 531.

(12) W. L. Russell. 1958. Science. **127**: 1062.

(13) W. J. Schull. 1958. Empirical Risks in Consanguineous Marriages: Sex Ratio, Malformation and Viability. Am. J. Hum. Genet. **10**: 294-349.

(14) W. L. Russell. 1954. A. Hollaender (editor). Radiation biology. New York, McGraw-Hill Book Co., Inc. **1**: 825.

(15) J. V. Neel. 1958. A Study of Major Congenital Defects in Japanese Infants. Am. J. Hum. Genet. **10**: 398-445.

(16) The data here presented were collected under the auspices of the Atomic Bomb Casualty Commission, Field Agency of the National Academy of Sciences—National Research Council of the United States and the National Institute of Health of Japan. Analysis of these data was sponsored by the U. S. Atomic Energy Commission under a grant to the University of Michigan. Contract AT(11-1)-405.

A
Reappraisal

Part Six

Possibly no science has had as many political and social entanglements as genetics. Human geneticists were involved in the eugenics movement at the start of the century, in the outrages which occurred before and during the second World War, and today in debates on the consequences of nuclear weapon testing and the importance of skin pigmentation in a free society. L. C. Dunn, a pioneer geneticist and a past president of the American Society of Human Genetics, provides in this paper a commentary on some of the ways in which genetics has been affected by these quarrels.

291

Cross Currents in the History of Human Genetics*

L. C. DUNN

There is, I believe, general agreement that interest and activity in human genetics has today reached a peak never before attained. The periodical literature of the last ten years and the reports of the increasingly frequent symposia and conferences devoted to genetic problems in man provide convincing evidence of this. It is also clear that interest in these problems is likely to increase greatly in the next years so that what we may be witnessing now is only the beginning of a kind of renaissance in which genetics in general stands a chance of being greatly enriched by research on man.

There are probably many reasons for this rather sudden spread of interest, but I think that now is not the best time to try to identify the specific causes and influences of the change. For me, at any rate, a more interesting question is why this period has been so long delayed. Why did human genetics develop so slowly? It is, after all sixty years since the basic principle of heredity came to recognition. By 1915 the general architecture of the hereditary material was known (The Mechanism of Mendelian Heredity, by Morgan, Sturtevant, Muller and Bridges). Even if we date the definitive elucidation of the physical basis of heredity as late as from the publication of Morgan's *Theory of the Gene* in 1926, still that knowledge has been with us for 35 years.

I know the stock explanation of lack of progress used in those days when human geneticists were inclined to be apologetic: "You see, we can't experiment with man, and his generation time is long." True, no more can we do experimental breeding with him today, nor has his generation time de-

* Reprinted by author's and publisher's permission from Am. J. Hum. Genet. 1962. **14:** 1-13.

Presidential address presented at the meeting of the American Society of Human Genetics, Atlantic City, N. J., May 3, 1961.

Grateful acknowledgement is made to the Galton Laboratory, University College, London for hospitality and library facilities and to Professor L. S. Penrose for helpful discussions during the writing of this paper.

creased. Yet the rate of learning about human genetics has greatly increased today. Great progress has only recently been made in several fields in which essential steps opening them to investigation were taken long ago. The primary generalization of population genetics was adumbrated by Pearson in 1904 and clearly formulated by Hardy and by Weinberg in 1908, and its usefulness in human genetics demonstrated by Bernstein in 1924. By 1930 the groundwork of general theory in this field had been laid by Haldane, Fisher, Wright and others, but there has been a long lag period in the application of such methods to man. Many of the implications of Mendelian genetics for studying the transmission system, gene action, bio-chemical genetics and evolution in man were foreseen by Garrod in 1908 and some of them even in 1902 by Bateson. Yet they too have only recently been exploited in human genetics. Cytological study had, even in the 1920's, facilitated the resolution of genetical problems in other animals and in plants yet did not begin to serve this function in human genetics until the mid-fifties.

I do not mean to say that new technical and analytical methods have not had important effects in facilitating progress. They certainly have. I do mean to say that methods and ideas already available were not, for many years, applied vigorously and with good results to the study of human genetics.

I have recently been re-examining the history of genetics in the formative period from 1900 to about 1930. I have gained the impression that influences which played on human genetics during that period had a good deal to do with delaying its progress in the next 20 years and have not yet ceased to operate. It was then caught up in the crosscurrents to which all studies of man are exposed. The effects of science on human life are always immanent, yet never so immediately apparent as when man himself is the object of inquiry. In the period of which I speak, his confidence as controller of his own destiny had been aroused by recent scientific discovery and by social and political conquests of new environments. Rapid translations of new knowledge into terms applicable to improvements of man's lot is at such times likely to take precedence over objective and skeptical evaluation of the facts, a danger of which cautious scientists have long been aware. The testing of hypotheses by factual observations and the construction of general theory, the normal methods of science, are certainly no less important when human beings are involved, yet one often finds these neglected in human genetics in that period. Progress in human genetics seemed to have been impeded less by lack of means than by lack of a clear scientific goal, and this at a time when the major problems of genetics were taking a clear form. The particulate nature of the transmission mechanism of heredity had focused attention on the means by which genetic elements reproduce and maintain their continuity with opportunity for change and evolution, and on the means by which genes control metabolism and development. But most observations on human heredity were not oriented in any clear way toward such problems. Matters of greater moment seemed to be the inheritance of "insanity," of "feeble-mindedness" and other then vaguely defined mental ills, the effects of parental age or alcoholism or social status on the offspring, and similar studies pursued for immediate social ends.

An interesting comparison, which I shall not be able to pursue in detail, is that between such dominant interests of the period as those just cited, and the direction initiated by Garrod's paper of 1901 (Lancet, Nov. 30) on alcaptonuria and especially by his Croonian lectures of 1908. One reads today those lectures as published in successive issues of Lancet for that year with admiration for the depth and breadth of Garrod's scientific understanding of genetics and of evolution, and then turns with amazement to the reports of discussions on human heredity at the Royal Academy of Medicine which ran through five later issues of that same volume. Except for Garrod's strong supporter and genetical advisor, William Bateson, there is little evidence that the numerous participants in those debates realized what, in fact, the problems were. Karl Pearson, the director of the Galton Laboratory of National Eugenics, was reported to have said in the third debate: "His own view was that there was no truth in Mendelism at all." (Lancet 2, p. 1615.) He insisted that he had been misreported, although two independent records confirmed the quoted statement (p. 1768), and that he had said that "Mendelism had not been demonstrated for any one character." (Lancet 2, p. 1708.) But the main lesson we learn from the above is that Garrod's work had little effect until many years had passed; while those interested in the social applications proposed by eugenics largely dominated the field of human genetics.

It will, I think, be clear to anyone who examines the records of the period from 1900 to about the middle thirties that the manner in which the eugenics movement developed cast a long shadow over the growth of sound knowledge of human genetics. The ideals of eugenics as originally proposed by Galton in 1883 and restated in more concrete form in 1901 can hardly be held responsible for this, for they will appeal to most people as embodying a noble conception. But there grew up within the eugenics movement ambivalent attitudes through which it tended to become all things to all people, here a science, there a social movement, and in Germany an instrument, though the so-called eugenics laws of 1933, of the ferocious application of prejudice which seemed to many people to be the logical extension, the reductio ad absurdum, of ideas to be found in eugenic programs elsewhere. One effect of all this was to deflect attention from the essential scientific problems and to discourage persons interested in these from pursuing them with human material. It seems as though some perverse kind of Gresham's law might have been operating here, bad coin driving out the better.

A second cause of failure and delay in human genetics was the all too frequent relaxation of critical criteria and a lowering of standards which would not be tolerated in other branches of genetics. In course of time this, like the handicap imposed by eugenics, became less important in relation to the rising tide of good scientific work, both practical and theoretical, in human genetics. Signs of the change may be seen in Penrose's paper of 1932 and in Hogben's book of 1931 which contained a sharp attack on eugenics. As these changes went on, the name eugenics disappeared from several institutions and publications dealing with human genetics. On the other side some of the eugenical organizations (like the American Eugenics Society) tended to assume a more responsible attitude toward the scientific facts underlying social applications and toward research in human genetics.

I think it can be shown, however, that neither of the chief defects seen in the adolescent period of human genetics has in fact disappeared today. Now while I suppose that the chief function of historical analysis is to gain views that are more satisfying, intellectually and esthetically, than those afforded by studying only the present state of knowledge, still it has its practical side as well, since we can hardly overlook lessons for the conduct of our lives in the present and the future.

In both of these respects the history of connections between eugenics and human genetics has a special relevance. The connections were very close, and were especially evident in the United States, where interest in both fields was widespread at the turn of the century. Human genetics was often treated as part of eugenics, or as it was often called, human betterment or race improvement. It was that part concerned with acquisition of knowledge of human heredity. The association tended to be maintained because both subjects were frequently pursued and often taught by the same persons. Those who had been attracted by the promise inherent in the newly discovered work of Mendel often added to their repertoire the results of earlier studies like those of Dugdale (1874), and others who had dealt with mental deficiency and criminality as social problems.

There were, however, a few whose position was most clearly stated later by Bateson (1919). "The eugenist and the geneticist will, I am convinced, work most effectively without organic connection, and though we have much in common, should not be brigaded together. Genetics are not concerned with the betterment of the human race but with a problem in pure physiology, and I am a little afraid that the distinctness of our aims may be obscured." But in general the position in most countries was that implied by an index entry in the one serious attempt to trace, from documents, the history of some of the important ideas about heredity. That was the essay of Alfred Barthelmess (1952) in which under the entry *Mensch* we find "sieh auch Eugenik."

The nature of the relations between eugenics and the study of human heredity was strongly influenced by three facts. The first is that the formulation of the problems and program of eugenics antedated the recognition of the particulate nature of heredity. Early work in eugenics was thus guided by a view of heredity which proved to be without general validity. The second is that eugenics achieved organized forms before genetics did. It thus became at the very least a part of the environment in which genetics grew up. The third is that stated by Bateson: they had different goals.

The development of my argument now requires a brief sketch of the history of eugenics. The best source book for this is Karl Pearson's great four volume biography of Galton (1914-1930).

We may formally date the beginnings of eugenics in its modern form from Galton's Huxley Lecture to the Royal Anthropological Institute (published in Nature, Nov. 1, 1901) on "The possible improvement of the human breed under existing conditions of law and sentiment." Galton's ideas on this subject had been adumbrated long before this time, first in a paper of 1865. By 1883 they had been given the name of eugenics but had not then attracted active attention. Nor did the seed sown before the anthropologists in 1901 appear to have taken root quickly in England (although it fared better in the United States) and it took further effort on Galton's part to get a fellowship in eugenics established at University College, London, in 1904. This led first to the organization of a Eugenics Record Office and then in 1907 to the Galton Laboratory of National Eugenics (both endowed by Galton) and in the next year to the organization of the Eugenics Education Society. One should note two coincidences of date: 1865 was also the year in which Mendel presented his results at Brünn; and 1900 was the year of the famous "rediscovery" of these. But there was no more connection between the ideas of Galton and Mendel in 1900-01 than there had been in 1865. It was chance of the same kind which gave both men the same year of birth—1822.

Galton's ideas concerning eugenics had been formed first after reading the Origin of Species. The substitution of social control for natural selection in guiding human evolution was for Galton "the logical application of the doctrine of evolution to the human race," but the first ambivalence appeared when he added that the result of his study had been "to elicit the religious significance of the doctrine of evolution. It suggests an alteration in our mental attitudes and imposes a new moral duty." He had become convinced of the heritability of mental qualities through his studies first of Hereditary Genius (1869) and then of Inquiries into Human Faculty (1883), and had devised statistical methods for the study of inheritance which led him to his Law of Ancestral Heredity in 1897. His views on heredity were always based on this "law" which turned out to describe certain resemblances in graded or continuous characters between parents and offspring but of course provided no explanatory or general principle such as that discovered by Mendel. This is not to say that his eugenical proposals would have been invalidated by his acceptance of Mendel's principles. Those proposals were based primarily on the supposition that heredity was an important cause of differences in physical, mental, and moral qualities, and that was sufficient for his purposes.

Divergences soon appeared in England both among the supporters of eugenics and between these and the school which was shortly to call itself genetics, but was at first referred to as Mendelian. The internal cleavage in eugenics was that between the research and the propaganda interests, as represented by the Eugenics Laboratory and the Eugenics Education Society. The Laboratory resisted and resented interference with its primary function by the Society. "It will never do," wrote Galton to Karl Pearson (the director of the Eugenics Laboratory) on February 6, 1909, "to allow the Eugenics Education Society to anticipate and utilize the Eugenics Laboratory publications" (Life Vol. IIIa, p. 371), and he reminded the Society of the "differences between the work of the two classes of publication." The founder of the movement saw quite clearly the distinction between research and propaganda, and in his last public lecture on "Probability, the Basis of Eugenics" (Oxford 1909) he came out for research as the immediate need, social application as the distant goal.

But dissension between Society and Laboratory continued and finally Galton was impelled in a letter to the London Times (Nov. 3, 1910) to make his position quite clear vis-à-vis the Eugenics Laboratory and the Eugenics Education Society. "Permit me," he wrote, "as the founder of one and the honorary president of the other, to say that there is no other connection between them. . . . The Laboratory investigates without bias . . . large collections of such data as may throw light on many problems of eugenics. The business of the Society is to popularize the results." (Life, Vol. IIIa, p. 408.) This cleavage, which was to reappear time and again as the movement grew, marked a separation, often not well defined, between those interested in science and those interested in social and political questions. The progress of genetics may not have been directly affected by such disagreements within the eugenics movement, but the occasional excesses of persons with political motivation revealed the source of danger which eventually broke into the open in Germany.

The other cleavage which became apparent at once in England was that between the Mendelians led by Bateson, and the followers of Galton, led first by Weldon and then by Karl Pearson, and known as the Biometricians. The verbal battles between these sharply opposed schools certainly did delay the development of both genetics and eugenics in Great Britain. Karl Pearson, the first director of the Eugenics Laboratory, and, after Galton, the leading eugenist, never recognized the importance of Mendel's principles upon which genetics was founded. As late as 1930 he could say (Life of Galton, Vol. III, p. 309) "during the last 25 years we seem scarcely nearer the exact knowledge of the laws of heredity; the farther we advance the more complex does the problem become." It was not that he (or Galton) failed to understand the primary principle of segregation, although he did not appreciate the relation of dominance to it. Indeed in 1904 Pearson foreshadowed an important extension of the principle of segregation by showing that Mendel's ratio $1DD:2DR:1RR$ tends to maintain itself indefinitely in random breeding populations of large size (cf. Wright 1959). Galton likewise applied the term "atomistic" to Mendel's system; but neither Galton nor Pearson nor their followers found their interest satisfied by the new principles of Mendel. The heredity in which they were interested could not (they thought) be studied in that way. What they thought important to understand was quantitative variation in human intellectual ability, and Mendelism they considered to be of no help at all. In fact at that stage it was not helpful. This of course is only to say that the purposes of the biometricians and eugenists differed from those of the protogeneticists. Purposes, like tastes, may not be fair game for scientific dispute, although neither side admitted that.

In general the alienation between the two schools was a local British affair. One aspect of it however involved the beginnings of the eugenics movement in the United States. There the ground had been prepared by studies like those of Dugdale (1874) on the Jukes family and of Alexander Graham Bell (1883) on deaf-mutism. However in name and purposes the eugenics movement in the U.S.A. was clearly descended from the British one. It differed sharply from its parent in its attitude toward Mendelism. The first proponents of eugenics in the U.S.A., of which C. B. Davenport was the most active, were thoroughgoing Mendelians, and eugenists because they were Mendelians. In fact, Davenport might have been called a super-Mendelian. One has only to read his conclusions on the monofactorial inheritance of a violent temper or a wandering habit to realize this. The British eugenists correctly surmised that this attitude could (as in fact it did) bring the whole movement into disrepute. Dr. David Heron of the Galton Laboratory vigorously attacked in 1913 the first papers to come from Davenport's newly established Eugenics Record Office (founded 1910). Heron wrote (p. 5): "We have selected this rounded group of papers because they deal with a very pressing subject, that of mental defect, and in our opinion form a very apt illustration of the points just referred to, i.e., careless presentation of data, inaccurate methods of analysis, irresponsible expression of conclusions and rapid change of opinion. . . . The Mendelian conclusions drawn have no justification whatever." And further (p. 61): "The authors have in our opinion done a disservice to knowledge, struck a blow at careful Mendelian research, and committed a serious offense against the infant science of eugenics." Heron's criticism, it must be acknowledged, was more than merely another skirmish in the war being waged between the Biometricians and the Mendelians. In this case the point at issue was fundamental scientific method, and Davenport and his collaborators were at least guilty of a lack of caution from which the whole eugenics movement was to suffer. It was at this time, 1910-1915, that single gene interpretations began to be applied with great confidence (amounting in some cases to recklessness) to differences in mental ability and to mental diseases. The outstanding example was feeble-mindedness, and on the basis of the first pedigrees published by Goddard in 1910 Davenport (1911 Eugenics Record Office Bulletin 1) adopted the hypothesis that mental deficiency in general was inherited as a Mendelian recessive. In this he was followed by many others, and eugenical programs and some legislation were based on this assumption. Stanley P. Davies, who reviewed the history of this period in 1923, called it "the alarmist period." The first fruits of new methods of mental testing were garnered rapidly and widely, and the overemphasis on bad heredity as the cause of mental deficiency and mental disease, and on restrictive or negative eugenics as the only possible cure of a social ill brought on its inevitable reaction. H. S. Jennings in 1925 attempted to restore common sense by his critical attack on the whole concept of unit characters and on the unreality of the either-or distinction between heredity and environment in the determination of human (or any other) characters. Raymond Pearl in 1928 said: "Orthodox eugenists are going contrary to the best established facts of genetical science and are in the long run doing their cause harm." One of the signs that the public image of eugenics had been affected by this and similar criticisms was revealed when G. K. Chesterton published in 1922 *Eugenics and Other Evils*. These essays are not the best example of Chesterton's wit and journalistic skill, but the main point was made sharply clear to his large audience. These essays, he said, had been accumulating since before the first World War, and he had thought the defeat of Germany would have rendered them obsolete. But, he said in his foreword: "It has gradually grown apparent, to my astounded gaze, that the ruling classes of England are still proceeding on the assumption that Prussia is a pattern for the whole world. For that reason, three years after the war with Prussia, I collect and publish these papers." The essence of his objections to eugenics is revealed in one sentence (p. 51): "Even if I were a eugenist I should not personally elect to waste my time locking up the feeble-minded. The people I should lock up would be the strong-minded." Although his criticisms were not always cogent, his suspicion of eugenics, race hygiene, and "scientific officialism" of the German type proved to have been well-founded.

In Germany the eugenics movement took the name Rassenhygiene from a book of that title published in 1895 by Alfred Ploetz who also founded in 1903 the chief German journal in this field, the Archiv für Rassen-und-Gesellschaftsbiologie. In an article in this journal in 1909 Galton agreed with the editor that Rassenhygiene and Eugenik were to be regarded as synonymous. Any misunderstanding on this score was removed in 1931 when the chief German society in this field, the Deutsche Gesellschaft für Rassenhygiene (founded in 1902) added "Eugenik" to its title. The direction in which Rassenhygiene led had become evident long before Hitler came to power; and the advent of the new laws for sterilization of the unfit and unwanted, and for the exclusion of Jews from the new state were greeted with editorial acclaim in the Archiv. The speed with which the first of these laws were prepared and promulgated within the first few months of 1933 is probably to be explained by the composition of the committee of experts which drafted them. This included Ploetz and his fellow eugenists Rüdin and Lenz and others who had worked in this field together with Heinrich Himmler. Frick, Hitler's Minister of the Interior, whose department was charged with the administration of the laws said upon their coming into force: "The fate of race-hygiene, of the Third Reich and the German people will in the future be indissolubly bound together." (Arch. Rass. Ges. Biol. Vol. 27, p. 451.) The situation was made quite clear by von Verschuer in the introduction to his book *Leitfaden der Rassenhygiene*, published in 1941.

"Es ist entscheidend für die Geschichte eines Volkes was der politische Führer von den Ergebnissen der Wissenschaft als wesentlich erkennt und zur Tat werden lässt. Die Geschichte unserer Wissenschaft ist aufs engste verknüpft mit der deutschen Geschichte der jüngsten Vergangenheit. Der Führer des Deutschen Reiches ist der erste Staatsmann der die Erkenntnisse der Erbbiologie und Rassenhygiene zu einem leitenden Prinzip in der Staatsführung gemacht hat." (p. 11)

(Decisive for the history of a people is what the political leader recognizes as essential in the results of science and puts into effect. The history of our science is most intimately connected with German history of the most recent past. The leader of the German state is the first statesman who has wrought the results of genetics and race hygiene into a directing principle of public policy.)

This statement by a leading German human geneticist was made with some deliberation, for it appeared first in identical form in an article by von Verschuer in Der Erbarzt 1937, p. 97, and although it has been omitted in a recent edition of the above book (1959), the author has not to my knowledge publicly altered his position on enforced race hygiene. Although not all geneticists who remained in Germany thus accepted the eugenical and racial doctrines and practices of the Nazis, there is at least evidence that even the serious scientists among them underrated the dangers of the movement until it was too late. From this the melancholy historical lesson can be drawn that the social and political misuse, to which genetics applied to man is peculiarly subject, is influenced not only by those who support such misuse, but also by those who fail to point out, as teachers, the distinctions between true and false science.

In von Verschuer's book of 1941 Galton is acknowledged to be the modern founder of race hygiene as eugenics; but to Gobineau is given the greater credit of having first brought race into politics, thereby becoming the founder of political anthropology, a field in which the leading later exponents in Germany were Eugen Fischer and H. A. K. Günther. In contrast to the situation in Great Britain in which Galton had been unable to arouse the interest of anthropologists, the German eugenics movement had close connections with the kind of anthropology which was pursued by anthropometric methods. Since this was not guided by a theoretical rationale such as might have been supplied by population genetics, it fell the more quickly a victim to the pseudo-science of the promoters of the Aryan mythology. The chief research institute was the Kaiser Wilhelm Institute for Anthropology, Human Genetics, and Eugenics, of which Eugen Fischer was the director. Many members of this institute had become so politically involved with Nazism that after the defeat of Hitler's regime the institute was not continued by the West German State, thus fulfilling rather quickly Frick's prophecy of the interdependence of race hygiene and the Nazi state. It must be noted that in the debacle eugenics carried anthropology and human genetics down with it. There can be no doubt that in Germany, formerly a center of genetical research, the effect of its association with race hygiene was to delay for a generation the development of a science of human genetics.

In the United States, as in Britain, anthropologists in general did not respond to eugenical appeals. The kind of racialism which had become attached to eugenics was not calculated to appeal to persons whose profession it was to study and interpret human differences objectively and in socio-cultural as well as biological terms. Human genetics has today become a useful contributor to anthropology, mainly through gene frequency studies, and by the application of good objective methods generally untinged by racialism. However, there are still reminders of the uncritical use of what look like genetical methods applied to racial anthropology. What shall one say, for example, when three authors, after anthropometric examination of 44 Italian war orphans of whom the father was unknown but assumed to be "colored" draw sweeping conclusions concerning heterosis ("established with certainty"), inheritance of erythrocyte diameter ("very convincing") and other statements not supported by evidence. Yet these are statements made in 1960 by Luigi Gedda and his co-workers Serio and Mercuri in their recent book Meticciato di Guerra. R. R. Gates, who writes an introduction in English to this elaborate book refers to it as an important contribution to what he calls "racial genetics." Others will have greater difficulty in detecting any contribution to genetics, but may see in it, as I do, a reflection in 1960 of the uncritical naïveté of that early period of human genetics which delayed its progress. And the same year—1960—sees also the appearance of a new journal "Mankind Quarterly" devoted in part to racial anthropology of the above kind (again described as such by one of its editors—R. R. Gates) and embodying racist attitudes of the earlier period. Truly the past is not yet buried, and human genetics, in spite of its recent evidences of new life, is still exposed to old dangers.

Eugenics movements grew in many other countries in the period before and just following the first World War, but space will permit taking account of only one such development.

It may be regarded as an anomaly of history that in Russia eugenics did not appear in an organized form until after the revolution of 1917, and this notwithstanding the enunciation of ideas very similar to those of Galton by W. M. Florinsky in 1866. In 1919 a eugenics department was started in the

Institute of Experimental Biology in Moscow under N. K. Koltzoff, and shortly thereafter a Eugenics Bureau began in Leningrad under J. A. Philiptschenko. By 1925 thirteen research articles on human genetics, *sensu stricto*, had been published from these institutes. The Russian Eugenics Society was founded in Moscow in 1920, with local branches in Leningrad, Saratov, and Odessa, and the Russian Journal of Eugenics under Koltzoff and Philiptschenko began in 1923 (cf. Koltzoff, 1925). The difficulties and later suppression of eugenics in the Soviet Union were foreshadowed by an event in connection with the publication in 1924 of Philiptschenko's book on eugenics. While it was in production at the government printing office, according to Weissenberg (1926) there was inserted in the introduction a statement to the effect that measures with important eugenical effects were the destruction of the bourgeoisie and the victory of the workers. What part the existence of eugenics there played in bringing about the suppression of genetics in the USSR is not clear to me. The first institute to be suppressed appears to have been that concerned with human genetics, the Gorky Institute for Medical Genetics, but this may have been incidental to the condemnation and execution of its director, S. G. Levit, as a "traitor."

Although the chief crosscurrents operating on human genetics were generated by persons pressing for social and political regulation of human breeding, frequently to the neglect of sound scientific method, others of less marked and definite character traced to relations, or lack of them, between genetics and medical research. Apart from lack of understanding of genetics on the part of physicians, there were frequent expressions of active lack of interest, since principles discovered in peas and exploited and extended by experiments with flies were not thought relevant to human beings. And if, physicians often said, a disease was inherited, that meant it couldn't be treated and knowledge about it was not likely to be useful. The gap due to mutual lack of appreciation and of common experience and training as between medical men and geneticists has shown some signs of narrowing, but is certainly far from being bridged. This would require further will and effort on both sides.

Nor can one conclude as yet that the confusion between the aim of eugenics and the facts of human heredity which Bateson pointed out has yet been cleared up. As eminent an acknowledged leader in genetics as Professor H. J. Muller has recently restated the adherence to ideas on controlled human breeding which he outlined in his book of 1935 *Out of the Night*. The central idea, eutelegenesis, had been developed by Herbert Brewer (1935) who probably was unaware of an earlier similar proposal by A. S. Serebrovsky (1929). The essential feature of the proposal was to utilize the sperm of men, chosen on the basis of achievement as superior, and by increasing through the use of artificial insemination the numbers of offspring of such superior sires to raise the average level of ability of the next generation. In his reiteration of this proposal in 1959, Muller has refined and extended it. He now proposes to retain the whole genotype of such men (which the processes of meiosis would tend to break down) by multiplying samples of their diploid spermatogonial cells in tissue cultures and subsequently obtaining embryos from these by some form of ectogenesis. Even though the technical problems involved might in some future time be solved, several more important scientific ones would still remain. Such schemes assume that there is an ideal genotype for a human being. Plato could entertain such an ideal but can we do so after our experience of the variety of genotypes in successful populations? Can human cultures be maintained by an ideal genotype? Even though the proponents of eutelegenesis should admit that there might be several good kinds of human being, are there objective scientific criteria by which they might be selected? Even though choice of sperm or genotype donors were to rest with persons as benevolent and acute as I believe Professor Muller to be, selection would still be subject to changing tastes and ideals and thus to control by imposed power as in the Nazi state. Muller illustrates this in his own examples of the eminent men he might have chosen, for in his list of 1959 as compared with that of 1935, Lenin, Marx and Sun Yat Sen have been dropped and Einstein and Lincoln added.

To me such schemes seem to express the same sort of benevolent utopianism as did some of Galton's proposals of 60 years ago, but now they must be viewed in the light of some actual experience with them. Then as now they were backed by the prestige of men of deserved eminence in science, then of Galton, today of Muller, but this did not save the earlier programs from grave misuse and ultimate damage to both human society and science. In fact the high scientific standing of their proponents increases the dangers of uncritical acceptance of them as bases for social and political action, with the ever attendant risk of loss of public confidence in genetics as applied to man if or when their unsoundness becomes manifest.

Such considerations remind us of the dilemma which scientists face in their desire both to advance sound knowledge and to make it serve its essential social function. In the case of human genetics, I do not believe that the problems posed by the cohabitation of these two purposes are to be settled by divorce, as Bateson suggested. The problems posed by the continuing occurrence of diseases and defects ("Our load of mutations" Muller 1950) are real and they must be faced, both as biological and as social problems. Both sets of interests must be free to develop, and better together than separately for this is the condition under which common criteria for criticism and rigorous judgements, so badly needed in all fields affected by potential social applications, may be evolved.

If I have strayed somewhat from the limits of 1900-1930 that I had set for myself for a historical review, I suppose this is a reflection of my view that some of the cross currents operating in the earlier years of this century still play upon us. It seems to me that their influence in the first two or three decades was in part due to the lack of a clear vision of what studies of man have to contribute to the elucidation of general problems such as the mechanism of evolution and of gene action. The rise of population genetics and of physiological genetics have now turned attention to the rich source of material for these problems provided by human populations, and by the accumulated experience of medical and anthropological research. Recent discoveries, such as the identification of human genes controlling serological, biochemical, and developmental processes subject to the action of natural selection, should now give human genetics that orientation toward important biological problems which was not generally recognized in its early days. What seems to me to be most important, especially in its implications for the future, is the growing recognition of the logical unity of genetics, for its essential problems, being concerned with a system of elements having similar attributes in all forms of life, can be seen to transcend the special problems of the different categories of organisms. Human genetics, freed from the narrower bounds and conflicting purposes which hindered its early growth, seems clearly destined to play an important role in the advancement of the whole science of genetics of which it is a part. And that, in the long run, may constitute its best contribution to the satisfaction of human needs.

REFERENCES

(1) B. Bateson. 1928. William Bateson, F. R. S. Naturalist. Cambridge Univ. Press.

(2) W. Bateson. 1919. Common sense in racial problems. The Galton Lecture. Eugen. Rev. 11.

(3) W. Bateson and E. R. Saunders. 1902. Royal Society Evolution Reports 1902-1909. Report 1, Dec. 17, 1901, cf. p. 133 for Bateson's interpretation of the observations of Garrod in Lancet, Nov. 30, 1901.

(4) A. Barthelmess. 1952. *Vererbungswissenschaft.* Freiburg/München, Orbis Academicus.

(5) F. Bernstein. 1924. Ergebnisse einer biostatistischen zusammenfassenden Betrachtung über die erblichen Blutstrukturen des Menschen. Klin. Wschr. **3:** 1495-1497.

(6) H. Brewer. 1935. Eutelegenesis. Eugen. Rev. **27:** 121-126.

(7) G. K. Chesterton. 1922. Eugenics and other evils. London.

(8) C. B. Davenport. 1914. Reply to criticism of recent American work by Dr. Heron of the Galton Laboratory. Eugenics Record Office, Cold Spring Harbor, N. Y., Bulletin 11.

(9) S. P. Davies. 1923. The social control of the feeble-minded. Ph.D. Dissertation, Faculty of Political Science, Columbia Univ. Press.

(10) R. L. Dugdale. 1874. The Jukes; a study in crime, pauperism, disease and insanity. New York.

(11) W. M. Florinsky. 1866. Über die Vervollkommnung und Entartung der Menschheit. Petersburg.

(12) F. Galton. For detailed references to the publications of Galton see Pearson (1914-1930).

(13) A. Garrod. 1908. Croonian Lectures to the Royal Academy of Medicine. Inborn errors of metabolism. Lancet. **2:** 1-7; 73-79; 142-148; 214-220.

(14) G. H. Hardy. 1908. Mendelian proportions in a mixed population. Science. **28:** 49-50.

(15) D. Heron. 1913. Mendelism and the problem of mental defect—a criticism of recent American work. Univ. of London, Publication of the Galton Laboratory, Questions of the Day and Fray, Number 7.

(16) L. Hogben. 1931. Genetics principles in medicine and social science. London, Williams & Norgate.

(17) L. Hogben. 1933. Nature and nurture. London, George Allen & Unwin.

(18) H. S. Jennings. 1925. Prometheus, or biology and the advancement of man. New York, E. P. Dutton & Co.

(19) D. Joravsky. 1961. Soviet Marxism and natural science. 1917-1932. New York, Columbia Univ. Press.

(20) N. K. Koltzoff. 1925. Die Rassenhygienische Bewegung in Russland. Arch. Rassenb. **17:** 96-99.

(21) H. J. Muller. 1935. Out of the night: a biologist's view of the future. New York, Vanguard Press.

(22) H. J. Muller. 1950. Our load of mutations. Amer. J. Hum. Genet. **2:** 111-176.

(23) H. J. Muller. 1959. The guidance of human evolution. Perspectives in Biol. and Med. **3:** 1-43.

(24) R. Pearl. 1928. Eugenics. Proc. 5th Int. Cong. Genet., Berlin. **1:** 260.

(25) K. Pearson. 1904. On a generalized theory of alternative inheritance, with special reference to Mendel's laws. Phil. Trans. Roy. Soc. London. **A 203:** 53-86.

(26) K. Pearson. 1914-1930. The life, letters and labors of Francis Galton. Cambridge Univ. Press. **I, II, III, IIIa.**

(27) L. S. Penrose. 1932. On the interaction of heredity and environment in the study of human genetics (with special reference to Mongolian imbecility). J. Genet. **25:** 407.

(28) A. A. Serebrovsky. 1929. Antropogenetika Medikobiologcheskii Zhurnal **5:** 3-19 (Russian, as cited by Joravsky, 1961).

(29) O. von Verschuer. 1959. Genetik des Menschen. Urban. Schwarzenberg.

(30) W. Weinberg. 1908. Über den Nachweis der Vererbung beim Menschen. Jahreshefte Verein vaterl. Naturkunde Württemberg. **64:** 369-382 (cf. also C. Stern. 1943. The Hardy-Weinberg law. Science. **97:** 137-138).

(31) S. Weissenberg. 1926. Theoretische und praktische Eugenik in Sowjet Russland. Arch. Rassenb. **18:** 81.

(32) S. Wright. 1959. Physiological genetics, ecology of populations and natural selection. Perspectives in Biol. and Med. **3:** 107-151.